A Flaming Challenge

A Flaming Challenge

Extinguishing the Stressful Emotional Fires of Life and Changing Our Perspective on Chronic Autoimmune Disease

Mala Naidoo

A Flaming Challenge
Mala Naidoo

First edition: 2019

ISBN: 9780620832441

Disclaimer:
This book is presented to the reader as a record of observations that the author has made regarding certain techniques that appeared to reverse the author's symptoms, de-stress her body and mind and help her multiple autoimmune syndrome go into remission. This book is the author's personal story that she has told in the way in which she best remembers it. The techniques discussed were effective for the author. Others may not respond similarly.

The author of this book does not hold herself out to be a qualified medical practitioner, nor does she – directly or indirectly – dispense medical advice or prescribe the use of any technique as a form of treatment for physical, emotional or medical problems without the advice of a physician. The intent of the author is only to offer information of a general nature to help readers in their quest for emotional and physical well-being. In the event that readers make use of any of the information contained in this book, the author and the publisher accept no responsibility or liability for any consequences of such actions.

Nothing contained in this book is intended to be instructional for medical diagnosis or treatment. The information contained in this book is not intended to replace professional medical advice and is merely presented for general informational and educational purposes. The information does not relate to any particular individual or individuals exept the author, and under no circumstances should any reader rely on the information for the purposes of treatment and/or medical advice.

Any person requiring any medical advice or treatment should consult their relevant medical practitioner or other qualified healthcare professional to suitably diagnose any ailments or diseases and prescribe the relevant treatment.

All information in this book is provided 'as is' without any warranty, whether express or implied.

The poem 'Footprints' version by Timothy Keith, https://keithieopia.com/post/2018-02-10-footprints/

Printed by *paarlmedia*, a division of Novus Holdings
1718350

This human birth is a gift.

*May we harness the strength and wisdom to go through our destiny
with love, understanding and acceptance of the Divine will.*

To my children, Pavesan and Tharsheyen, and my husband, Rajin, whose strength, love and wisdom are reminders of the gifts I embrace every day as I unravel the mystery of healing.

Thank you for giving me the space to grow.

Contents

⌒

Praise for A Flaming Challenge

On a cold winters night in Grahamstown, I was most pleased to meet a vibrant, dynamic woman who appeared at my talk on the 'Third eye and your brain' at the Science Cafe. I wasn't expecting many people, but seats filled up and people had braved the cold to hear a neuroscientist mixing science and philosophy in a talk on 'Protecting the aging brain.' After the talk, I had the pleasure of interacting with Mala and learned her intriguing journey of torment and then rising above it all. Her story, for me, tied together what I had been trying to convey. We as medical scientists who so firmly believe in the exactness of the doctrines of science have to concede that there is a strong spiritual element to the healing process. Constant bombardment of the mindset by adverse events and what we believe in, can have devastating consequences on our immune systems, unmasking underlying immune disorders. *A Flaming Challenge* demonstrates that changing your mindset with positive thoughts and following a diet, not harmful to your body, to restore your immune response can provide remarkable results. Mala has emerged triumphantly from the 'fires' that surrounded her, and lives not only to tell the tale but to publish her book, which I am certain, will give a great deal of courage to many who find themselves in a similar situation. The book also highlights the importance of family support and connectedness as part of the healing process.

— Santy Daya, Ph.D.

Neuroscientist and Professor of Pharmacology

The book is an insightful read which is aligned to the principles of natural medicine. The focus on the mind-body connection as well as resolving underlying emotional baggage is the start of any healing process. A book to inspire and motivate the community towards looking at health in a holistic way.

— Khalida Sabi

Naturopath

Dear Mala

I am eternally grateful that God has intertwined our lives and decided that we must meet. Reading your book has left me richer and with so much more hope for health and wellbeing that I knew, but never understood in detail as I do now. Living your truth with you through the pages of your book, has been an exceptional privilege.

A *Flaming Challenge* is a life story that movies are made of – a family's business is burnt to the ground, their home is destroyed, and Mala is diagnosed with multiple autoimmune diseases. The prescribed medicine has severe side effects. Mala questions whether it is the illness or the drugs causing the devastating symptoms.

Yet, the promise for every one of us is that we are never given more than we can cope with. The body simply does not lie. We need to understand the cause, as the cause determines the treatment. And what is the right treatment? From the first chapter, the reader is gripped by the unbelievable life experience and journey for Mala and her family to find the answer to living with multiple autoimmune diseases and overcoming trauma. A must read for all!

— Estie Schreiber

Chairman SA Natural Products

⌐

An inspirational read! Mala Naidoo takes us into the emotional world of a person not only suffering from a chronic autoimmune disease, but also having to endure numerous calamities seriously threatening the existence of her family. Every human being strives and deserves to be happy and healthy. Mala describes her journey out of abject misery and despair to ultimate healing that can only come from within, utilizing her own resources of mindfulness, gratitude and meditation.

This book challenges the approach of conventional allopathic medicine and offers the liberating healing powers available to everyone. The daily stressors of life lead to emotional turmoil and paralysis of the immune system which in turn lead to mental and physical disease as we know it. The power of now and mindfulness can reverse this dysfunctional state and lead to health, success and happiness. Mala Naidoo depicts this beautifully…. a must read for the caring profession and everyone.

— Henning Steinhagen, M.D.

Family Physician

∽

From adversity to wellness and a winning formula to contend with illness. Brilliantly written Mala – Thank you.

— Jay Bhagwan, M.D.

Anaesthesiologist

∽

Foreword

I am an Integrative Life Coach, Founder of Mind Enhancement Systems and Wisdom to Nourish and facilitator of *AWAKENING The Shift Experience*.

I first met Mala at the BRC, a beautiful and serene Buddhist Retreat Centre situated in the rolling foothills of the Drakensberg Mountains in KwaZulu-Natal, a province in South Africa. Mala was an attendee of the retreat entitled 'The Awakening Shift', which I was conducting there.

During the retreat, I described the transformation of consciousness by fire, thus: There is an ice block, solid, separate and resistant to change, secure in the material world. A world based on certainty and predictability. However, the dynamic nature of the universe favours change, growth, and expansion, operating outside of our comprehension and limited human perspective. So, in its infinite wisdom, universal consciousness places a fire beneath the ice block. Gradually it begins to melt, an uncomfortable experience for the ice block, which, becoming more fluid and flexible, starts to flow into new shapes and forms, transforming into something more than it had ever dreamed it could be.

The universe, seeing still more potential for expansion, then places additional fire beneath the pool of water, and once again a transformation is initiated. The pool of water heats up, expands beyond its former boundaries, and transforms into expansive, formless steam, lighter than air, yet with the potential to drive giant mechanisms, create great movement and momentum in the world.

Then I asked the participants, including Mala, to put their hands together, and rub them fast with great pressure. I then asked them what they experienced, and they uttered in unison, 'Heat!' I then suggested that we are that ice block, rigid and fixed; as the flow of life comes along, it presents us with challenges and opportunities to change. Many of us resist change with a big inner 'no!'; we prefer to reside in a 'comfort zone' of familiarity and certainty. However, this resistance builds up an inner heat, which many people experience as anger; some choose to resist this anger, turning it inward where it grows into depression. This inner resistance and heat leads to inflammation of the body and mind, where it can lead to 'incurable', heat-based diseases, like cancer, or autoimmune diseases like arthritis, in my case. I was told I would be on chronic medication for the rest of my life.

That day at the BRC I suggested to the retreatants that incurable means curable from within. Rather than outsourcing either the cause or remedy for my disease, I decided to take responsibility for it; I came off all medication, and slowly, painfully, changed my life from one of resistance to one of acceptance, changing my diet, the way I treat my body, my career and relationship, and today, 20 years later, I am completely arthritis free, having been so for many years now.

That day I had no idea of the incredible debilitating and fiercely painful journey Mala Naidoo had travelled. At the end of the retreat a glowing Mala came up to me, and after thanking me, briefly mentioned the journey of healing she had been on herself; one which resonated powerfully with what I had articulated over the previous three days. She mentioned she was writing a book detailing her experiences of self-healing and asked me to write a foreword to it, and I immediately agreed to do so.

The journey detailed in these pages is both heart-breaking and astounding. She writes with such depth of feeling, insight, and wisdom that the reader is drawn along at a fast pace as she relates her descent into the fires of hell as she was diagnosed with not one, but four painful and incurable diseases, one of which would be enough to slay a normal mortal, and her rise like a phoenix, renewed and reborn. She openly and intimately relates how the calamities of her life affected her physically and emotionally, and how these in turn impacted on her husband and family. Her journey is both an inspiration to others and guidance for healing the 'incurable', extinguishing the fires of challenge and resistance with the healing waters of rationality and responsibility; demonstrating the capacity to respond with consciousness and love.

It's not what we go through that determines our successes, but rather how we go through what we go through. It's our attitude and the effect of that on those around us that really matters in life. It's not what we achieve, nor what we accumulate, nor is it what others think of us that really matters, in the end; it is love. And that is the purpose of the crucible of the universe, to transform us, sometimes through the fire of extreme personal challenges, into the love that we are destined to be, living in alignment with the flow of life, rather than resisting life. This path to love is one that inevitably creates heat within our mind, body, and soul, and the inevitable fire of suffering.

To end, I quote Mala's wise words from within the pages of this book: 'Fighting doesn't win the battle – love does'. Thank you Mala for being courageous enough to share your journey with the world. Your book will, I am certain, help many others traverse their own very fires of hell with a bit more ease and insight gleamed by your heart-felt sharing , helping them emerge with greater wisdom, peace and serenity.

John Homewood

Preface

My journey in life thus far has been filled with profound shifts that some people might even call miracles. By the grace of the Divine I was constantly given the tools that empowered me or introduced me to people who would help me with challenges to come. I am in awe when I reflect on the synchronicity of my life journey. Reality is certainly not random; rather, it is beautifully orchestrated and steeped in meaning and growth.

According to medical science, I should be in a wheelchair. But I have defied these limiting beliefs. The human body and mind have the most astounding ability to find balance and harmony. I have fallen many times, but time and again I got back on my feet. My passion for the innate intelligence within every human being is my secret to surviving the many disasters that life has hurled across my path. I am walking proof that the human body and mind have the extraordinary ability to activate healing within themselves. With this book, I want to inspire you, too, to heal from the inside out.

My story will take you through the fires of hell I experienced, only to rise from the ashes like a phoenix. Just when everything seems to be in balance again, your emotional state is engaged through my rollercoaster journey towards wellness. Many who want to heal, yet feel helpless, will be able to relate. We need to realise that wellness is a responsibility. This book highlights everything I did to bring about improved health and wellness even though I was diagnosed with conditions for which medical science has few answers. If we want to effect change, we need to start with our thoughts. I changed my perception of my circumstances and now the 'new me' is slowly creating the world she wishes to live in. My healing kit includes taming the mind and taking care of the body with modalities based in sound, colour, light, breathing, movement, visualisation and meditation, while paying attention to the food I eat, nurturing my relationships, and being aware of the effect that stress has on my life.

This book will allow you to draw on the many healing techniques developed from my personal experience. I have written it in the hope that it will inspire you to find the things you need to help you improve your health and wellness. I invite you to embrace the belief that we are living in a matrix of infinite possibilities: believe that everything is possible and find the motivation to start your personal healing journey – emotionally, mentally and physically.

A stressful lifestyle and the demands of modern society are wreaking havoc on our bodies and minds. Stress is an epidemic in the western world – and an extremely costly one at that. I trust that this book will assist those who are experiencing stress today. I want to inspire you to unlock the immense power within yourself to let go of the stressful thoughts associated with your circumstances and thus heal and thrive.

Whether you are experiencing challenges in your relationships, your place of work, your country or your health, the mental noise is the same. We all want a way out. We all want our pain to evaporate. When we ignore the signs of the effects of stress on our bodies and minds, pain becomes the final message, the only way we can learn. Our journey in life is one of growth – physically, mentally, emotionally and spiritually. When we don't have the means to change a situation, we are challenged to change ourselves. We have to drive change from the inside, instead of trying to change external circumstances. When we become more at peace with where we are, rather than where we want to be, we allow our problems and challenges to catapult us to our full potential. Without these challenges, our strengths often lie dormant.

The caterpillar is squeezed out as it goes through its metamorphosis into a butterfly. For the caterpillar, metamorphosis is death but, for the butterfly, metamorphosis is life. Instead of taking the caterpillar's perspective and viewing our situation as a crisis, let's choose the perspective that we are breaking free, taking flight and soaring with life. When we see every challenge as another opportunity to fly, the Divine will move heaven and earth to breathe wind beneath our wings.

Part One of this book focuses on the financial challenges my family and I were suddenly faced with after a number of tumultuous events, and the emotional transformation that came with them. It then introduces the three autoimmune conditions I was diagnosed with, for which medical science has no clearly defined cause or cure. Part Two is an invitation to join me on a journey to reassess and redress the 'no cure' label many autoimmune and chronic conditions have received. It is filled with healing modalities that could transform our perspective on improving wellness for patients diagnosed with chronic conditions as well as the autoimmune-disease community.

My intention is not to disrupt or criticise any patient's conventional medical protocol. Instead, I want to encourage patients to take back their power and explore the boundless ways in which the human body and mind can repair and heal itself. Medicine often tells us that a condition or disease is incurable, but more and more people are finding ways to recover, or at least drastically improve their general level of well-being. May this book be a valuable tool for those who are willing to take responsibility for their lives and their personal growth.

The process of writing this book was a healing experience in itself. Embracing a positive attitude gave me the ability to accept the challenge and inspired me to do research, document my practice and share my experience. The greatest shifts came on days when I just sat still with awareness of the Divine, devoid of purpose and agenda, with no expectation of results. When I did finally let go, it felt like the noose of the 'incurable' disease was removed from my neck. When we dare to go against the commonly accepted paradigm and believe with openness that something inside us is more powerful than our challenging circumstances, we find the strength to try something different and open ourselves to miracles.

My healing is an ongoing journey of control and maintenance – controlling my thoughts and maintaining a positive, winning attitude. May this book be a source of help and inspiration in your healing journey.

Much love,

Mala Maidoo

Part One
Caught in the Flames, Caught in the Flood

1
Fire on the outside

My story starts off like a typical nightmare, only I wasn't dreaming. The harsh ring of the telephone in the middle of the night jarred me out of a deep sleep. It was the alarm company. There was a fire at our business property!

Makybe Diva Luxury Day Spa and Wellness Centre was our dream project. We had created the perfect setting to pamper the body while healing the mind. The spa and conference centre was a work of art, boasting a rustic yet modern look with a majestic thatch roof. It was located on the Midlands Meander in Hilton, twenty-five minutes from our home in Pietermaritzburg. I can't remember how I got to our garage – I was that quick. I picked the more powerful car and hooted persistently for my husband to hurry up and jump in.

'Move over', he said, 'I'll drive'.

'No!' I snapped, feeling the anxiety starting to build up inside me. 'We don't have time to swap seats. Jump in please, Raj!'

I drove, trying to ignore the frightening possibilities my mind was conjuring up. It was a still, clear night, unusual for Hilton, which was normally blanketed in thick mist at this hour. The roads were quiet, but my head was a cacophony of panic. I was driving at top speed. As I took the bend that brought the spa into view, I started to tremble. The smoke and flames were raging towards the sky. I could feel myself go limp. The car was slowing down. I had no energy to press the accelerator.

'Drive, Mala, drive!' Rajin screamed.

My foot obeyed.

The police and alarm company greeted us at the gate. We were not allowed to enter the property until the fire department arrived. The two forty-five-kilogram gas cylinders that had fuelled the beautiful fireplace, where hundreds of couples had cuddled over the last few months, could explode at any moment. I stood at the gate and helplessly watched our dream go up in smoke.

This can't be real!

This was not just an ordinary business. This was our retirement. Rajin and I had invested all the money we had, and then some more from friends and family, to create a luxurious and therapeutic environment for our clients. Now we were watching our ambitions and our future go up in smoke.

Rajin and I had long shared a passion for empowering our community in the matter of wellness of body and mind. He had been active as a respected pharmacist in Pietermaritzburg. We also tackled projects together: between 1992 and 2003, we hosted the largest Drug Wise campaign in South Africa, the largest diabetes screening campaign in the province of KwaZulu-Natal and free talks on numerous health topics. We hosted free soccer, Tae Bo, tai chi and Indian classical dance classes. The Tae Bo group grew to be the biggest in South Africa: we reached numbers between eight hundred and one thousand participants. It was incredible. We invited the mayor of Pietermaritzburg to our Tae Bo group's first birthday party, and the participants shared how the class had built up their self-esteem and confidence and brought joy back into their lives. To think I had invited them for a mere cardio workout. Over the years we came to realise what an amazing tool these programmes were in fostering physical, mental and emotional wellness in our community.

We had owned a beautiful, vibrant pharmacy in Pietermaritzburg and enjoyed giving back to our community. However, in 2003, when the dispensing fee for retail pharmacists in our country changed, it destroyed the passion of many in the profession. The South African Department of Health amended the Medicines and Related Substances Act 101 of 1965, which involved regulations related to a transparent pricing system for medicines and scheduled substances. The resulting reduction in profitability threatened the viability of retail pharmacy. For us, it meant that we had to reduce our projects, retrench staff and drastically alter our lifestyle. All retail pharmacists were affected, and numerous independent pharmacies closed down throughout the country. Watching his peers give up everything they had worked so hard for destroyed Rajin's love for the profession. Not being able to practise pharmacy the way he loved to do it – serving beyond the call of duty – broke his heart. The industry was in distress and no one was interested in buying a pharmacy. But, in December 2006, the local newspaper carried an article on our decision to close down our pharmacy and that very evening we had an offer on the table that would cover all our outstanding commitments to creditors. We accepted the deal.

Still having to pay our home mortgage bond, the children's school fees, car instalments, personal insurance, medical aid and living expenses, we knew that we had to work fast to find a source of income. We decided to remain in the wellness industry and, after we had done our research, Makybe Diva Luxury Day Spa and Wellness Centre was born. It felt so good to see Rajin 'get his happy back' as he went about supervising the fifteen companies involved in the renovation of the property we acquired for the spa. He was in his element – like a six-year-old with a new toy at Christmas. We worked well together as we created a unique luxurious and comforting healing space for people to reconnect to their inner magic.

We shifted all our money and energy to the business; we had no other source of income. Our vision was to use the spa as a vehicle to empower our community in improving and maintaining wellness in body and mind by combining conferences and health workshops with spa treatments. We had, however, underestimated the set-up costs of a luxury health spa. At the time of opening, prioritising our insurance was the least of our concerns. We were insured for the bare minimum and promised to redress this as our income grew.

5

Watching the fire engulf our spa, we knew we were losing everything. We had invested our all in this venture. And now there it was, going up in flames.

By the time the three fire engines got there, the entire spa was ablaze. The thatched roof and all the wooden furniture were fuelling the fire. The flames were devouring our hard work like a pride of lions at a kill.

My stomach knotted up. My ribcage was crushing my lungs. My mouth was dry. I battled to focus. My brain just wanted to shut down.

So, this is what shock and panic feel like.

My legs were wobbly and I felt faint, but I didn't want to give in.

Breathe, Mala, breathe – deep diaphragm breathing.

I knew if I focused on my breath, it would calm my mind.

How is Rajin going to cope with this disaster?

Just then I heard him say, as if he were reading my thoughts, 'Mala, we're going to get through this'. I turned to look at him: his eyes told a different story.

He called my parents. When they arrived, the unfolding events rendered them speechless.

We watched as the conference room, with its high-tech equipment and executive furniture, was swallowed up by the fire. Rajin had made the builder replace its majestic door three times. It had to be perfect. Everything that was being burnt to ashes was still brand new. The spa was still an infant, not even two years old. As I gazed into the blue of the flames, I wondered what the universe was telling me. The notion that I was being punished crossed my mind, but I consciously quashed that thought.

I have always believed that the creative energy of the universe never punishes us; it strengthens us. As I said this to myself, I felt, at a deep level, a sense of not being alone. I'm not talking about the company of other people. I'm talking about a universal knowing. I sensed that the days ahead were going to challenge me in ways that would be beyond my comprehension. Life was about to become extremely demanding. But I was not alone. Even though the universe had thrown me into a catastrophic nightmare, it was still on my side. That's the beautiful paradox we embrace daily as we grow to our full potential.

The spa was set on a beautiful property with breathtaking views and surrounded by a garden designed according to feng shui principles. As the building blazed into the early hours of the morning, the garden's tranquil energy seemed frozen. Our therapists had done foot massage treatments in the lapa, which was strategically placed among the lush foliage. Both they and the clients had loved nature's sounds, sights and smells. The spa treatment package also included guided relaxation under the 'Buddha Tree', where a serene statue of the Buddha was the focal point. Although the absence of wind meant that the garden was not physically destroyed, the raging fire swallowed up the peace of our paradise with ruthless persistence.

Only a few months before, Rajin and I had attended a spa conference in Johannesburg, a four-hour drive from Pietermaritzburg. On our way back, we received a call informing us that there had been a runaway fire the night before. When we got back to the spa, there was burnt grass all around, as far as the eye could see, but – incredibly – our spa was okay. Our neighbour from the adjacent plot said that the fire had literally jumped over our property.

Perhaps that fire was a sign from the universe that I shouldn't have ignored. But at the time I simply thought that the garden's special energy would not allow for it to be destroyed by fire. I had looked at our unharmed property surrounded by burnt land, turned to my husband and exclaimed, 'There's something special about this place, Raj. Our spa is here to stay!'

Then, on the night of the devastating fire, I realised that nothing in this world is permanent. In a flash, we lost it all.

The fire department worked hard to bring the blaze under control. When they finally succeeded, there was nothing left. Our spa was razed to the ground.

My mother, who had worked tirelessly all her life, had joined us at the spa as part of her retirement plan. We worked well together: her culinary skills and creative flair complemented the ethos of our business.

Rajin, Mum, Dad and I stood with our arms around each other, resisting the urge to put into words the horror of what was unfolding. The darkness felt like it was leaving the sky and entering its new home, my heart.

As the sun began to rise, I suddenly remembered – our children! Our two sons were alone at home, hopefully still asleep. 'I have to go back home immediately to check on the boys!' I said.

When I got home, Tharsheyen, our younger son, aged ten at the time, was already up, wondering what had happened to us. Pavesan, our elder son, aged thirteen, was just waking up.

'I'm so sorry I left you alone for so long', I said. I sat them both down, held their hands and tried very hard not to burst into tears.

'Before I tell you the sad news, I want you to know that no one was hurt'.

'What's wrong, Mum?' Pavesan asked.

'Our spa caught on fire last night and it burnt to the ground'.

'Oh no, Mummy, no! Why? What happened? Why did it have to burn down?' they asked.

'I don't have any answers yet, boys. Let's be strong for each other and thank Baba Ji for keeping us all safe'. We just sat in silence.

'Okay, Mummy. We love you', Tharsheyen said, breaking the silence. The three of us hugged each other tightly.

The news that everyone was all right allowed my children to continue as normal. I got them ready for school, dropped them off and headed back in the direction of turmoil.

The news reporters, police and insurance agents were waiting to question me. I spoke to all of them briefly before I sat down on the beautifully manicured grass and stared at the still-smouldering ruins. And then it happened: I burst into tears. It was an explosion of pain and sadness. I sobbed loudly and uncontrollably. My friends and family had already gathered to show their support and couldn't help crying with me. They had enjoyed many hours at the spa being pampered and knew full well how much it meant to us.

And then our twenty-four massage therapists arrived. The shock and horror of what confronted them had them screaming in anguish.

'This is not fair!'

'Who did this to us?'

'This is our bread and butter. What's going to happen to us now?'

We hugged each other, repeating, 'I'm so sorry' and 'This is so sad'.

I had employed local women, paid for them to be trained as massage therapists and then schooled them in the Makybe Diva Spa philosophy of inner wellness. They loved their work, and their clients kept coming back, asking for specific therapists by name.

Rajin and I were obsessed with attention to detail with layout and cleanliness, and this brought many smiles to our clients' faces. We deliberately made all our treatment packages affordable so that middle-income clients could also enjoy a royal pampering experience at a luxury day spa. We had many first-time spa-goers, but the backbone of our repeat business was the upper-income market. At the time of the fire, we were fully booked for the next two months. The spa had been steadily gaining popularity. It had taken us fifteen months to get to that point. We had invested everything, hoping that we would be fully booked in the first month. It had, however, taken longer, so there was quite a financial backlog.

I just couldn't stop crying. It felt as though my insides were being ripped out. My heart felt sore. We were only just beginning, and now it was over.

While the tears were still flowing, a friend came up to me, bent down and spoke close to my ear. He said, 'Mala, I want you to watch your relationship with Rajin closely. Do not blame each other at all. Now, I want you to get up, wipe away your tears and go do something good for someone else'.

Our friend doesn't recall this conversation, but it definitely had an impact on me. As if in a trance, I got up and, abandoning Rajin and the smouldering building, drove to town. I decided that I wanted to take food to those less fortunate than me. My parents taught me that feeding people is a blessing. I bought a big bag of biscuits and went looking for the people who often beg at traffic lights. But no one was around. So I decided to go to the public hospital, which is not far from where we live.

Still reeling from the morning's disaster, I got to the hospital, in tears, and just stood at the entrance. Now what? I asked the security guard to point me in the direction of the children's ward. When I walked in, I had to stop. I was speechless. It was the burns unit of the hospital. The children in the ward were all badly burnt. Some of them were crying in pain. Some burn wounds were bandaged and some were open. The universe was showing me what hadn't burnt in the fire – my clients, my staff, my family and me! What a strong message indeed. The smell of pus was suffocating as I walked around the ward, handing out biscuits to the little children and their parents. They were so grateful, smiled at me and sent me many blessings. I was quickly learning that the most important things in life are not possessions, but people.

The previous day, hours before the spa had caught fire, we had had twenty-four pensioners visiting, to whom we had given complimentary spa packages. It was a gift from Rajin and me to a group of older women who had never been to a spa before. I shudder to think of the consequences if the fire had started while everyone was having treatments. Or, since I sometimes worked until late doing online marketing, I could have been trapped by the fire. I had been reminding my clients daily about the joy and wisdom of gratitude, and now it was time for me to go to a place of gratitude amidst the cinders.

That afternoon another incident brought a powerful realisation to me: I wasn't the only one going through extreme challenges. I had gone to fetch our sons from their school, which was just down the road from the spa. A stranger walked up to me in the car park. She introduced herself: she was a new teacher at the school and had heard about the fire that morning, just like everyone else. Then she said, 'I'm so sorry for your loss. I feel your pain. I would like to share with you what I've recently gone through'.

She was from Rwanda. She and her family had fled the country because of genocide, with nothing more than the clothes on their backs. She was four months pregnant at the time and would go days without food.

'I have no idea how my body produced breast milk to feed my other baby son', she told me.

The family had slowly moved down through Africa, looking for a way to take care of their children.

She also told me about another woman who had tried to avoid the bullets and grabbed her baby with his blanket from his cot. She reached safety only to open the blanket and discover that she had grabbed the frightened cat that had crawled under the blanket. She had inadvertently left her baby behind to die.

'People are going through much worse out there', she said. 'Just hang in there. Life will get better, I promise'.

This woman had lost not only all her wealth, but also her home, her country and her people. Her story brought new depth to my courage.

It was clear that the universe was not going to allow me to stay sad forever – oh no! After the hospital visit and this stranger's story, the magnitude of what had happened to us was diminishing in my mind. Life was sending me a positive attitude adjustment. With the right attitude, everything is possible. That evening my mind was all over – the hospital scene, the Rwandan woman, our burnt spa.

The next morning the newspaper posters on the street read: POSH SPA BURNS DOWN. Not the way I had envisioned making the front page of our newspaper. The days that followed were absolute hell, even though our friends and family poured in to show their support. My mother spent the entire day, every day, talking to them about the fire, while Rajin and I were consumed with dealing with the police and the insurance company. The energy in our house was heavy. There was so much crying, it felt like death had arrived; just the body was missing. I didn't want to talk about the fire any more. I was simply drained.

I remember an aunt of mine scolding our sons for being cheerful.

'Stop laughing, boys! Can't you see how sad your parents are? This behaviour is disrespectful', she said.

Thank God for our children, was my thought instead. They brought light back into our home. As long as they saw Rajin and me every day, their world was complete. Nothing else mattered to them. Children live in the now. Unlike adults, their thoughts do not project a bleak future. Right now all is well, and this moment is the only reality that exists for them.

It was a few days before my birthday. Rajin had usually spoilt me with extravagant parties, but this year we had tickets to a pity party. I just wanted to get away from it all. I needed a place where I could be silent, in the present moment. I had always wanted to go to the Buddhist Retreat Centre in Ixopo, in our province of KwaZulu-Natal, which is renowned for its peace and tranquillity. My family agreed that this was exactly what I needed. My mum took care of Rajin and our boys while I took the time to start healing my mind.

I spent five days at the retreat centre. Most of the day was spent in silence surrounded by the indigenous valleys, forests and undulating hills. The retreat focused on mindfulness meditation, led by Louis van Loon. We were taught how to stay in the present, the now. At this point in my life, this was exactly what I needed. The past reminded me of the devastating fire and the future looked insurmountable. Being present in the moment felt comforting. I experienced the profound power of being in the now.

We were taught to focus on our breath and feel present in our body. We had to feel where our body met the chair and our feet touched the ground. We did all this with our eyes closed. This simple yet powerful technique kept my thoughts on the peaceful present moment. To be removed from the depths of despair and be allowed to find my centre again was a lifeline. I learnt that on the other side of rage and sadness is clarity and strength. By the end of the stay I felt recharged and ready to take on this new challenge in my life.

Despite an intensive investigation, the police never found out what had caused the fire. The insurance company paid out a pittance. The disappointing reality was that, at the time of taking out the policy, we had little income, so we covered ourselves well for public liability and told ourselves that, as the business grew, we would top up our general policy. The ridiculously low payout couldn't rebuild what we had created. There was no money to restart the spa.

What was left of the property was sold for the amount outstanding to the bank. We had started our venture by investing millions into renovating the property, to create a luxury spa and wellness centre, and now we had nothing to show for it. We were almost bankrupt.

That night Rajin and I held one another as if for the first time, so grateful for the strength each of us brought to our relationship. Lying on my husband's chest with his arms around me, I could feel his emotional pain.

'Raj, if there's anybody who knows how to start again, it's you', I said. Trying to be brave for him and not let the tears pour, I just held him tightly.

He kissed me. 'Together we're not just going to come out of this, we're going to enjoy the process. I love you', he whispered.

We fell asleep entangled in each other's support and love.

Right now, we needed to find a way to survive the financial ruin of the fire. A few months before the incident, Rajin had been approached by an investor to open a pharmacy in Dalton, a little town fifty kilometres outside of Pietermaritzburg. It was time to reconsider this offer. We had to put aside everything that we had grown to dislike about the pharmacy profession and find a way to earn an income quickly. Rajin is a brilliant pharmacist, and we both felt it would be the best option. It takes guts, determination and deep love to do what my husband did. And I know that he did it for us, for our family.

We approached the investor, who was delighted to have us. The only problem? The shopping complex would only be ready in six months' time. We expressed our desperate need to earn money as quickly as possible. He was so pleased to have a pharmacist of Rajin's stature as a tenant that he agreed to let us use another building that he owned. We said yes, only to discover, when we went to see the premises, that it was down a passageway opposite a noisy bottle store and shebeen – and that it needed a lot of work. We walked back to our car, despondent. We got in and held each other, crying our hearts out.

My husband is such a good man, he doesn't deserve this. But we've got to keep moving forward.

'We can't give up. We have to take the premises', I said.

'Not today, Mala. I just want to go home. Please'.

When we got home, Rajin mapped out a plan. He decided to use this tiny premises as a health shop, while waiting for the new complex to be built. He would do locum work in Pietermaritzburg in addition, in order to raise funds to set up the new business. This would allow us to earn an income while we embraced the six-month-long wait for the processing of a pharmacy licence for the new complex.

Now that we had a plan, we decided to take a long drive to strategise further. Over the years, our greatest business concepts had been born on the road. The comfort of our luxury car seemed to kindle groundbreaking business ideas. It was our boardroom on wheels.

We had made quite a bit of progress during our drive, so I was surprised when, later that same day, Rajin came to me with tears in his eyes again.

'I'm so sorry, but the dealership wants an answer regarding the outstanding amount on our car'.

We still owed a substantial sum. The dealership suggested that we voluntarily return the car. That evening a consultant arrived at our door, took the car and said they would sell the car to cover the amount due. In that moment, losing the car seemed like the least of our worries. We would have to give up a lot more than our 'boardroom'.

Our spa had been fully booked for the next two months at the time of the fire. Now we had to refund all this money. We had exhausted all our lending options, so it was time to part with our lives as avid racehorse owners.

We had entered the sport in the most absurd way possible: in 1999 a pharmacy customer of ours was unable to pay his account, so he offered us his share in a racehorse as settlement. We said yes and entered a world we had never imagined we could be part of.

Rajin's passion for horses was easy to see; he seemed to come alive in their presence. He studied the bloodlines and followed the champion horses with great interest. As for me, I relished wearing specially designed avant-garde outfits and mingling in the parade ring at the racecourse at big race day events. For Rajin's thirty-fifth birthday, I had given him the lease to a beautiful suite at Greyville Racecourse that was flanked on either side by the giants of horse racing, the Oppenheimers and the Jaffees. We had shared many fun times there, but now it was time to let it all go. We had to give up everything that was considered a luxury. Our house and the children's private school would be next.

I tried to take things one day at a time but, even though I looked so composed on the outside, I felt ashamed on the inside. My ego didn't just get bruised; my ego got assaulted. I went from driving a luxury car to driving an old dilapidated one. Initially I cringed every time I sat behind the wheel and encountered friends who still had all their wealth. I was surprised by my response. *What happened to the gratitude, Mala? The old car is still getting you from A to B, isn't it?* My ego felt that people were belittling me. How absurd is that? I quickly realised that people were all so worried about who was looking and laughing at them that they had no time to look at me. So I asked myself: *Why are you so worried about what other people think of you?*

My ego felt like a heavy mask that was covering up my true self. This was the first time in my life that I observed my ego. The ego is sustained and fed by constant thinking about the past or the future. The ego cannot concern itself with living in the joy of the present moment. Being in the present threatens the ego's very survival. In the past, I always felt driven to succeed, and I did. I did not come to this world to be average. I was determined. *It's not about how low you fall, it's about how high you bounce back.* At the same time, I had to keep my ambition in check. *Don't let your ego drive you into a depression. Keep your compass on appreciation.*

2
Acts of kindness and the power of gratitude

Gratitude ignites abundance. Nothing manifests abundance like an act of gratitude: an action that shows concern for the happiness of another human being, without hope of reward for oneself. I had often read about the joy of gratitude, but I had made it part of my life only in a small way, meaning I always thought about giving but rarely got down to doing it. Even though I valued the deep transformation that happens for a human being in the act of practising gratitude, I didn't make the time to do it much.

But I did always encourage gratitude. In our spa's garden we had designed a unique steam room to offer a simultaneous combination of psychoacoustic therapy, colour therapy, hydrotherapy and aromatherapy. This truly rejuvenating experience was followed by a gratitude session outside. We encouraged clients to write a letter of gratitude to themselves and put it in a self-addressed envelope that I would post three months later. The idea was to give the client a feeling of joy months after their treatment. We often get caught up in the routine of our busy world. We take things for granted and miss out on experiencing the joy around us. Receiving this gratitude letter from oneself three months after writing it was a great way to be reminded to be conscious of the blessings each day brings. This letter was a reminder for clients to start cultivating gratitude as a way to improve the quality of their lives.

Some clients were tremendously challenged by this gratitude session in the garden. I remember a gentleman who sat there, staring at his blank page.

'I have nothing to write', he said.

I patiently reminded him of how much he had and how we all often take this for granted. 'Well', I said, 'are you happy that you have hair on your head?'

'Yes', he replied.

'So, write it down. Are you grateful for the fact that you can walk so easily?'

Yes again.

'How about the time you gave yourself to be here today?'

'Oh yes ...' And so the page was slowly filled.

I recall another client being so upset with the twenty-minute gratitude session that she accused us of squandering her time and demanded a refund for the full day package.

After the fire, I had to examine my own relationship to gratitude. Had I been so arrogant to believe that it was my right to have things a certain way? Gratitude is more than just saying 'please' and 'thank you' out of habit. Gratitude is a deep feeling of joy and appreciation for what we have. When we are in a state of gratitude, our mind is calmer and our body is more relaxed. Gratitude is a gift from our Creator to initiate healing of the heart during emotional trauma. So simple, yet so life-changing.

Since my initial visit just after the fire, our sons and I started visiting the hospital burns ward to give out gifts and meals every Friday. I actually feel that one should not speak about this kind of act, because it loses its essence. But, for the purposes of this book, I wanted to share the profound effect this simple act of gratitude had. We all felt like we were a part of something that mattered. The blessings we received from the children and their parents carried us for months to come.

The children started to look forward to our visits. Their faces lit up as soon as we entered the ward. Their joy filled our hearts. As it turned out, we weren't there only to give. In my down state, it was easier for me to pick someone else up and, in doing so, I automatically found myself on the rise. What a beautifully orchestrated exchange in nature. When we bring joy to someone, we cannot help feeling joy in ourselves too.

It was only years later that I learnt about the biochemical impact of an act of kindness. Research into the neurobiological link between compassion and love shows that our body releases our 'happy' neurotransmitters during an act of compassion[44]. They cause elevated levels of oxytocin and dopamine in the brain, which give us a natural high. While dopamine is known as the neurotransmitter of pleasure, oxytocin is often referred to as the love hormone. When it's released, it produces a feeling of love, contentment and satisfaction. It reduces anxiety and stress. New mothers form a bond with their babies and forget the pain of childbirth because of oxytocin.

An act of kindness releases a flood of this hormone into our bloodstream. Those performing the act of kindness, those receiving the kindness and those observing it are all filled with the warmth of oxytocin. This oxytocin-induced happiness has many health benefits. Research shows that oxytocin reduces levels of free radicals and inflammation in mice[162]. It lowers our heart rate and our stress-hormone levels[65]. It improves the cardiovascular system and slows the aging process. What a fabulous way for nature to say thank you for an act of kindness.

I noticed how my choice of attitude in the morning set the tone for the rest of the day. An optimistic, hopeful attitude made my day more manageable. A sad, negative attitude drained and exhausted me. Hugging our children always helped to put a smile on my face and lift the energy in our home. A good hug is a fast way to release oxytocin in the body. We all need hugs for survival, growth and maintenance of our well-being.

I had to keep monitoring my attitude. Even days when my eyes were full of tears, I would remind myself that I still had more than most people in our country and much to be grateful for. Of course, adjusting to life after the fire remained difficult. With us being so close to personal bankruptcy, everyone in our family was preparing me to give up our beautiful house. I put it up for sale just under its market value. It didn't sell. I dropped the price further. It still didn't sell.

I wrote a detailed email to the bank explaining what had happened, highlighting our determination to get through this financial setback. I asked them to believe in our dream to heal our community and outlined our business plan to establish a pharmacy in a town that had no pharmaceutical or healthcare facility. The pharmacy would be run by a pharmacist with vast experience and expertise in the industry, who could deliver quality health care to the community. Then I asked for a six-month grace period on the bond. My family thought I was crazy to make a request like this. But the bank granted the request. I knew it: the universe was on our side. Looking back, I'm so grateful that our house never sold. It's a beautiful living space.

Next, our sons would have to change schools in order for us to be able to afford school fees. I made an appointment to speak to the headmaster of our sons' private school, a very caring and approachable man who adored and valued our sons. He frequently praised them for their abilities on the sports field and talents in the arts and sciences. I entered the headmaster's office with my head held high, determined not to cry, but as soon as he greeted me, I burst into tears. My children loved this school. It felt like one big family.

I explained to the headmaster: 'Sir, the fire destroyed our business. We have no money and no stable income yet. We are not coping financially. Our children love this school, but we just cannot afford it'.

'Just leave it to me', he said.

He went to the board of directors to plead our case and they came up with a financial plan to keep our sons in the school. This was huge for me emotionally. I felt so relieved that we wouldn't have to disrupt our children's world and pleased that they wouldn't have to deal with the stress of starting at a new school.

We live in a kind world. As soon as I acknowledged this and surrendered to it, I attracted kindness. Seemingly impossible things were happening. By acting with an attitude of love and gratitude, and through our built-in survival spirit that becomes amplified when children are involved, we were moving forward in leaps and bounds. Rajin and I suddenly stopped seeing obstacles. I wasn't fighting back. I surrendered to the moment and went with the flow. I would do something and then leave the result to manifest on its own, free of interference. Saving our home and giving our boys a good education was the miracle of gratitude.

I encouraged our sons to tell their dad how grateful they were for what they did have. I thanked Rajin sincerely every time we spoke. I also spent many, many hours visualising all four of us happy and having fun together, laughing, expressing our love for one another. The driving force of love can indeed move mountains. We kept reminding each other that no lives were lost in the fire and that a better financial state was something we could always get back. A life lost is gone forever.

To be able to draw strength from another human being is powerful and inspiring. I knew it was important for me to keep Rajin motivated and focused on rebuilding our business. Yet developing and sustaining a positive attitude is not just a quick-fix motivational technique; it is a disciplined skill that must be learnt and practised. I picked my discussions with him very carefully. I decided that the one place he should always be able to find some solace was in my arms. We labelled this 'disaster' an experience that was written into our destiny. We both believe that our Creator gives us only what we can handle. Yes, instead of telling God how big our problems were, we chose to tell our problems how big our God is. This shift in attitude solidified our trust in each other. The worst was behind us. Or was it?

3
The mind plays the field while the body keeps score

The mind can enslave us or empower us. Just as we had started reaping the fruits of focusing on positivity, the unconscious impact of negativity on the human mind made its bold presence felt in our lives.

It was six weeks since the fire had destroyed our spa. The telephone rang. It was my mum.

'Mala, I don't feel too well', she said. 'Something is wrong'.

'I'm on my way, Mum', I replied reassuringly.

My parents' retirement home was twenty minutes from our house. I immediately dropped everything and drove over there. My mother is an incredibly strong woman with a passion to succeed and conquer. If she says something is wrong, it is. When I arrived at the flat, she was so apologetic for taking me away from my work.

'What's the matter, Mum?'

'My entire body is covered in these massive blisters. It's so painful. I also feel a burning and itchy sensation all over my body. At first, I thought it was an allergy to something I had eaten, so I took an antihistamine', Mum explained. 'But it didn't help. It's getting worse'.

I rushed her to our family doctor. Upon consultation, he immediately contacted a dermatologist and asked for an emergency appointment. We got back into the car and were off to the dermatologist.

While I was with Mum at the dermatologist, Rajin and my dad were on their way to Johannesburg to visit my mother-in-law in hospital. She had just been diagnosed with a serious condition and needed an urgent operation. Rajin couldn't wait for me to accompany him. He felt that his mother, aged seventy-five then, might not recover from the anaesthetic and that this might be the last time he saw her alive. I wanted to be there for him, but my mum was so ill as well.

When the dermatologist examined my mother, I saw the blisters properly for the first time. They were the size of my palm and she had them all over her body. It looked extremely painful. The doctor went back to his desk, consulted a textbook and asked Mum and me to take a seat across from him.

'Mrs Naidoo', he said, 'your mother has a severe case of a rare autoimmune condition called lichen planus. It's an inflammatory condition of the skin. The best way for me to describe the severity of your mum's lichen planus is as first-degree burns'.

I sat in absolute shock. The doctor wasn't aware of my mum's emotional state since the spa had been destroyed in the fire. She hadn't been in contact with flames, yet she was presenting with something akin to first-degree burns. Just from standing there, watching the fire burn everything we had worked so hard to achieve, and from talking about the fire over and over again to everyone who visited us, and from feeling more and more traumatised by our financial loss, my mother's mind had come to believe that she might as well have been in the fire. The survival stress pathway in the human body doesn't know the difference between what is imagined and what is real. It is triggered by the negative emotion of fear. Every time we think about a negative incident, the body responds as if it is happening in that moment[9]. The body's chemical response activates our fight-flight-freeze survival mode every time we harbour negative thoughts. Yes, thinking about a shocking incident and talking about it in a negative way again and again can take its toll on the body. My mother was living proof.

The doctor went on to say that medical science has no conclusive idea what causes lichen planus and that there is no cure, although it does sometimes resolve by itself. But, in light of the severity of her case, he wasn't all that optimistic, so he gave her a prescription for an immunosuppressant. It would suppress the immune system and hopefully relieve some of the symptoms, although my mother's body would have to try to cope with horrendous side effects. The doctor told me that I would have to use a syringe to drain the fluid from every blister and then medicate and bandage them like burn wounds. My heart went out to my mum. She didn't deserve this. She was suffering enough emotionally. Still shaking from the news, I went outside to call Rajin.

He answered the phone: 'Mala, you're not going to believe this. Dad and I just had an accident. The tyre burst and the car rolled three times. We were pulled out through the window. We're covered in glass. The car is a write-off.'

I dropped the phone, feeling myself going faint.

Not now, Mala! Mum needs you! Just breathe, breathe deeply.

I picked up the phone and called my brother, Jeevan, who lives in Benoni just outside Johannesburg. He was already at the scene of the accident.

'Jeevan, tell me the truth', I demanded. 'Are Rajin and Dad okay?'

'Yes, I think they're going to be okay. Just shocked and covered in glass right now. We're waiting for the ambulance to arrive so that they can be taken to hospital to have a full check-up'.

Jeevan is a rock in our lives, and I was so glad that he was with Rajin, helping to ease the trauma of the situation. He took control for the moment. I hadn't had a chance to tell him about our mother.

I walked back inside to my mum, who was trying to make sense of what the doctor had just said.

'How far are Rajin and Dad?' she asked.

Oh dear! How do I answer this question? How much more can she take?

I decided not to tell her. This was terribly hard for me. I tell my mum everything. She is our tower of strength and emotional support in the family. Now my main support system was falling apart.

Rajin made it to visit his mother in hospital. She was fragile. He sat at her bedside while my brother picked out bits of glass from his hair.

I hadn't told my mum about the accident and I hadn't told Rajin and Jeevan about Mum's diagnosis. I knew we would make it through but, with both our mothers so ill, the air around me felt thick with pain and suffering, physically as well as emotionally.

I drove my mum to our home. I started the treatment on her 'burn wounds'. She screamed in pain as I drained the fluid. There were so many lesions. I have no idea where I got the strength to nurse the sores while watching her suffer as I worked. I love her so much. She is the most kind and beautiful person in my world. I dressed the wounds and then went into the bathroom to cry my heart out.

The next day my husband and dad were back home. Rajin looked at the prescription from the dermatologist. He explained to me that the drugs recommended were so toxic that my mother would have to have her liver function checked weekly for the next four weeks. We discussed how we could help her.

'Before we try these drugs, we have to find some other way to help your mum. These drugs don't guarantee relief and they have so many side effects', Rajin said.

'Raj, I can't do this any longer. I'm weak at the knees. I'm mentally and physically exhausted', I said.

'I know', he replied. 'This too shall pass, I promise'.

'It's not easy, Raj'.

'You're not alone. Together we can do this. Your mum and I need you now', he said.

'I feel empty. I don't think I have anything left to give', I said, curling up into a foetal position on the bed, wishing I could be back in my mother's womb where everything was perfect.

'I'm extremely sad too. But just knowing you're with me gives me strength', Rajin said.

Hearing these words, I realised that being strong does not mean that we are not hurting on the inside; it just means that we are choosing to trust that *this too shall pass*.

'Help me, Raj. What can we do to get Mum out of her pain?' I asked.

'Let's be real here', he said. 'She brought on this condition with her mind. So I want both of you to take the time to figure out how to reverse it'. He spoke with such certainty. I related our thoughts to my mum, and she was willing to try a natural way to bring relief to her condition.

My life journey up to this point had often been concerned with observing the mind and practising to befriend it. Our mind is one of our greatest assets. More and more, science is showing us how our thoughts and emotions influence our state of mind and our physical well-being. This is very exciting information. In my opinion, it puts us directly in the driver's seat. We are in charge of our thoughts. Nobody can force us to have a particular thought. Only we can decide what to think. The choice is ours. We can decide if we want to have a positive thought or a negative thought. *We can choose!*

My brother contributed significantly to the start of our mother's decision to heal. He told her, 'Mum, if Mala was injured or killed in the fire, you would have said that God could have taken everything, but he should have left your child. Well, Mum, God took everything away, but he did leave your child'.

Hearing this statement, my mother did a complete turnaround in her mind. It looked as if a massive weight was lifted from her shoulders. She looked at me with a glow in her eye and said, 'I am so grateful you weren't trapped in that fire'.

We hugged one another, this time crying with joy for the blessings we had received.

'Okay, Mum, it's time to let go of the lichen planus. I'm going to help you', I said.

My mum has much respect for my research into healing the body with the mind. She was willing to surrender to my suggestions.

My mother's distressing thoughts about the fire had created a perception or awareness in her world that was so destructive, it manifested as burns on her body. We have to take a moment to pause here. If reading about the power of her mind doesn't knock your socks off, you must be reading barefoot! Everything my mum valued materially, everything she had treasured over the years, was kept at the spa. She collected brass artefacts and designer brass items. The collection was her symbol of financial abundance. These items added a touch of class to the décor in the spa. The fire had destroyed everything she had worked so hard to obtain. She had grown up in abject poverty and had been determined to give her own family a better life. With hard work and many sacrifices, she achieved this. I grew up in luxury compared to those around me.

I had underestimated the impact of her losses in the fire. Her material possessions represented her success in life. In a flash, it had all been turned to ashes. Her painful thoughts about the incident were causing her physical illness. Yes, thoughts are powerful. Very powerful. Our thoughts are the foundation of everything we feel and experience in our lives. It's all in the mind. If the mind could be so destructive that it manifested massive burn blisters all over my mother's body, surely it could also be constructive and heal the blisters.

'Mala, what exactly is stress doing to my body?' she asked. 'And why is it that the stress can make me so ill?'

'Those are very good questions, Mum', I said. 'I'd like to explain it to you'.

My mother knew how passionate I felt about stress management. It had all started in our pharmacy twenty years ago, when Rajin pointed out to me that the number of people diagnosed with chronic diseases had increased drastically. He wanted me to do research into the relationship between stress and chronic disease and then implement a programme to help our clients. In my research I was most intrigued to learn about the magnitude of the impact of stress on the physiology of the human body. My consultations with our pharmacy's chronic patients all pointed to stress as being the major factor in their lives, together with poor lifestyle choices. The hundreds of clients that I counselled all felt that it was impossible to find time for themselves. With my background knowledge in biochemistry and chemical pathology, I made it my sole purpose to study the intricacies of the effects of stress on the human body. This journey kindled in me a passion to understand the human being from the perspective of:

- the complex mind-body connection

- the impact of the quantum wave–particle duality on our perception of things
- the ramifications of stress on our physiology and neurobiology.

I was amazed by my findings and wanted to share the information. I compiled a Chronic Disease Management Workbook for our pharmacy's clients. Whenever the occasion presented itself, I wrote articles highlighting the negative impact of prolonged stress on the human body. I also ran numerous stress management workshops at schools and companies, and through other public platforms.

Human beings, just like other animals, have an internal system that is designed to help us save ourselves from harm. Stress is designed to keep us alive. When our brain receives a threat signal, our stress response is activated. Science calls this the fight-flight-freeze response. In a stress situation, our body prepares itself for a physical response. Our reptilian brain signals the release of adrenaline, cortisol and norepinephrine to mobilise the body for action. The body moves into a state of hyperarousal. Brain function is minimised to allow maximum blood flow to the most important muscles needed to fight or flee. Adrenaline increases our heart rate and our breathing becomes more rapid. Our digestive and immune systems also take a backseat to give the body maximum energy to save itself.

In the face of real danger, this stress response will allow us to do things that we sometimes cannot fathom. We have all heard of people jumping over high walls while running from danger or picking up a car that had trapped their loved ones. Our body will go to great lengths to keep us alive when we are threatened.

There is, however, something really important that many of us fail to realise. This fight-flight-freeze stress response starts with a feeling of fear in our mind. If we don't feel this fear in our mind, then our body has no reason to release the stress hormones into our bloodstream. Our body and mind stay focused on digestion, healing, repair and learning. But, when we keep playing a past traumatic experience over and over in our mind, our body does not know that we are just remembering a past experience. The survival stress response gives us the ability to protect ourselves when faced with physical danger. Chemicals including cortisol and adrenaline help to kickstart the body, pushing blood towards the major muscles that give us strength. However, the exact same stress response kicks in when we imagine danger, also producing cortisol and adrenaline and pushing blood around the body. The same chemistry is produced regardless of whether the danger is real or imagined. The brain assumes that everything that our mind focuses on is real and responds accordingly. The problem, then, is that our repetitive negative thoughts move us into an inappropriate hyperarousal state, where we remain stuck.

Merely *thinking* of a past traumatic experience can trigger the fight-flight-freeze response in our body. This build-up of energy has nowhere to go, since the danger is only in the mind. The mind becomes more anxious. Over time, repetition of this thought process creates a toxic environment for our cells and interferes with the harmonious functioning of our organs. Blame, guilt, resentment and regret are fears that trigger a stress response in the body. By contrast, thoughts of acceptance, fun, joy and love shut down the stress response and trigger 'happy' chemicals like endorphins, oxytocin and serotonin in the body. The thoughts we choose and the subsequent feelings we evoke can either hurt us or repair and nourish us on the inside.

'Really, Mala!' Mum exclaimed. 'I had no idea what damage my thoughts and words were causing to my body. I thought I was merely relating our sad story to our family and friends. So many people came to show their support. Everyone wanted a full version of the incident, so I was talking about the fire in such detail over and over to different people on the same day. I've repeated the tragic tale so many times, I've lost count.

'You're right', she continued, 'every time I related the story, I could feel the heat of the flames around me. The feeling of sadness and loss felt more intense every time. When I speak about the fire, I remember myself standing next to you, watching you look so numb with shock while our dream spa went up in flames.

'You are my baby', Mum said. 'How can I stand by and watch my child go through this painful loss? I understand now that I have to stop talking or thinking about the fire. But I don't know how to do this'.

'I can help, Mum', I said. 'Let's do this together'.

The first thing I did was disconnect her from making or receiving any phone calls. No more discussion about the destruction caused by the fire. It was in the past, and we can't change what happened in the past. I then switched off the television and radio. In this way, I was minimising any negative talk or news that would add to the stress my mother was experiencing in her mind. Yes, the fire was traumatic for all of us, but her mind was stuck watching the fire destroy our business. She had spent weeks telling friends and family the traumatic story over and over again. She relayed the incident in minute detail every time she told the story, so much so that her body was living in a stressed fight-flight-freeze mode. That's why her vivid negative emotions and prolonged stress were wreaking havoc on her body. So there Mum was, sitting in the comfort of our home, surrounded by people who love her, yet her system was busy calculating its fight-flight-freeze strategy. This behaviour culminated in a diagnosis of lichen planus. We needed to change her perception of the past.

I believe the exciting news is that we are all just pure energy. At our core, we are consciousness. We are spiritual beings vibrating in an ocean of love. At any moment, we can hit the reset button and restore balance and harmony in our lives. This action is an inside job. We have to close our eyes and consciously enter the inner door to reach our motherboard. Our mainframe, our hard drive, is on the inside. The mind does not like this journey. The mind prefers to stay on the outside. 'Let someone else heal me', says the mind. The mind will do everything in its power to make us believe that we are not skilled or powerful enough to make this inner journey. But our heart, intuition and higher consciousness know better. We are all born with an inner voice that knows – an inner voice that knows how to love and how to heal ourselves.

To help my mum tune in to her inner voice, I intuitively felt that exposing her to soothing sounds would be a good method. Sound healing is one of the oldest forms of healing known to man. Although music therapy is not very widely used clinically, it has been practised by cultures around the world for centuries. Music can move through the brain's auditory cortex directly to the centre of the limbic system[10]. This system governs emotional experiences and basic metabolic responses such as body temperature, blood pressure and heart rate. It can help create new neuropathways in the brain, too.

For Mum, I switched on some Indian classical music. I was raised as a Hindu and introduced to its sounds at an early age. Indian classical music has been shown to excite peptides in the brain and stimulate the production of endorphins – natural opiates secreted by the hypothalamus – producing a feeling of natural euphoria and joy[113]. This might be one of the best natural antidepressants available. I originally felt drawn to the positive impact of sound on the body and mind through the works of sound master Fabien Maman. I learnt about his work while studying Resonance Repatterning under Chloe Faith Wordsworth in the early 2000s.

But even before my interest in sound, I had already started to think about more natural forms of healing. After completing my honours degree in biochemistry, I obtained my master's degree in chemical pathology at the Nelson R. Mandela School of Medicine at the University of KwaZulu-Natal. My brief corporate work experience doing DNA fingerprinting on maize lines came to a halt when we started our family. With a pharmacist as a husband, healing scenarios were a constant battle when our children were still babies. We always questioned the risk-to-benefit ratio of pharmaceutical drugs and looked for the most effective and least toxic option. This stimulated me to pay more attention to the intricacies of healing the human body the way nature intended. So, when I came to Resonance Repatterning, I was glad to be introduced to the healing effects of intention, colour, light, movement, breathing and sound, among many others.

With the help of Indian classical music, Mum chose to let go of the negative talk about the fire at the spa. She filled her time with beautiful, soothing sounds, deep breathing and meditation. She trusted the process. She also changed the way she spoke about the fire to me. She kept reminding both of us that money can be replaced but human life cannot. We kept our thoughts on gratitude.

She set the intention to heal. About six times a day, she would lie down, set her intention for her body to heal itself and consciously listen to the music. I watched my mum take on a peaceful persona. She was sending a very clear message to her body that she believed in its intelligence to heal itself. It worked. Within three weeks, she managed to surprise the dermatologist at her follow-up visit. He couldn't believe what he saw. The blisters were gone and all that remained were some scars. He wanted to know if he could help her by bleaching the skin to bring back its original colour.

She looked at him and smiled. 'No thanks, Doctor. My body will bring back the colour by itself', she proudly declared.

I too was in awe of the speed of her recovery. While mild cases of lichen planus can clear within two years, healing severe cases like my mum's is unpredictable.

My mum is such an inspiration in my life. For as long as I can remember, she has started her day with meditation, followed by a shower, and then she goes outside to perform her sun salutations. She deeply values our magnificent sun and pays homage to it daily, showing her gratitude. I have learnt many valuable lessons from my mum and made them part of my world. Beyond self-respect and discipline, determination, resilience and faith stand out.

My mother had to leave school at the age of twelve to help her family survive. She was a determined child: she ran many businesses, which ultimately culminated in a successful take-away business as an adult. She believes that, if you don't like your situation, do something about it. It's only in challenging times that we can find our strengths and true potential. She has shown me this so many times in her life.

Although she faced many hardships as a young woman, she never gave up – she was resilient. As a young teenager, she took it upon herself to be the breadwinner in her family when her father lost his job. She financially supported her five sisters and two brothers with absolute love. After getting married, she continued to work hard and contribute financially to her family and friends. She sprinkles kindness and compassion wherever she goes.

No matter what the circumstance, she strongly believes in a higher power. The combination of her determination, resilience and faith is in her go-to line: 'Get up and make the effort, then leave the rest in Baba Ji's hands. He knows best, and He always comes through for us'.

4
Riding the waves to unbeknown disaster

The joy we felt over Mum's speedy recovery was unfortunately short-lived. Two weeks later, my mother-in-law came to Pietermaritzburg to recover further from her operation. Rajin was both stressed about our finances and despondent about his mother. I drove to the pharmacy where he was the locum at the time, while we were waiting for our Dalton pharmacy's licence. We were sharing one car, so I wanted to pick him up during his lunch break, because I felt that he needed to be with his mother. He needed to feel a mother's love telling him that everything was going to be okay. I picked up a chocolate cake for her and we were on our way. He was so sad, he didn't even want to drive, so I drove. I took a route that we use daily. I was trying to encourage him to be more optimistic about his mother. It hurt so much to see his pain. We were chatting when suddenly he screamed, 'Watch out!'

All I heard was a massive bang and then I felt the car spinning out of control. Lights out.

I woke up to find Rajin slumped against me. The front of the car was completely smashed.

A young woman was standing next to our car repeating, 'I'm so sorry, I'm so sorry. I didn't see the stop sign. I'm so sorry. Don't move. The ambulance is on its way'.

She had gone through a stop sign and driven into our car.

Rajin wasn't moving. I tried to shake him. Not for a second did I consider that he could be badly injured.

'Wake up, Raj, you're crushing me', I said.

He opened his eyes. 'What happened?' he slurred.

The ambulance arrived. We were taken to hospital.

Rajin was concussed and suffering visual disturbances. Everything was blurred. 'How am I going to work like this?' he panicked.

In my case, I experienced severe pain in my chest area from a hairline fracture in my ribs. The next day, vertigo set in. The dizziness was extreme. As soon as I stood up, everything around me would start to spin. I was basically bedridden.

Our family and friends were shocked to hear about our accident. 'How much more can a couple endure?' they asked. Rajin and I were too afraid to answer that question. We celebrated both of us surviving the accident. It felt as if we were becoming numb to the drama of life. We didn't analyse. We just picked ourselves up and continued. We realised that not reacting didn't mean that we were okay with what had just happened; it just meant that we were choosing to rise above it.

A week after the accident, I attended a school function, hanging on tightly to my dad as I entered the venue. The headmaster walked up to me to find out why my dad couldn't walk on his own. When I related the car accident to him, and that I was the one who couldn't walk on my own, he just shook his head and said, 'Well, Mala, even gold has to endure the extreme heat purification process to become a brilliant precious metal'.

My doctor informed me that the vertigo was here to stay. He said I would probably never drive again. No amount of medication alleviated the dizziness. After spending two weeks in bed, I decided to try something different. I created a safe space in our carpeted bedroom. I asked my mum to be there when I did this exercise: I would stand up and, even though I felt the room was spinning, I would start turning clockwise, twenty-one times, with my hands outstretched at shoulder height, palms open and facing downwards. I did the exercise five times a day. Initially, I fell down many times. But I persisted. Within a week, the vertigo symptoms were gone forever. I had hit upon my own vestibular rehabilitation therapy that worked.

Our car was written off. Since it was an old car, the insurance pay-out was not enough to replace it. At least, with God's grace, Rajin's eyes were back to normal in three weeks.

Without a car, getting our children to and from school was a challenge. We managed to organise lifts for them, but we missed our special morning routine in the car. It included chanting eleven repetitions of a verse from the Rigveda called Mahamrityunjaya Mantra, which goes as follows:

Om tryambakam yajāmahe sugandhim puṣṭivardhanam
urvārukamiva bandhanān mṛtyor mukṣīya mā'mṛtāt

This would be followed by our prayers of thanks and positive affirmations for the day.

'Thank you for our happy family'.

'Thank you for helping Aya get well today'.

'I have fun with my friends today'.

'Maths and physics are simple and easy. I pass my test with ease'.

'I am superfast in the pool today. I excel in swimming'.

This had been our special time, getting ready for the day ahead. Although we were grateful to everyone who helped us, the boys couldn't help being unhappy with this new arrangement. They wanted their mum to drive them to school.

The next thing I knew, my sister Devi arrived from Johannesburg and handed me her car keys.

'Mala, you need to get your children to school', she said. 'Don't worry about me, I will join a lift club'.

'Thank you so much, Devi', I said, choking up with tears. 'I don't know what else to say'.

I hadn't driven a manual car in ten years. Devi gave me one lesson and returned to her commitments in Johannesburg. Rajin and I were simply blown away by this act of kindness. My sister was willing to compromise on her own comfort so that our boys could get to school in comfort. I kept her car for six long months. She never once asked for it back.

The new shopping complex was ready in Dalton. The only problem was that we weren't. Rajin left me with the responsibility of getting the new pharmacy fitted while he tried to bring in additional income by doing locum work.

'How do we do this, Raj, without any money?'

'Go on, Mala, work your magic', he said.

'Come on, this is a tall order. We have no money and no equipment and fittings. The last time we refurbished our pharmacy, I spent close to a million rand on the renovations, remember'.

'I honestly don't know what to do', he said, frowning.

I sat in the empty building and just smiled to myself. The Creator was certainly testing my creative skills. I approached our landlord and discussed our unique situation with him. He saw the potential of our pharmacy in his centre and valued Rajin's experience and good name in the pharmaceutical industry. He agreed to install the air-conditioning at his cost and to build us a concrete wall that could be used as a counter. He also said that I could help myself to a trailer full of old shelving.

With zero carpentry skills, our gardener, Patrick, as my assistant and a spirit level and hammer in my hand, I set off to get our pharmacy fitted. Rummaging through the pile of old discarded shelving, I was in tears, remembering the cherry-wood furnishings that I had picked out for our previous pharmacy. In a flash, we had gone from living in financial abundance to being financially challenged.

Let go of the past. Make the best of this moment! You got your foot in the door, Mala. Don't complain that the foot is squashed and feeling pain. You got your foot in the door!

It was hard to remain positive. I kept reflecting on my past decisions: I am a fairly intelligent woman. How did I not invest appropriately? Sometimes I blamed myself for our financial state. I felt angry. I felt cheated. I felt guilty. I felt humiliated. These emotions would greet me each morning. I made every effort to shift into a space of gratitude. Focusing on gratitude instead of fear gave me the strength to take positive action. Once I became fearless, life became boundless with opportunity and kindness.

What was so interesting to me was to see how differently my ego and Rajin's ego responded to our challenging situation. For me, it was painful to watch my husband restart at forty-three. Where was this emotional pain coming from? My ego was producing it. I felt that we had failed. Up until that point, our challenges had been mere bumps in the road by comparison. It was no easy task getting up every morning only to be reminded of our financial burdens.

Rajin, on the other hand, was completely oblivious to what others might think. He was focused on moving forward. Like the alpha male in the jungle, he made every effort to provide for and protect his family. He refused to entertain any conversation that hinted at disaster. His secret was to take it one day at a time. He understood his pain so well. He never allowed himself to dwell on the difficulty of the situation.

He kept reminding me of our blessings. 'Don't be sad', he would say. 'I promise I'll work hard and get it all back. I'm just grateful that I didn't lose you in that fire or the car accident. To you, things may look hopeless right now. Not to me. God saved you, Mala. For that I am eternally grateful. I have nothing to mourn. Together you and I are unstoppable'.

'I agree. We have to trust that things will get better'.

I pushed myself. I started a gratitude journal. With tears flowing down my cheeks, I would write in my journal: *I can see. I can walk. I have a bed to sleep in. I have food on my table today. I have a beautiful family. I have an awareness of the divine intelligence that permeates everything.* There were so many blessings to be grateful for. I repeated the words 'thank you' throughout my day. *Thank you, thank you, thank you.*

Focusing on gratitude instead of fear gave me the strength to take positive action. I focused my energy on getting the new pharmacy in Dalton ready. Doing physical work made the time go faster. I cleaned the old metal shelves and knocked them straight. It took Patrick and me a few days, but we got the entire pharmacy fitted. The next step was computers and software. But how? Time to negotiate again. Thankfully we got it all installed based on our excellent long-standing relationship with our software company. Then our stock materialised as if by magic. Everyone in the industry wanted to help. When the doors opened, it felt like a ray of sunshine had entered our hearts.

Rajin appreciated the beautiful drive to work. He had no complaints about the jalopy we had bought which was very different to the luxury cars he was used to driving. With a deep sense of trust and faith, he opened his pharmacy doors on time for business every day and waited patiently. Business was slow initially, but every day was busier than the previous one, with more and more wonderful people coming in. His leisurely days at work were very short-lived. News of this highly competent and committed pharmacist spread rapidly in the area. As the business grew, the debt quickly reduced.

Money to buy more stock for our pharmacy remained a problem, however. Luckily a businessman who was keen to start up his own pharmacy approached us to help him design his business according to the South African law. We helped him to draw up the plans and saw it through to completion. We also helped him to employ the right staff for his business and put him in contact with the best computer companies and wholesalers. This was hard work that took many hours, but we could use the consultation fee we received to buy stock for our business in Dalton. It was certainly a blessing from the Divine to have had this financial opportunity.

With enough stock on the shelves, our business grew steadily every day. The community around us realised what a wealth of information Rajin held when it came to healing. His love and care for his customers, coupled with his exceptional work ethic, quickly attracted clients from far and wide. We worked long hours to ensure the success of our new business. I was exhausted all the time. My list of commitments did not allow time for ensuring that our sons' homework was complete. My emotions fluctuated between gratitude for our source of income and guilt and sadness for not paying enough attention to our children. I had to remain focused on maintaining our pharmacy customers and growing our business so that we could sustain our income. Our children were very supportive and understood that not having Mum around applauding on the sports field or fetching them from school and spending the afternoons and evenings together, as we had always done, was only a temporary situation. Once we could afford more staff, I worked only half-days at the pharmacy and spent my afternoons and evenings with our boys again.

Looking back, I realise that the best thing we did during those tough times was to communicate with each other. We would have daily discussions with our children about our financial situation. Rajin was very tactful with the way he spoke to us. He kept emphasising that it was just a temporary setback and we would definitely get back on our feet very soon. In the meantime, we wanted to come up with new ways to enjoy our time together as a family.

'Okay, boys, I need your help. Let's brainstorm how we can spend less money and still have fun', Raj said.

'I know!' shouted Tharsheyen with excitement. 'Let's play soccer at the school grounds'.

'That's a brilliant plan!' Raj replied, matching his enthusiasm.

So we entertained our children on the weekends by going to the school grounds and kicking a ball around. It was *free*. We had sandwiches and water as our snack. We enjoyed long hours in the sun just talking and laughing with our children. Looking back, I would guess that this was the magical miracle antidepressant that got us through our week.

One evening, years later, when we were all seated at our dining room table, I casually asked our children, 'What do you consider the happiest time in your life thus far?' and their answer simply blew me away.

Both our sons agreed that it was the time when Mum and Dad played soccer with them and laughed and chatted with them so much on the field.

'What about our trip to Cape Town together, or the golf weekend at Pezula Golf Estate in Knysna?' I asked.

'No', they replied, 'soccer with Mum and Dad was better'.

'How about the trip to Kruger National Park or the golf weekend we enjoyed at Sun City?'

Again, they shook their heads. 'Yes, it was fun, Mum, but the soccer days were the best!'

As our pharmacy business grew, the paperwork also grew, and the only time Rajin could complete it was on the weekends. So the soccer days decreased, and the PlayStation hours increased. After all, we could now afford to buy them PlayStation games. We thought that's what they wanted, since all their friends had it.

It was certainly an eye-opener to experience our children describing one of the lowest times in our lives as being some of the best times that they had enjoyed with us. It hadn't cost any money – it had cost us our time and undivided attention. We didn't have to go out there and look for happiness. Our love for one another filled us with joy. We all received tremendous strength and comfort from simply holding and hugging each other and playing and laughing together.

Two years after our spa had been razed to the ground, soccer brought another potent pick-me-up to us all: the 2010 FIFA World Cup arrived in our country. The four of us bonded deeply thanks to South Africa hosting the World Cup. Watching the opening game on TV, armed with our vuvuzelas, our children and I were ecstatic when South Africa scored the first goal. Even though we were watching the game at home, it was still electrifying.

We are passionate about soccer in our home. With the lead-up to the FIFA World Cup, we discussed our financial situation as a family and agreed that we could afford one first-round match in Durban. The tickets for the first round were affordable and, since Pietermaritzburg isn't too far from Durban, we wouldn't have to worry about accommodation costs. We went online and bought four tickets for Germany vs Australia. Rajin had supported Germany for all of his adult life and wanted to watch them play in person.

The day finally arrived when we could take our sons to a World Cup soccer match. Sitting in the Moses Mabhida Stadium with my husband and our sons made me feel incredibly happy. Rajin had a good feeling about one German player, Thomas Müller, a young up-and-coming talent. He got the three of us so excited about watching Müller play – and he was brilliant. He scored the third of Germany's four goals.

Germany won the match 4 – 0 and we followed the team closely for the rest of the tournament.

The energy in our country soared with the World Cup. And how we wished we could go to more games. We had the best soccer players right on our doorstep. We joined a few screenings at fan parks, which was great fun, but the boys and I wanted just one more game. The Germany vs England round-of-sixteen game was the one we all wanted to be at. We are avid followers of the English Premier League and we felt it would be a dream come true to see these world-class soccer professionals in person.

Rajin came home from the pharmacy one day with a big smile on his face. 'I have been doing the maths: our business is growing. It's going to be a bit of a squeeze again for the next few months, but I think we deserve to give ourselves a treat. We have all been through so much. Let's not miss this opportunity. Germany vs England, here we come!'

This is amazing. Is this really happening?

The match was in Bloemfontein, a six-hour drive from our home, on a Sunday evening. We couldn't afford a locum for Monday at the pharmacy, but we didn't let that bother us. We would deal with the logistics of getting home on time later. This was an opportunity to celebrate.

Prior to the match the atmosphere outside the stadium was filled with exuberant expectation. The four of us were mingling with passionate soccer fans from around the world. The match exceeded all my expectations. Both teams were so close to the quarter-finals. The stadium was filled with fans who believed that their team simply had to go through. The zoom on my camera even captured David Beckham's expression on the sideline when England's goal was disallowed. So much action.

I was overjoyed watching the talent of some of the greatest players to grace the soccer pitch at the time, including Miroslav Klose, Lukas Podolski, Steven Gerrard, Frank Lampard and Wayne Rooney. What a delightful feast for my eyes. I can confidently say that on the day of the match every bit of trauma of the events that had followed the destructive fire just melted away. The match, the fans, the players, the atmosphere – it was all so intense, there was no room for past pain in my mind. Just big smiles and absolute joy. I felt so free.

On a deeper level, I must admit that I was enjoying the healing that came with this opportunity. It was so refreshing to laugh and smile from the inside. After losing the spa, it had been brutally exhausting trying to put up a front that I was okay with everything that was happening around me. I was trying so hard to hide the shame and disappointment I felt towards myself. On the outside, I had created a tough image of myself. I wanted to be strong for Raj and our boys. I would smile and look composed, yet on the inside I was hurting. Being part of the FIFA World Cup gave me a chance to focus on something fun and exciting instead of all the financial drama that had consumed me for the last two years.

The match ended late on Sunday night and it was hours before we left the parking lot. It was past midnight.

'Okay, Raj, I will drive us home and you try to get some sleep', I suggested.

The heavy mist made the driving conditions difficult. I had never driven these roads before and felt uncomfortable behind the wheel. At the rate I was driving, we would never get home on time to get Raj to work. *Come on universe, I need some help, please.* The next thing I saw was a brightly lit bus entering my lane.

It was the first time I had seen a bus so lit up at the back: its entire rear was covered in lights. It felt as if I was being guided home. The bus driver seemed to know the contours of the road very well and was driving at the speed limit, which was much faster than I was going. *Stick with him, Mala. Don't let him get too far ahead.* For the next two hundred kilometres I managed to match his speed. By the time the mist cleared I was on familiar roads again. We reached home just in time for Rajin to shower and leave for the pharmacy. He worked a full day, so euphoric from our adventure, he forgot how tired he was.

The pharmacy was getting busier every day and my Resonance Repatterning consultation business, which I had set up at home, was taking off. Resonance Repatterning is a system of healing that enables us to take unconscious beliefs that are limiting us and transform them into coherent life-enhancing opportunities. I was also successful in starting up an agency in our province for a natural product that I believed in. Riding on Rajin's popularity in the wellness industry, my agency took off very quickly. I used all my research, marketing and presentation skills and brought in an income that was quite phenomenal, given the short space of time. We had worked so hard and now the sting of financial loss was starting to ease.

Our entire country was FIFA World Cup crazy. Everywhere we looked, we were reminded of this unbelievable opportunity that our country had given us. We were hosts to the most watched game in the world. For the entire month, the whole world had their eyes on South Africa. The resonance of joy in our country was filtering into our home. All our family members were mesmerised by World Cup excitement. The final was going to be epic. No one in the house said it, but we were all thinking it: we wanted to go to the final.

'Let's be fair', Rajin said. 'Even if we could afford it, it's impossible to get tickets to the final at this late stage'.

We all agreed. And yet the four of us gravitated to the computer room to put this issue to bed. Rajin opened the website and requested four tickets to the final. The result on the screen left us speechless. Tickets were still available.

'Okay, guys', Raj said with a naughty grin across his face, 'what does this mean?'

We were all having so much fun with the World Cup. Our children had been so patient with us. We wanted the ultimate experience: to be at the final. They were old enough to remember this exhilarating experience for the rest of their lives.

'Let's go for it!' we declared.

We were so caught up in the moment that we felt that Jeevan and my nephew, whom we love to socialise with, should be there too. We went online and bought not four but six tickets to the final. I remember smiling so much my face hurt.

For many people being at the final was a special, enjoyable moment. For my family it was more than special – it was healing. I am eternally grateful to my husband for making the decision to be part of this happy moment. He was fully aware of the financial pressure he was putting himself under when he bought the tickets. It was a gamble he felt he had to take. We had so much fun at the game. The closing ceremony felt like the end of sadness and heartache for our family.

Rajin expressed the delight he felt at watching our sons enjoy the games live at the stadium. It made his heart so much lighter. It gave him the drive to get up in the morning and try harder. Instead of feeling sorry for ourselves and licking our wounds, Rajin used the World Cup to catapult our family into a world of joy, fun and laughter. The endorphin high before the final kick-off in the Soccer City stadium in Johannesburg was the medication our family needed.

Although financial challenges would still crop up from time to time, including shortly after the World Cup, Rajin and I focused on growing our pharmacy with appreciation and gratitude for the people who supported us. My Resonance Repatterning wellness practice flourished and I accepted many invitations to speak on stress management in the corporate world. Before we knew it, the fire was five years behind us, and Pavesan was writing his final matric examinations. The energy in our home was comfortable and hopeful. There were no more discussions about tightening up – perhaps because we wanted less. We had more appreciation for what we had. Every day we paid attention to the comforts we enjoyed. Our family drew much strength from staying close together and being honest with and supporting each other. We discussed everything at our dinner table. Having a solid connection with our internal divine source made the experience profoundly enlightening. We are still in awe of the strength each one of us brought to the table.

Contentment can be a powerful force. It allowed me to let go and just be. It removed my shackles of worry and opened the door to the possibility of feeling joy again. The former spiritual leader of the Divine Life Society, Sri Swami Chidananda Saraswati[140], makes it clear: 'Contentment is the true secret of affirming your abundance. Whatever comes, feel full. Once you have contentment, there is nothing that can make you unhappy. If you don't have contentment, nothing can make you happy'.

The next few years were spent happily rebuilding our business and appreciating the blessing of getting back on our feet. We enjoyed each other's company. Life seemed to be smiling brightly on the Naidoo family. Pavesan was away at university studying pharmacy and Tharsheyen was just three years away from completing high school. The community served by the pharmacy embraced us as family. We enjoyed mutual respect and appreciation from our customers.

We learnt to respect and appreciate our financial abundance. We were much more conscious about distinguishing between what we needed and what we wanted. Our children had learnt to appreciate how fortunate we were with the luxuries we enjoyed. We all became more conscious about sharing. The joy of giving to strangers and those less fortunate than us was nature's way of allowing our family to transcend the theme of destruction and suffering.

Another great lesson Rajin and I were learning was the joy of simple pleasures. Through our children, we learnt that, as long as Mum and Dad are happy around them, their world is complete. I hadn't realised how true it is that a child's greatest joy doesn't come from things. As parents, we work so hard, believing that having more money will allow us to buy more for our children and that this will make them happy. But what they desire most is our time.

Our business was now fully stocked. The days of standing in the pharmacy idle, waiting for customers to arrive, were far behind us. I remember when Rajin used to read novels at work to help pass the time. Now he could barely find a couple of minutes for a loo break. As the business grew, we ensured that every person we owed money to was reimbursed. We could even afford a second car. The experience taught us that, together, Raj and I have the strength to get us through anything. But we had no idea what we were yet to face.

I remember sitting in the restaurant full of smiles. We could afford to eat out. I had spent the day at the pharmacy and driven back to Pietermaritzburg with Rajin. It was rare to have him with me so early in the evening. We had fetched Tharsheyen from school and decided to go out for supper together. Waiting for our food to arrive, we could hear the rain coming down heavily. It continued pouring buckets throughout our meal. Watching the rain and enjoying our food, we never imagined that something sinister was unfolding at home.

As we drove up to our house, we could tell that this was no ordinary downpour. There were fallen branches strewn across the road. Water was gushing out of the manholes. Our driveway looked like a river. We pulled into the garage and parked the car. Rajin unlocked the door and stepped into the house.

'The floor feels wet!' he exclaimed. Then he turned the lights on.

Nothing could have prepared us for what we saw. There was water and thick sludge everywhere. Rajin and I froze. Tharsheyen walked ahead.

'Dad, the water and mud is everywhere! It's a disaster!'

'Oh no! No! No! Now what do we do?' Rajin cried out in horror.

We continued to walk through the house in absolute shock, water spluttering with every step. All the rooms were covered in mud. I felt a hollow sensation in my chest and my legs grew heavy.

'Don't touch anything until we've had a chance to contact the insurance company', I said.

The beautiful stream that entered our garden from the forest on the hillside behind our house had turned into a powerful river that tore down our retaining wall and flowed right through our entire house, bringing debris and destruction with it. Every piece of furniture was standing in water. The mud had even flooded the pool at the front. Our home was completely ruined.

Do not cry. Do not break down, Mala.

The house was so badly damaged that it was unsafe for us to stay there. Unfortunately, our insurance company made our living arrangements and our life hell. We had to switch accommodation again and again, because we trusted that our home would be restored as promised, within two weeks. Instead it took four long months.

The insurance company dragged out the claim. I spent a huge amount of time fighting a losing battle with them as well as the assessors and the construction workers. I was oblivious to the fact that the strain and stress of my response to their behaviour was draining the life energy out of me. I was just so desperate to have the house fixed properly with the least possible financial strain on Rajin. There were countless on-site meetings and back-and-forth emails and telephone calls. The unpleasant discussions even led to arguments. The longer the insurance company took, the less patience I had.

Over the four months, to ensure that all the repairs were carried out properly, I worked eighteen hours a day at home, having discussions with the insurance company and the construction workers under difficult conditions. I set up a work area on the veranda, the only spot in our house that didn't need renovations, for emailing and paperwork. All the other rooms were under construction. The pool had to be fixed and a new retaining boundary wall had to be completed. The problems were endless.

I had to make sure that the insurance company did not shirk their responsibility. Halfway through the claim, they changed the assessor. He kept trying to reduce the insurance company's liability, so I had to constantly be on guard to see that we were not financially compromised. This was frustrating and exhausting for me, both physically and mentally.

Every day for those four months, Rajin would arrive home from the pharmacy and point out all the flaws in the workmanship of that day's construction. The list of snags was never-ending. The next day it was my task to ensure that the work was corrected. The construction company showed no commitment to getting the job done correctly. Every day a different team arrived on site, and I was left with the task of managing them.

I never once questioned why our house was flooded. I accepted it as my destiny. But I did fail to realise how often I felt infuriated by the standard of workmanship the insurance company expected us to accept. I made no time for myself. I rationalised that, the harder I worked, the sooner we could get our house and life back to normal. I ranted and raved at the absurd suggestions of the assessors. I remember the one day I screamed over the phone to the construction company, because they had started another job and couldn't tell me when they would be back to complete ours. I was trembling with anger for being treated this way. Rajin decided that working with the insurance company was pointless, so we agreed to start over on our own financial strength. The stress continued. As we were doing this on an owner-builder basis, I now had to manage many individual tradesmen and their teams to get the job done.

Finally, all the work on our house was completed, but our finances were once again challenged. The many difficult calls to the insurance company, and the toxic emotional battle that had ensued, dampened the relief of our house being beautiful again. My collapsing body mimicked my exhausted mind. By the time the renovations were complete, I was bedridden with exhaustion. I couldn't manage the fatigue.

Tharsheyen was in grade ten at the time. It became impossible for me to drive him to school. I had neglected him for the last four months while trying to renovate the house after the flood. Now that the house was complete, I still wasn't there for him. I remember the look of abandonment in his eyes when I remained in bed instead of helping him with breakfast and driving him to school. He had been so patient with me for so long.

I suddenly found myself experiencing dreadful mood swings. There was a deep sense of emptiness and worthlessness in me. I would become angry and bitter towards Rajin and the rest of my family for no particular reason. Every word Rajin said seemed to annoy me. I could not understand what was happening to me. I felt a strong urge to swear and shout, something that was totally out of character for me and not common practice in our home.

I visited my doctor with Rajin, in the hope of getting a diagnosis. After examining me, she said, 'Mrs Naidoo, your symptoms clearly point to burnout, considering how hard you've pushed yourself physically and emotionally for the past months. I suggest that you take some time out to relax and allow your body to recuperate'.

I turned to Rajin and reassured him: 'See, there's nothing to worry about. I'll be back to normal in a jiffy'.

'Okay', he said, 'take some time to rest'.

I spent many hours moving from the jacuzzi in our beautiful garden, which overlooks a golf course in the distance, to the sauna in our gym. For the past twenty years, I had always enjoyed my time in our jacuzzi, sipping cocktails while listening to the sounds of nature and taking in the beauty of the lush garden around me. I relished sitting there, bubbling with life and watching the birds take a drink of water from the cascading water feature. The strong-scented *Brunfelsia*, a yesterday-today-and-tomorrow shrub, with its fascinating display of purple and white flowers, added to the relaxation. The tall banana trees, fighting for attention alongside the exotic palm trees, transported me to a tropical paradise island. But now, as I sat in the jacuzzi, the pleasurable sensation of the water against my skin was gone. I only experienced numbness and fatigue.

I increased the time I spent indulging in these two activities, unaware that they were dangerous and detrimental to my undiagnosed condition. I reasoned that being in the jacuzzi, in the beautiful garden setting, was the perfect way to relax my muscles and soothe the aches and pains and thus rejuvenate my body. The next day I would opt for the sauna with its far-infrared feature, designed to detoxify and heal. My body was so numb from all the tingling that I couldn't feel the heat of the sauna and overdid my stay often, nearly dozing off while listening to my favourite love songs.

I was exhausted all the time and desperate to feel better again. I was convinced that the soothing hot water in the jacuzzi and the therapeutic far-infrared radiation of the sauna would invigorate my body and facilitate my healing. Sadly, instead of emerging relaxed and revived, I felt sicker and more indisposed. I was weak, exhausted and miserable. Holding up my head felt too difficult – so heavy. I didn't want to get out of bed. I just couldn't seem to get into gear. My get-up-and-go had got up and left.

The exhausted feeling from the flood renovations was, however, only one of many symptoms. It was 2014, almost six years after the fire at the spa, in the chilly month of June, when I started experiencing an inferno of a different kind – on the inside. Relentless burning, tingling, prickling pains throughout my body. Even my tongue started to burn – an exceedingly uncomfortable sensation. It didn't matter how much I tried to get better, my body seemed unable to function normally. I was still convinced that I was just burnt out and needed a few more days, but none of my remedies and no amount of rest seemed to work. I looked and felt drained, exhausted, ill. Having spent quite a while cooped up at home, I thought that spending a day out at a prestigious racing event might cheer me up as it had in the past.

5
When you can't get back in the saddle

The Durban July is Africa's greatest horse-racing event, abounding in glitz and glamour. It puts the continent's best thoroughbred horses on display to more than fifty thousand visitors and is televised around the world. Every horse owner dreams of winning this race and every horse-racing enthusiast dreams of attending the event.

I remember in 1989, as a student majoring in genetics, going to my very first Durban July Handicap, as it was more commonly known back then. I was intrigued by both the unique fashion designs the visitors flaunted and the rich history of the horses' bloodlines that is an integral part of the sport. For racehorse owners, the prestige of winning the race lies in the champion going on to become the most sought-after stallion or mare in the breeding barns of South Africa.

My best Durban July experience was in 2003, when Rajin enthused about a horse called Dynasty. His admiration was born of our encounter on the racetrack against this horse. In 2002, one of the best horses we owned, a six-time winner, Dancing Alliance, was attempting to win the Grade 1 Cape Derby when his colours were lowered by Dynasty. We knew then that Dynasty was a very special racehorse.

Dynasty was attempting to win the Vodacom Durban July from draw twenty. This is considered an impossible task, because it's the widest draw on the racetrack, meaning the horse actually has to run a greater distance. Dean Kannemeyer, the trainer, had engaged South African-born jockey Robbie Fradd, the then resident Hong Kong duel champion, to ride the horse. He was famous for his ability to read the race situation and make split-second decisions to get the best out of his horse.

The build-up to the Durban July is four months of pure excitement for Rajin. On the day, the two of us were standing on the third floor of the Greyville Racecourse in breathless anticipation. We were wearing matching avant-garde outfits, designed especially for us for the glamorous occasion.

Finally, the moment arrived. In my mind I can still hear race commentator Craig Peters saying, 'And away they go in the 2003 Vodacom Durban July!' It was a rough race, but Fradd kept Dynasty out of trouble at the back of the field. He had to make up almost twelve lengths in the home straight. As they turned for home, Craig Peters said, 'Here comes Dynasty, swooping through on the outside'.

I joined the thousands of racing fans on the course as we shouted and urged him on. I can still hear the thundering hooves as Dynasty sliced through the field, getting up to win with absolute authority. I was tingling with joy. Both Rajin and I were delirious. We stayed for all twelve races and partied late into the night at the traditional July After Party at the racecourse. The thrill of Dynasty's victory was exhilarating and lasted for weeks to come. There was no doubt that both Rajin and I had fun at the races.

Eleven years later, at the 2014 Durban July, one of Dynasty's sons, called Legislate, was attempting to repeat his father's feat of 2003. Rajin was certain that Dynasty's progeny had the class and pedigree to win the race. However, as much as he loved attending this event, he felt that I was in no condition to go. But I insisted on our attending the race meeting, hoping that it would be a distraction from my pain and discomfort.

I remember walking through the gates of the racecourse in a pair of jeans and a medical moonboot to brace my right foot. I had no energy to dress up. My ankle was throbbing and my body felt numb with pain. As I made my way up to our usual spot on the third floor, this time round, instead of the euphoria, excitement and expectation, I was drenched in discomfort and sadness. I felt depleted of energy. As the commentator's voice echoed, 'And away they go in the 2014 running of the Vodacom Durban July', I wished it was me that could go … away from the racecourse.

As the horses turned for home and Legislate started to make his move forward, the crowd went wild with excitement. Their cheering in anticipation of his victory and the thundering of the hooves in the home straight distressed me: the loud noise felt like an explosion of pain in my body – everything was tingling and burning. The loud, high-pitched voices felt like thousands of needles pricking me all over. I couldn't hide the pain and discomfort any longer.

Rajin was shouting and jumping with joy as the horses approached the finish line. He turned to me to share his elation, but all he saw was tears of misery running down my cheeks. He dropped his race card, grabbed hold of my hand and took me to the car. He drove straight to the hospital. The next morning, when he came to visit me there, he brought the Sunday newspaper. The headline read: LEGISLATE REPEATS FATHER'S FEAT IN WINNING THE 2014 VODACOM DURBAN JULY.

That was our last Durban July and the first of numerous visits to the hospital. After doing a few blood tests and a nerve conduction test, the neurologist said he couldn't find a cause for my symptoms. I told him it was possibly due to burnout. He discharged me and asked me to come back if the symptoms persisted.

Rajin started to worry about my medical condition. More visits to the hospital didn't help. The doctors picked up nothing, but my symptoms persisted. I could barely move to the bathroom. I was tired all the time, the life seemed to have been sucked out of me. No appetite. What was happening? I was drained and moody all the time. All my muscles and joints started to hurt. The tingling intensified.

More visits to the hospital and still no answers. Another nerve conduction test: the test showed that everything was fine.

The doctor looked me in the eye and said, 'There's nothing wrong with you, Mrs Naidoo. You may go home'.

But I was far from okay. My body felt as if I had barely survived being hit by a train. I may not have looked physically injured, yet every part of me felt hammered. I hurt from head to toe.

I tried to reassure Rajin that I was just suffering from burnout from dealing with the insurance company and renovating our home after the flood. He wasn't convinced. He persisted with his own investigation to help me. I was very ill. Movement was becoming a challenge. My legs felt heavy. The tingling pain was intense. Disorientation and depression were setting in. After three months of discussions with our doctors, Rajin finally persuaded the neurologist to look into a brain tumour.

The doctor ordered an MRI. A magnetic resonance image of the brain gives a clear view of brain function. I was still convinced that this was all unnecessary, that my body just needed a bit more time to recover from the burnout.

The results of the MRI arrived while I was asleep. I opened my eyes to find a big white envelope on my hospital bedside table. I opened it, intrigued at the thought of my brain being photographed. But what I opened was a Pandora's box. Looking at the results was a gut-wrenching experience. I knew that events were already unfolding, and I was powerless to stop them. I felt like I was in the path of a massive tornado – destined to be annihilated.

6
The debilitating symptoms that come with a dreaded diagnosis

Throughout my master's studies in chemical pathology and my experience in the medical research field at the Nelson R. Mandela School of Medicine, I never had the opportunity to focus on the details of this condition.

I called Rajin. 'Raj, I'm scared. What do you know about multiple sclerosis?'.

'Oh no ... Are you ... are you sure?' he stammered

'That's what the scan showed', I replied.

The next thing I knew, he was at my bedside sobbing.

We looked at the MRI scans together. There were so many lesions in my spine and brain: my MRI scan had lit up alarmingly. We both realised that I was in serious trouble.

The neurologist arrived and suggested that we work fast. There was a sence of urgency around my hospital bed. He ordered a lumbar puncture to test for oligoclonal bands and a full list of blood tests. Oligoclonal bands are proteins that collect in a patient's blood plasma or cerebrospinal fluid when there is inflammation of the central nervous system. The lumbar puncture was positive for oligoclonal bands, so it was confirmed: I had MS.

'Multiple sclerosis', the neurologist explained, 'is an inflammatory disease of the central nervous system that affects the brain and spinal cord. It's an unpredictable, often disabling disease that forms lesions in the brain. The lesions disrupt the flow of information in the brain and between the brain and body'.

'What does this mean?' I asked.

'When a disruption happens, the nerves can't conduct information properly so, depending on the area of the brain under attack, the body loses its function. In your case, Mrs Naidoo, I'm so sorry ...' He shook his head. 'Your case is extremely difficult! There are many lesions in your spine and over twenty lesions in your brain alone, most of them situated in the cerebellum. That's the structure at the back of the brain responsible for balance, movement and coordination. It helps you to make adjustments so you can maintain balance, and it coordinates the different muscle groups to produce fluid limb and body movements. But, when the nerve fibres in this part of the brain are damaged, they can't send the correct signals to the muscles to flex or contract. Movement is going to become a challenge for you'.

'What caused this? And how do we fix it?' I asked, trying to hold back the tears.

'Mrs Naidoo, medical science, with all its advancement, has no conclusive explanation as to the cause of MS. And there is no cure. It's a destructive disease: over time the symptoms get worse and more debilitating. Eventually you'll experience loss of certain functions. I'm afraid that disability is inevitable'. He briefly glanced down; despite his professional demeanour, his eyes betrayed his sadness. 'You're going to need intensive medical intervention'.

He went on speaking, but I have no idea what he said. My mind was preoccupied. I couldn't take in any more new information.

I tossed and turned for nights in hospital, trying to make sense of what was unfolding. Even though I was on strong medication, my right eye started to go blurry. In MS, the optic nerve is sometimes attacked by the immune system, which can lead to blindness.

To add to the terrifying diagnosis of multiple sclerosis, the blood results had shown that inflammatory markers were substantially raised, and a confirmation of rheumatoid arthritis (or RA) was also given. In RA, the body attacks its own tissues, causing chronic inflammation of the joints. Where I had previously had an injury, my right ankle was throbbing, together with my hip, wrist and finger joints. Alas, bad things come in threes, and the blood tests also confirmed Hashimoto's thyroiditis. In people with Hashimoto's, the immune system attacks the thyroid, leading to a gradual decline in function and eventually an underactive thyroid, referred to as hypothyroidism. This meant that my thyroid wasn't making enough hormones for my body's needs.

The brain fog I was experiencing, paired with my feelings of shock and bewilderment, clouded my ability to search the internet and understand the diagnosis. It was only months later that I got a clear understanding of what it all meant: my body was riddled with autoimmune conditions. The extreme level of inflammation measured was essentially a sign of fires burning all over inside my body. With a combination of three or more autoimmune disorders, I had what is called multiple autoimmune syndrome. Individually, these conditions are already challenging. I had to wonder if there was any chance of survival for me with all three. *Will I ever lead a normal life again? What am I to do, diagnosed with conditions for which medical science has yet to figure out definitive causes or cures?*

I was so ill that colleagues of the neurologist and rheumatologist made special stops at my bedside to meet me. They repeated the neurologist's sentiments about the diagnosis. 'MS with RA is one of the cruellest combinations. Once they've got a grip on you, there's no release. You will spend the rest of your life fighting an uphill battle'. They looked sad for me and said how sorry they felt about the diagnosis.

I remember feeling confused and overwhelmed. I was put on 1000mg intravenous immunosuppressant medication for five days. The drug is designed to totally suppress the immune system, but, unfortunately, it comes with many harsh side effects.

The medical logic is this: until we know why the immune system is attacking the body, we have to suppress it completely. Suppressing the immune system means that the risk of contracting and perhaps dying from an infection, because the body can't fight back, is suddenly outweighed by the reality of living a life with the consequences of immune disease – going blind, losing body function, becoming physically disabled and mentally incapacitated. My future in medical terms looked unpromising, to say the least.

Immunosuppressant drugs were initially designed to be used for a short period of time to reduce the strength of the body's immune system in order to help it accept a transplanted organ like a kidney or liver. In the case of autoimmune disease, these drugs also help to reduce the strength of the immune system and hence the impact of the disease on the body. However, in autoimmune disease, they have to be taken chronically, although they present a temporary rather than an ultimate solution for most patients. They do not increase the remission rate significantly and do not stop the disease from progressing further in the long term. Yet the first basic principle in the current approach to autoimmune disease is immunosuppression, rather than looking into the patient's poor lifestyle choices, which might be triggering the disease.

The next class of drugs is disease-modifying drugs. These drugs are intended to slow down disease progression. Apart from their adverse side effects, which include tiredness, depression, flu-like symptoms, muscle aches, heart failure, anaphylaxis and liver damage, they are very expensive and carry the inconvenience of intravenous administration.

While the neurologist and the rheumatologist researched the best way forward in terms of chronic immunosuppressant medication for me, I was given the standard entry-level immunosuppressant drug. Even though Rajin and I had refused to give this drug to my mum when she had it prescribed for lichen planus, I agreed to take it. I was consumed by fear of the diagnosis and the unknown. And I was consumed by symptoms of the disease: awful, incessant headaches; persistent nausea and vomiting; severe heartburn; painful constipation; dizziness; endless pins and needles; and muscle weakness. It was all too much to handle. I cried for hours when I couldn't manage the crushing pain in my head, chest area, wrists and ankles.

One of the drugs that was to bring me relief arrived at my bedside with a bold label – 'cytotoxic drug' – meaning that it has a toxic effect on the body's cells and may result in the death of cells. The copious side effects of my treatment regime fill a number of pages. From the package inserts, I learnt that they included but were not limited to fluid retention, weight gain, high blood pressure, potassium loss, headache, muscle weakness, puffiness of the face, hair growth on the face, thinning and easy bruising of skin, glaucoma, cataracts, peptic ulcers, high blood sugar (hyperglycaemia), irregular menstrual periods, convulsions, nausea, vomiting, heartburn, dizziness, trouble sleeping, appetite changes, increased sweating, acne, psychiatric disturbances, and injection site reactions (pain, redness or swelling).

The last time I had been in hospital had been sixteen years ago, to give birth to our beautiful baby boy. It was a magical water birth experience. I was a pioneer for water births in the hospital in my city. What made it even more special was that my body coped well with the experience even though I had delivered our first baby via caesarean section. I had been blessed with a healthy life. Little did I realise that, with the diagnosis, this was the start of many, many visits to the hospital.

Initially, I blamed myself for the autoimmune conditions. I felt that I had failed my body and mind. I had let myself down. My entire life had been dedicated to wellness and here I was, so ill. My tears flowed nonstop. At the time, I felt that Rajin and I told people about the diagnosis too soon. There certainly was no rush. I underestimated the time I needed to understand the impact of the condition. I wasn't ready to deal with people's pity and the pain in their eyes when they saw me. With each new moment, I felt like I was treading further into terrifying territory. It felt like time had stopped, yet I was supposed to go on. The people who visited me loved me dearly, but their expressions of helplessness made me feel more depressed. None of them understood the condition fully and, every time I explained the diagnosis to them, I felt more ill. Nothing people said could quell the anxiety building up inside me. The energy around me was low. I was desperate for answers, but all I got was a sad shake of the head from everyone around me. I could hear my hospital visitors standing in the passage outside my room discussing my dreadful future.

How could they possibly know how I feel? They are all well and have so much vibrant energy.

The sting of the diagnosis remained strong. Looking back, I wish that someone had reminded me that the intensity of these feelings does not last forever. As Winston Churchill said, 'When you are going through hell, keep going'. Had I been given more time to digest the diagnosis, I would have welcomed the support of my visitors with more love and appreciation. Choosing whom to tell and lean on for support is a significant part of the initial process when one is coming to terms with a scary diagnosis. I allowed my personal space to be invaded and this compounded my depression.

To add fuel to the fire, someone unwittingly shared the news on Facebook before I could tell Pavesan.

'Mum, is this true?' he asked over the phone.

'I'm so sorry that you had to find out this way. But yes, it's true. I'm dreadfully ill'.

'Don't worry about me, Mum. Just focus on trying to feel better. I'm here for you'. We both burst into tears.

On the outside my body was numb and in pain from the disease, and on the inside my spirit was numb and in pain from the news of the diagnosis. I was completely overwhelmed and in shock. All I wanted was some alone time to digest the reality of what medical science terms a 'dread debilitating condition'.

My emotions were all over the place. I oscillated between bouts of anger and the depths of sadness. I felt helpless and confused. The gloomy energy around my bed was suffocating me. I wished I could just run away to a place where nobody knew my name or knew about the diagnosis. Tharsheyen's visits made me realise that I wasn't the only one hurting. Lying in the hospital bed, I asked him how his day at school had been.

'Mum, today during my English lesson I knew my teacher was talking, because I could see her lips moving, but I couldn't hear a word she was saying. All I could think about was that my mum was dying on the inside'.

My heart went out to my child. 'I love you, son'.

I was so consumed by my own sad feelings about my illness that I had failed to see how much it was hurting my family. It was only months later that my mum revealed to me that Rajin would go to her and cry in her arms every night after returning home from the hospital.

Then, just when I thought I couldn't go any lower, I hit rock bottom. The neurologist informed me that he had booked an occupational therapist to educate me about some practicalities of my new life: 'She will help you to change your home environment to accommodate your wheelchair', he said.

The nausea welled up inside me as I heard these words. My entire world was crumbling before me. A wheelchair for the rest of my life!

My spirit was crushed. *Oh Mala, you'll never be able to dance again!*

I left the hospital in a wheelchair and was told that from my MRI scans and current symptoms there was a high possibility that I might never walk again.

I suddenly found myself as the observer. Events and decisions were just unfolding with or without my consent. With all the challenges that life had thrown at me, this one finally felt absolutely insurmountable.

It would be some time before I could come to terms with everything that was happening to me – before I could reconcile the shock with some of the wisdom I had been exposed to in my life. The spiritual teachings I had learnt from for many years, referred to as Surat Shabd Yoga or Sant Mat, had taught me that we must face our karma or destiny[128]. Surat Shabd Yoga is a spiritual journey of self-realisation with meditation as the central practice, as taught by a living guru.

Have you ever given much thought to why you were born into a particular family? Why you have certain likes and dislikes? Why you are drawn to certain people and jobs? Why you are faced with certain illnesses and challenges? Is the Creator punishing you or are you just living out your destiny? Most of our mental misery and negative attitudes come from our belief that people or events are against us. We believe that life is hard, life is unfair, and we cry and get depressed. However, when we understand the laws of karma and destiny, we willingly adjust to the events of life, because we understand that they do not change.

We all have a set destiny that we have to face. We have to be prepared to deal with these events of life. We cannot change them; we can only adjust to the events of life. When we refuse to adjust to the events of life, we become miserable and we suffer. Winter has to come. Summer has to come. If we refuse to adjust to the weather, we will be miserable. When we adjust and change our clothing accordingly, winter or summer will pass without being a problem. Similarly, we have to face the events of life whether they are good or bad. Sometimes we will be happy, sometimes we will be sad. We have to prepare ourselves to face destiny. Nonetheless, a destiny with an autoimmune condition is not an easy one, because it is in conflict with our understanding of the human survival process.

According to our regular understanding, our immune system is a sophisticated defence mechanism that responds only to proteins made by foreign invaders. Normally it guards against and should only respond to germs like bacteria and viruses. When it senses these foreign invaders, it sends out an army of fighter cells to attack and destroy them, thus keeping us safe and well. But, in an autoimmune condition, the white blood cells of the immune system, which are normally responsible for fighting disease and infection, start to attack the body's own tissues instead. To date, more than eighty autoimmune conditions have been identified. Why our immune system, which has a sophisticated defence intelligence, turns on the body it is supposed to protect, is the million-dollar medical question. While there are no reliable figures on how many people suffer from autoimmune disease in South Africa, according to Dr Amy Myers, author of *The Autoimmune Solution* [102], autoimmunity is the third leading cause of chronic illness in the USA, right behind heart disease and cancer.

Over time I did a great deal of research into my seemingly conflicted destiny of a body attacking itself. When I learnt the art of research during my tertiary education, I never imagined that I would someday need this skill to save myself. I felt compelled to understand as best I could what was happening inside my body at the cellular level. I wanted to understand the pathophysiology, that is, the functional changes associated with the disease, so that I could recognise its progression. I wanted to gain medical knowledge of the severity of the diagnosis and to further understand why I felt the way I did. I used a wide range of research articles on the internet and had many discussions with my neurologists and friends in the medical profession. Below I have summarised some of what I found.

Brief Pathophysiology of Multiple Sclerosis

Multiple sclerosis is generally accepted to be a potentially disabling disease of the brain and spinal cord. It is an autoimmune demyelinating disease of the central nervous system. The immune system attacks and destroys myelin. Myelin is a fatty substance that insulates nerve cell axons, which are responsible for transmitting electrical signals between nerve cell bodies or from a nerve cell body to a muscle. The damaged myelin forms scar tissue or 'sclerosis', which gives multiple sclerosis its name. The multiple focal areas of myelin loss are referred to as plaques or lesions. MS affects each person differently, depending on where the lesions form in the brain or spinal cord.

Whenever a part of the myelin sheath is damaged, nerve impulses travelling to and from the brain and spinal cord are distorted or interrupted. The messages are delayed and either misinterpreted or not received. This causes communication problems between the brain and the rest of the body. Eventually, the disease can cause the nerves themselves to deteriorate and become, according to current medical understanding, permanently damaged, producing a wide variety of fluctuating symptoms, many of them invisible. In my case, my legs suddenly felt strange and heavy when I tried to walk. I would lose my train of thought mid-sentence. Swallowing food was difficult. Urinating was frustrating. An electric shock ran down my spine when I bent my head.

Just as the electrical cord in a kitchen needs to be insulated to transmit its electrical impulse to where it is needed, nerve cells need the myelin sheath as insulation to transmit their information correctly. We use insulation tape to repair and re-cover a damaged electrical cord in the kitchen. The million-dollar question is how to re-cover or remyelinate damaged nerve cells.

According to the World Health Organization, MS typically first occurs in people between the ages of twenty and fifty years and is the most common disabling neurological disorder in young adults[166]. The National Multiple Sclerosis Society in the USA estimates that more than 2.3 million people around the world have MS [106]. Anyone can get MS, but it's at least two to three times more common in women than in men.

Research is under way to investigate whether MS is hereditary or has a hereditary component. Prof. Carles Vilariño-Güell from the University of British Columbia and his colleagues published work on the NR1H3 gene in MS in 2016 . According to Vilariño-Güell [55, 155], the mutation they focused on put people 'at the edge of a cliff but something has to give them the push to set the disease process in motion'. Although only one in one thousand MS patients appears to have this mutation, the study was received with much interest, because many of the individuals concerned had a rapidly progressive form of the disease.

MS is typically classified into types. Some types may also be seen as stages, since the disease may progress from one to the next over time. For some patients, the symptoms alternate, with periods of remission and relapse. For others, the disease may continue to get worse without periods of remissions. I was initially diagnosed with relapsing-remitting MS. Eighteen months later, after a severe relapse that showed new lesions, I was diagnosed with the start of secondary-progressive MS. The many lesions in my spine made the condition even more destructive and hinted at a more advanced stage of MS. The four different types of MS are listed below.

1. Relapsing-remitting multiple sclerosis (RRMS) is the most common form of the disease. It is characterised by clearly defined relapses, exacerbations, flare-ups or attacks of new or increasingly severe neurological symptoms. These relapses are followed by periods of partial or complete remission. Some symptoms may disappear while others may continue and become permanent.

2. Secondary-progressive multiple sclerosis (SPMS) is characterised by worsening of symptoms over time, with or without relapses. According to the USA's National Multiple Sclerosis Society, most people diagnosed with RRMS will eventually transition to secondary-progressive MS, which also includes the onset of disability [105].

3. Primary-progressive multiple sclerosis (PPMS) is less common. A patient with PPMS experiences worsening of neurological function and disability right from the start, without relapse or remission.

4. Progressive-relapsing multiple sclerosis (PRMS) is a rare form of the disease, characterised by a steady worsening of symptoms from the beginning with acute relapses but no remission.

MS symptoms vary widely from person to person, because the location and severity of each attack can be different[58, 106]. The Genetic and Rare Diseases Information Center (GARD)[58] describes the symptoms of MS as follows:

- Muscle symptoms may include dizziness and loss of balance, muscle spasm, numbness or abnormal sensation in any area, problems moving arms or legs, problems walking, problems with coordination and making small movements, and tremor or weakness in one or more arms or legs.

- Bowel and bladder symptoms may include constipation and stool leakage, difficulty beginning to urinate, frequent need or strong urge to urinate, and incontinence.

- Eye symptoms may include double vision, eye discomfort, uncontrollable rapid eye movements, and vision loss.

- There may be numbness, tingling, or pain in the face, muscles, arms or legs.

- Other brain and nerve symptoms may include decreased attention span, poor judgement, memory loss, and difficulty reasoning and solving problems.

- Individuals may also have slurred or difficult-to-understand speech and trouble chewing and swallowing.

- Sexual symptoms may include erection or vaginal lubrication problems.
- Depression or feelings of sadness also occur.

Brief Pathophysiology of Rheumatoid Arthritis

Rheumatoid arthritis is a systemic inflammatory disease mainly characterised by inflammation of the synovial membrane, which produces synovial fluid to lubricate the joints. If the membrane becomes inflamed, this is referred to as synovitis, which can ultimately result in joint destruction. The exact cause of synovitis remains unknown. Patients diagnosed with RA usually have several permanently inflamed joints. This causes the joints to become deformed and stiff. My dearest maternal aunt suffered from advanced RA with severe joint deformity. We unfortunately lost her early at the age of forty-nine, because the strong medication she used to manage the disease caused kidney failure.

I had experienced pain in my ankle almost a year prior to the diagnosis as a result of posterior tibial tenosynovitis brought on by gym training. An orthopaedic surgeon picked up the early onset of RA from blood tests. I refused to take any medication for it, because none of my other joints hurt. But the pain in my ankle never eased completely and I often used a medical moonboot to help with movement. Following our house flood renovations, the pain in my ankle became more intense. I mentioned this to the neurologist when I was admitted to hospital to have my first MRI done and he picked up high levels of rheumatoid factors in the blood tests. Rheumatoid factors are proteins produced by our immune system that can attack healthy tissue in our body. I was told that I had a severe case of RA together with the MS. My wrists, finger joints, hips and ribs all hurt. The pain was always worst when I got out of bed in the morning or after a long rest, which is typical of RA. The relationship between MS and RA remains unclear and further studies identifying the risk factors that lead to their comorbidity still have to be carried out[135].

Although genetic factors can increase our chances of developing this autoimmune disorder, the genetic basis is not sufficient to explain the triggering of the immune insult. As outlined in the book *Rheumatoid Arthritis* [70], the symptoms include:

- sensitivity to cold
- pain and inflammation
- fatigue
- low-grade fever and weakness
- muscle pain
- joint pain
- joint redness
- pins and needles
- stiffness in joints, especially early in the morning and after sitting for a long period of time
- deformity of joints over time
- swelling of joints
- limping
- anaemia
- rheumatoid nodules.

Brief Pathophysiology of Hashimoto's Thyroiditis

Hashimoto's disease is an autoimmune, endocrine disorder of the thyroid gland. The thyroid gland is a butterfly-shaped endocrine gland located in the lower front of the neck. The endocrine system involves our hormones and how they transmit and receive information in the body. Our bodies mainly secrete hormones from the thyroid gland and the adrenal glands. The production of thyroid hormones is controlled by another hormone, the thyroid-stimulating hormone, that is secreted by the pituitary gland in response to stimulation by the hypothalamus in the brain. In Hashimoto's, the immune system mistakenly attacks and destroys the normal thyroid cells, resulting in an underactive thyroid. The term 'thyroiditis' refers to inflammation of the thyroid gland. This inflammation disturbs the important role the thyroid plays in the metabolism, repair and growth of the human body. The thyroid contributes to regulating a number of vital bodily functions, including heart rate and body temperature.

According to the American Thyroid Association, women are five to eight times more likely than men to be diagnosed with thyroid problems[4].

The low thyroid hormone (free thyroxine) levels and elevated thyroid-stimulating hormone levels present in my blood results indicated the onset of Hashimoto's thyroiditis. Evidence for common biological factors involved in the autoimmune response in MS and Hashimoto's thyroiditis still need to be investigated[117]. It's interesting to note that Hashimoto's thyroiditis is often observed with other autoimmune disease, which is referred to as poly-autoimmunity. It is defined as the presence of more than one autoimmune disease in a single patient. However, when three or more autoimmune diseases coexist, as in my case, this condition is called multiple autoimmune syndrome. Research published in the *American Journal of Epidemiology* demonstrates the coexistence of RA and Hashimoto's at higher than expected rates but found reduced comorbidity between RA and MS[135].

I was unable to clearly differentiate between the symptoms of the three autoimmune diseases. It was overwhelming. Looking at fellow MS patients, I realised that, in my case, the intensity of the classic MS symptoms was amplified by the other two autoimmune diseases being present. Plagued with debilitating fatigue, aches in my joints and feeling as if someone gigantic was sitting on my chest, I just camped out on my bed, in pain, wondering how much more I could endure as I awaited another excruciating symptom to rear its head. I felt powerless to fight the psychological manipulation of the autoimmune police inside me, who were using my body as an interrogation room to torture me.

Hashimoto's thyroiditis is the commonest cause of hypothyroidism, in which the thyroid gland doesn't release enough thyroid hormones into the bloodstream. As a result, the body's homeostasis is greatly compromised. This imbalance results in a host of symptoms, which include[25, 93, 97]:

- sensitivity to cold and heat
- pain and inflammation
- extreme fatigue
- shortness of breath

- brain fog
- depression
- enlarged thyroid (goitre)
- weight gain
- joint pain
- infertility
- heavy menstrual periods
- joint stiffness
- constipation
- puffy face
- forgetfulness
- slow heart rate
- swelling in extremities
- hair loss or dry hair
- brittle nails and dry skin.

Understanding the conditions I had been diagnosed with was the first step. The question of how to truly face them and deal with them, however, remained unanswered. The lack of answers from the medical doctors about these conditions devasted me. I felt marooned on an island of pain and inflammation.

7
Crumbling under silent symptoms

Upon diagnosis, every part of my body was either hurting, tingling or burning. There was no room in my mind for rational thought and understanding. I couldn't see the bigger picture yet. In fact, with double vision and the intense burst of pain – like an electrical shock – that ran down my spine and into my legs every time I tilted my head, I could barely see properly at all.

When I discussed this electrical sensation with the neurologist, he said, 'Yes, Mrs Naidoo. We call this Lhermitte's sign. Unfortunately, it's unlikely that it'll go away. The scar tissue that has formed as a result of the damaged myelin is blocking the messages travelling to your brain and spinal cord'.

'It hurts so much', I complained.

'Yes, I know it's uncomfortable. Try not to bend your neck', he suggested.

But how do I live with this symptom for the rest of my life?

I felt figuratively and literally crushed. The crushing pain around my chest – commonly known as the 'squeeze of death' or the 'MS hug' – was relentless. It was like being caught in lift doors that were determined to shut on me.

The doctors were trying their best to help relieve the many symptoms from my multiple conditions. I was given mountains of medication. I could feel my gut and insides burning. I couldn't figure out if it was the

69

medication or the conditions that were causing this. Or possibly both? Or was my gut burning from the conditions and the medications weren't helping? There were no answers, just a ravaging fire of inflammation. I was on fire on the inside from the inflammation caused by my body's own betrayal.

After ten days in hospital, on our way home, I mentioned to my husband that all I needed was to put my head on a harmonium. The harmonium is an Indian keyboard instrument that I enjoy listening to. I cannot adequately put into words how strongly I felt that I needed this sound energy. That very evening, Rajin arranged for a live performance of sweet harmonium music at our home.

The musician arrived and Rajin led him to our bedroom. He then lifted me out of bed and onto the floor so that I could get my head as close as possible to the harmonium. The musician rendered an hour-long musical session that felt incredibly peaceful.

I had spent over a decade informing people about the dynamic and profound ability of the body to heal itself. I understood fairly well that I needed to change the frequency of my diseased body as soon as possible in order to start the healing process. I needed to spiral up to a higher energy state. My gut instinct told me that I should re-establish balance with the help of a powerful sound frequency to stop my immune system from destroying my brain cells, my thyroid gland and my joints. My background knowledge of and passion for the connection between the body and mind drew my attention to sound frequencies as a healing modality. Being a research scientist and a Resonance Repatterning practitioner, I had spent several years investigating – just as I currently still study – the relationship between the body and mind when it comes to healing.

The sound of the musician's calming voice, the powerful Sanskrit and Hindu mantras that praise our Creator and the gift of our human birth, the vibration of the harmonium, the incredible energy of love – they all soothed my mind and body. My family was there too. They wept openly at the thought of me never walking again.

I remember Sunisha, my sister-in-law, holding my hand while I lay on the floor, listening to the musical sounds. She was sobbing uncontrollably. Both of us had our children in the room with us, so we tried not to make the crying audible; our bodies simply shook. She squeezed my hand to let me know that she was there for me. This calmed me for a bit and allowed me to turn my focus inward. I surrendered myself to the sound of classical Indian devotional music. I just closed my eyes, became still and allowed the power of sound to work on me physically, mentally and emotionally.

Then my body went very still. I felt as if I was being enveloped by a cloud of beautiful peace. The next thing I knew, I was no longer in my body – I was floating outside, looking down on myself. I felt perfectly at peace. I could sense that my family was around me, crying. I watched myself lying on the floor under the white covers – simply serene. Then I saw petals being showered on me in a rainbow of colours. I watched as people blessed me with flowers. The heaviness in my heart seemed to fall away under the spell of peace so pervaded by love that it glowed with a soft radiance. I felt light. My body radiated with happiness, and I felt a profound joy deep within me. In that instant I knew that everything was going to be okay.

When the musical rendition was over, I opened my eyes to find everyone's eyes on me … they looked stunned. I smiled.

'How could you do that to us?' my brother asked.

'What did I do?' I gently enquired.

'You were so still under those white covers for so long that it felt like I was sitting at your funeral. Your face took on this peaceful radiance'.

Now I was the one who was stunned. I too had felt as if I was at my funeral.

This experience was a reminder to me that we are so much more than just a physical body. We are instead spiritual beings having a human experience.

The day after the music session, I started to walk again – with help, of course. I used a walker and walking stick. Not too many steps, though: my muscles felt weak and my insides were burning. As if the symptoms of the condition weren't torturous enough, the side effects of the immunosuppressant drugs administered in hospital were unleashing their wrath in my body. The pain in my head seemed to intensify by the minute. I felt drowsy and dizzy. The nausea was relentless. The heartburn felt as if a petrol truck had exploded inside me. My entire body was in pain: the muscles and joints were all sore. I fluctuated between constipation and diarrhoea. My teeth became sensitive to hot and cold and started to loosen. My gums were bleeding. I sometimes had to get up in the middle of the night to change my pillowcase, which was covered in blood. My skin was dry and flaky. I felt drained and exhausted all the time. The muscle spasticity and tight cramping pain continued. The electric shocks that shot down my spine whenever I moved my head and the jolts of sharp nerve pain that ran into my legs were unmanageable at the best of times.

After many hours of uncontrollable crying in my mother's arms, I just closed my eyes and started crying on the inside. The diagnosis brought so much sadness to my family, and my response to it just deepened that sadness. The thought of being a burden to my family was overwhelming to me.

My friends would visit and try to cheer me up with happy stories, but I couldn't follow conversations. After a few minutes, I would open my mouth to say something, only to realise that I had no idea what they had been talking about or what I had intended to say in response. I started to mimic their facial expressions to avoid embarrassing myself when we were in a group. I felt confused so often. The neurocognitive decline was affecting my memory, attention, perception and social cognition. This mentally confused state cost me some friends.

Rajin tried to discuss Tharsheyen's school activities and routine with me. I noticed that he often went very quiet when I would reply. It was only months later that he told me that my responses were nonsensical when it came to planning. I had usually been the planner, coordinator and problem-solver in my family. But not any more. I was stripped of my cognitive ability to prioritise and think clearly. Medical science calls this 'brain fog'; I called it 'brain embarrassment'. The depression I was experiencing compounded my cognitive decline.

For an MS patient, the cognitive impairment is a blow to our self-esteem. Our thoughts race around. The never-ending cycle within is overwhelming.

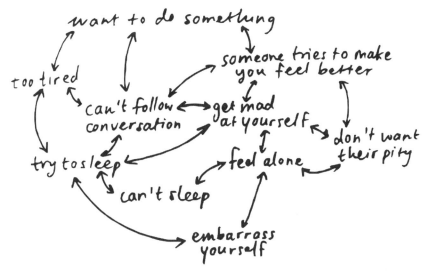

Thoughts racing around in the MS mind

It didn't matter how much medication Rajin brought home from our pharmacy, nothing alleviated my symptoms. The aching and burning pain around my eyes, cheeks, jaw and mouth varied in intensity throughout the day, ranging from mild to excruciating. Damage to the myelin sheath that covers the trigeminal nerve was causing my facial pain. I dreaded the simple act of brushing my teeth, which sometimes triggered the pain. The pins and needles and swollen and burning sensation on my tongue felt as if the dentist had half-anesthetised my gums and now I was sipping scalding hot tea. This sensation never subsided, even with the intravenous immunosuppressant. In addition to difficulty swallowing, I lost my appetite, so eating was unpleasant. I also lost my ability to taste. I would inhale the delicious aromas rising from my plate, take a wary but hopeful nibble, and then drop my fork in despair and disappointment. I was slowly losing my taste for life too.

I tried watching a movie to help distract my mind from all the discomfort. In the past, this had been one of my favourite pastimes. Now I found myself rewinding the movie every few minutes. I was unable to focus and follow the conversations. I had to keep the volume low, too. Loud sounds felt like explosions that were being set off inside me. I felt like an alien in my previously familiar world.

I decided to seek a second opinion. We went to see a neurologist in Durban. The drive there triggered my nausea. Most of the lesions in my brain were concentrated in the cerebellum, the area that controls balance. Vertigo and dizziness in MS are usually caused by the growth of an existing lesion or the appearance of a new lesion on the brainstem or cerebellum. As we arrived at the doctor's rooms, the intense nausea, painful headaches and tingling-burning sensation throughout my body were driving me insane. To make matters worse, as we sat in the waiting room, Rajin kept insisting that things be done his way.

'I think you need to come to terms with the fact that you may never get better. We need to make some drastic changes in the way things are done at home', he said, annoyed at the long waiting time and the thought of the difficult life journey that lay ahead for both of us.

'I will get there, Raj. I just need to understand what's happening inside of me. Can we discuss this at another time, please?'

'We have to employ a driver immediately', he continued.

'We can't afford a driver', I countered.

'Why do you have to be so difficult!'

'I'm sorry. The inconvenience of this diagnosis seems to be really upsetting you'.

'I wish you would just come to terms with it and realise that you will not drive again and that we now have to employ more help to ensure that life continues as normal for the rest of the family'.

I felt he was writing me off a bit too quickly. I started to feel bitter.

The neurologist confirmed the MS diagnosis and the high risk of disease progression and disability due to the many lesions in my brain and spinal cord. We left his office gutted.

After the appointment, I was hungry and desperately wanted to have some lunch by the beach. I just wanted to hear the sound of the ocean. When we arrived at the beachfront restaurant, Rajin was upset with me, fed up with the diagnosis and dissatisfied with the added responsibility of taking care of what had previously been my responsibilities. In his world, there was no more time to give. He was so upset that he just sat there and watched me eat; he ate nothing.

As we walked back to the car, I felt an urge to get as far away from him as possible. I tried with all my strength to 'make a run for it' with my walker. I moved in the direction of the ocean. In my mind, I just wanted to get as deep as possible into the water. I was consumed by anger and despair.

If Rajin can't understand what's happening to me and doesn't believe that I can get better, nobody else will. I am all alone!

I wobbled towards the ocean.

Thank heavens he ran after me, because I can't swim.

As he grabbed hold of me, I screamed at him: 'I wish you would realise that *I* have the dreaded condition, not *you!*'

This seemed to stun him. It was as if his brain recalculated. 'I'm so sorry. I didn't realise what I was doing to you', he said before he burst into tears.

I didn't tell him how strongly I had wanted to submerge myself in the ocean forever. This wish frightened me. I love life. Where was all this destructive emotion coming from? I felt like a prisoner trapped in a body full of painful symptoms and a mind full of anger and hostility.

Looking at an MS patient is like looking at the iceberg that sank the Titanic. The little bit we see on top is no indication of what lies below the surface. If an MS patient doesn't have walking difficulties, speech problems or tremors, the average person believes there is nothing seriously wrong with them. The chronic pain and fatigue, spasticity, numbness, vision problems, bladder problems, dizziness and vertigo, swallowing difficulties, cognitive problems, anxiety, depression, and bowel difficulties go unnoticed.

These 'silent symptoms' are a big challenge with an MS diagnosis. Until something like paralysis or blindness in one eye develops, the internal disaster a patient is subjected to is hidden from the rest of the world. 'But you don't look ill' was something I heard daily from people who didn't live with me. These insensitive words brought on new pain. There I was, looking so normal and well on the outside, yet on the inside there was just pain, pain and more pain. Why couldn't they take my word for it? All I wanted was for them to understand that the pain and all the other symptoms were debilitating.

Why was it so important that other people understood my pain? Maybe I was afraid that I was being judged by everyone for my lack of effort to be helpful. I didn't want to be seen as the one who had no responsibilities. On the one hand, I didn't want to look helpless; on the other, I felt that no one understood just how helpless I was.

When an autoimmune condition lays into us with its ruthless invisible daggers, it penetrates to the deepest core of our being without breaking the skin. We can feel it. We, the autoimmune patients, know it's there. But, because nobody can see all of it, it's hard for others to be aware that it's always there, constantly causing havoc within.

I tried to avoid situations or discussions that reminded me of the pleasures that MS was depriving me of. It hurt to be trapped indoors because of a disease. But it wasn't always all bad: many people tried to be conscious of what they said around me and on group chats. They focused on ensuring our discussions were encouraging and motivating, especially for me.

'I can't walk in your shoes, Mala, but I'm here when you need a friend'.

'I'm so happy you are doing better these days'.

'You are in my daily prayers. Know that you are not alone'.

'So sorry for discussing our party events on the group chat, knowing you can't attend. It was insensitive. It won't happen again'.

'We'd like to bring our girls' Christmas party to your bedroom. It's not the same without you, Mala'.

'If you feel like talking about it, I'm interested in learning more about MS'.

'You are such an inspiration to me when I see you researching and investigating different methods to reverse your condition'.

'I want to make a meal for you. Tell me what foods you're allowed to eat on your programme. It's no trouble at all'.

'I'm buying you a ticket for the event. I totally understand if you have to cancel on the day'.

I used to go to bed beaming with appreciation for having such kind and thoughtful friends and family.

However, even when one is surrounded by much kindness and understanding, managing triggers can be a challenge. Since so many factors can suddenly trigger a flare-up in MS symptoms, they are yet another thing to try to explain to people. My husband, our sons and my mum truly understand the intense pain and discomfort I go through when I disrespect and ignore the triggers. They can see the impact, because they live with me. They have witnessed my painful days, my lows, my mood swings and my angry outbursts all too often. That's why our household is in agreement on making every effort to keep the triggers away through our choice of actions and, more importantly, our choice of words.

People outside our home need more frequent reminding of the factors that can trigger an MS relapse. Unfortunately this has often led to my integrity, character and intentions being questioned. I became exhausted from constantly having to explain what would happen if I risked going on social outings in hot weather, neglected my special dietary needs or overwhelmed my mind with intense or argumentative conversations. I finally stopped explaining. Over time I slowly learnt that I was not going to be everyone's cup of tea, and I am okay with that. Today I finally understand that I will never be able to get everyone to treat me the way I want to be treated, and that's okay. I wasted so much energy trying to educate people about the silent symptoms instead of focusing on starting the healing process.

In comparison to dealing with friends and family, dealing with strangers was another matter still. When I was newly diagnosed, I had extreme difficulty with walking, so I had to use a wheelchair when I was outside my home. One day, I accompanied Pavesan to a mall in the wheelchair. We entered a clothing boutique that specialised in unique styles and classic pieces made with modern fabrics. Pavesan has a keen eye for fashion and, while he browsed around, I sat patiently in my wheelchair. Spotting a stunning jacket in the aisle a little distance from me, I asked the manager if it was on sale.

'Everything in the store is 50 per cent off', he replied.

'Oh yippee!' I exclaimed and got up out of the wheelchair to go to the jacket.

His eyes just popped out. 'You can … you can walk!' he stammered. 'Is this a miracle?'

For a brief second there he thought that the news about the sale had inspired movement in my legs. The three of us laughed so hard we had tears rolling down our cheeks. Well, I couldn't blame him. Most women love a good sale. That day the manager learnt that not everyone in a wheelchair is a paraplegic. Funny as the experience had been, the rest of my day was spent observing how people treated me in the wheelchair. I felt sad when I noticed how people avoided eye contact with me or spoke down to me.

Just as I had wasted energy on trying to explain the silent symptoms to people, I also wasted many days feeling out of control with anger because I felt helpless. The underlying hurt was grounded in the fact that my specialist medical team, reliant as they were on the pharmaceutical industry to provide the drugs we needed to facilitate healing, were at a loss when it came to effectively managing and reversing my condition.

When I turned to the community of fellow patients, I discovered that social media could be very discouraging for autoimmune patients, even among patients themselves. People were entirely comfortable with me when I spoke about my pain. But, whenever I spoke about a cure, they were up in arms. They were rude when I suggested exploring methods to better manage our condition or cure ourselves. Some were happy with the word 'remission'. 'Cure', however, seems to be a big no-no, because our medical professionals said so. The many stories shared on the internet of people successfully managing chronic diseases seem to go unnoticed by most, because we only see what we're looking for and overlook positive options that are right in front of us. Our internal healing system reflects only what we believe. Becoming aware of our limiting beliefs and transforming them opens up a new world of healing opportunities.

Over time, I would learn to let go of external factors I could not control and turn my focus inward, to manage my inner energy to encourage healing in my body and mind. This meant letting go of wanting everyone to understand my symptoms and what might trigger them. It meant letting go of the fatalism I felt medical professionals and patients subscribe to too easily. Perhaps most challenging of all, it meant facing the many hardships that multiple autoimmune syndrome caused in my marriage and dealing with them from the inside out: starting with myself rather than blaming my husband. Given how my condition affected me physically and emotionally, this wasn't easy. Too often I let circumstances cloud my heart and my mind. I expected Rajin to be in two places at once. I accused him of neglect, because I was bent on having my cake and eating it too. He moved mountains to keep our family afloat financially. While he was achieving this, I sometimes felt abandoned.

It's only now that I realise how hard Rajin had tried to make me a part of his world throughout our marriage. He invited me into the business and gave me the opportunity to add to it in whatever way I desired. He praised my work and valued it. I couldn't fully commit to the business, because in my heart I was set on raising our sons. So Rajin worked very hard to keep us financially comfortable, and he excelled in his profession. He was our province's pharmacist of the year in 2002, and in 2003 the pharmacy he was owning at the time was the national runner-up in the prestigious Boehringer Ingelheim Community Pharmacy of the Year competition.

He also invited me to share in his passion for horse racing. I have already painted some of our fairy-tale experiences in this sport of kings at events like the Durban July. Our family and friends thought we were crazy to enter this world reserved for the rich and famous. We simply revelled in the adrenaline rush on race days when we had runners and the exhilaration of being interviewed for TV when we had a winner. The joy and fun we shared as racing partners bonded us deeply. Looking back, I'm so glad we had this bonding opportunity, because the diagnosis would end up testing the very limits of what our marriage could endure.

After the diagnosis of any chronic illness, it's normal for the person diagnosed, and for those close to them, to experience the classic stages of grief, including denial, anger, bargaining and depression. While some people eventually reach the acceptance stage, the grieving process can also become more intense and often shifts between stages throughout the course of the disease, as relapses occur or the disease progresses. In the past, Rajin had described me as the rock in our relationship, but now the rock had been blasted from the inside and was crumbling fast.

While his respect for my opinion had always strengthened our relationship, his commitment to his professional responsibilities compromised his ability to spend quality time with me. With the diagnosis, my interpretation of this situation was often greatly exaggerated. Instead of focusing on the love we shared, my mind could only look for faults. Nothing hurt Rajin more than when I accused him of neglecting me.

Even though we had made the decision together that I would be a stay-at-home mum and he would run the business, the long hours he devoted to his practice were hazardous to our romantic relationship. Although I previously understood that it was not his fault that he had to work so much, that it was simply the circumstances we were in, with the diagnosis that understanding evaporated. We had no idea how much our relationship was going to be tested. He was completely unaware of the fact that he had taken his wife to the hospital but had returned with a stranger. I looked like Mala, but I didn't act like Mala. The MS and RA had metamorphosed me into a monster that my family and I could never have imagined.

The continuous pain, nausea, burning and tingling first made me sad, then angry. The neurological damage in my brain triggered a chemical imbalance. I became bitter and hostile. The bitterness and hostility were aimed at Rajin and my mother, the two people closest to me, whom I love dearly. I would lie in bed and contort my interpretation of the past. I couldn't help thinking only negative thoughts. I felt driven to pick fights.

The conversations in my head were irrational and intense.

'Mum, I deserve better than this. I know you worked hard, but you worked so much, you forgot that I needed you too. The only way I could spend time with you was to join you at work. I never got to play like other children'.

'Rajin, when I helped you set up our business, I never imagined I was creating the very monster that would rob me of your time. In life we always make time for what is most important to us. For the rest we make excuses'.

Instead of coming from a place of gratitude, acknowledging all my husband and mother did for me, I created a picture of suffering in my mind, believing that I lived in a lonely world. At the same time, my mind would go back and forth between directing the resentment at them, then at myself: I imagined that they would make me feel guilty if I asked for their time, because they had and did in fact provide amply for me.

I would spend entire days crafting plans of attack. Steeped in despair because of my illness, I directed my negative emotions at Rajin. He has always been sincere in his commitment to our marriage, yet, in my depressed state, I would accuse him of every possible indiscretion.

He would barely make it through the front door before I would lay into him: 'No man could work the hours you work and spend so much time away from his wife without negatively impacting the marriage. You must be attracted to someone at work! From the time you get up in the morning, it's go, go, go! You can't seem to get to the pharmacy fast enough. Who are you so eager to be with?'

'Where is this coming from?' he asked.

'I miss us, Raj. For all of the twenty-five years of our marriage, all you have done is work. Day in and day out! You say you are working so hard for me. Do you ever consider how much I pine for your company, for just the two of us to spend some time together?'

'You know how difficult and demanding the pharmacy industry is. It's only because of my professional responsibility that I am trapped in this situation' was his go-to line whenever this conversation came up. He always wanted the best for his business and his customers and didn't trust that anyone else could deliver to his standards.

'Why is it so difficult for you to acknowledge that all I want is to have some new experiences with my husband, my favourite person in the whole world? Right now we aren't living; we are merely existing. Do you even love me any more? Your obsession with work is insane!'

'That's not fair', he responded angrily.

I would scream and say hurtful things to him all the time. I was hurting so much physically and emotionally that it came spilling out. In truth, nothing could be blamed on our marriage. But I had become desperate for my husband to take some time off and spend a few days with me, as if this was what would fix everything. For the past twenty-five years, Rajin had explained to me that, in his line of work, taking time off was rarely an option, and I had accepted it. But the despair brought on by my disease unearthed my longing to spend time with him. I thought I had buried it, but the despair dragged in anger, hostility and irritability.

I wanted Rajin to give me his physical presence, to 'hold my healing space'. As Danielle Bernock[16] writes, 'Trauma is personal. It does not disappear if it is not validated. When someone enters the pain and hears the screams, healing can begin'. While studying Resonance Repatterning, I learnt the value of holding the healing space. When we try to fix others, we prevent them from drawing on their inner strengths. Just by *being there* for the patient, free of judgement and doing nothing, something very beautiful happens. The patient feels loved and supported enough to move through their experience, as opposed to pushing it away – that's when healing manifests. A profound shift happens for a patient when someone can sit still with them in their suffering, with no expectations of an outcome. Paying attention while being present to comfort another with an open heart is a spiritual practice in itself.

But, given the difficult circumstances, it would take us a significant amount of time to learn to foster healthy interactions with one another. With my ability to reason clouded, I was unaware of how harshly I spoke to my family. In my mind it was all too much to handle. Everyone around me felt sorry for me, pitied me. And then – it happened so quietly: depression set in. Like a tiny thorn in my foot, depression was making its presence known, a little more each day, until it began to fester. I felt myself spiralling into a bottomless pit. My entire world felt bleak. The intensity of my headaches increased every day. The constant nausea made it difficult to eat. The air around me was thick with despair. The disease was suffocating me.

I was put on antidepressants and started seeing a psychologist. But nothing worked. I continued harassing Rajin daily. One evening I made him so angry, he punched our bedroom wall and was left with bleeding knuckles. I didn't care. I responded by leaning on the wall and furniture for support as I moved to the kitchen for a knife. He assumed I wanted to use it on myself, to slit my wrists. He couldn't have been more wrong: I had no intention of using it on myself.

Tharsheyen was the one who disarmed me and calmed me down. This behaviour shook me to my very core.

What have I become? Who is this person wearing my clothes and living in my body?

Over time, I became obsessed with the thought of losing mobility in my limbs. A friend accompanied me to a local support meeting of the Multiple Sclerosis Society of South Africa, where I met an MS patient who had symptoms similar to mine. He told me that one morning in his thirties, he had woken up to discover that all he could move was his hands. He was paralysed from the hips down. Many years later, he was still in a wheelchair. This was the reality of MS, staring me in the face. I felt I was moving on borrowed time, and I longed to spend the time I still had left to move with Rajin. In my mind, his not taking time off to have some final good times with me – before life as we knew it would forever be over – was unacceptable. I didn't care about the world around me. I was preoccupied with my anxiety at the prospect of living life in a wheelchair.

The weight of Rajin's responsibilities was beyond my comprehension. I didn't appreciate that, in addition to lacking appropriate human resources at work and working out of town, he also had to manage our sons' school and university demands, maintain our house, do the weekly shopping, plan and prepare meals for the family, organise my medicines and nurse me at night. I couldn't see that I was demanding the impossible of him when I asked him to take some time off from work to help me come to terms with the diagnosis.

Depressed as I was, my thoughts became toxic. There was a single refrain in my head:

The MS clock is ticking.

The MS clock is ticking …

I started harassing Rajin during working hours. Our relationship became hostile. He just couldn't take it any longer. One morning he shut the pharmacy early, drove home, and sat down with my mum. He wanted out of our marriage. He was sobbing as he told her that, in our twenty years of marriage, I had never once spoken to him in such a rude and offensive way. My behaviour was simply hurting him too much.

'I can't live with the monster that Mala has become. I can't handle this emotional rollercoaster ride any longer', he said.

My mum begged him to stay. She moved into our home to help out.

The possibility of losing Rajin shook me out of my angry mindset. At that point I realised what an important role he was playing, in spite of not being able to give me the time that I desired with him. He was keeping us financially afloat. He was taking care of our family. He was making sure that the household was running smoothly. I had been finding non-existent faults in our marriage.

I was forced to come face to face with who or what is responsible for my joy and happiness. I hadn't realised how often I had been quick to blame someone else, most frequently my dear husband, instead of taking responsibility. Making him responsible for my happiness and wellness was a sure way to destroy our marriage. I had to learn to respect who I was and what made me happy. Over the years I had been so focused on always ensuring that Rajin got his desires and needs met that I had lost sight of what I wanted. He had, however, never placed any demands on me; he was not to blame. I needed to let go of my anger. The autoimmune diagnosis gave me a much-needed wake-up call.

Rajin also made a conscious effort to step away from my drama. Whenever I said mean and hurtful things, he would respond with, 'I know that's just the MS talking, Mala, it's not you'.

His response shifted the anger in me. He encouraged me to practise gratitude. I apologised to my family and made every effort to show my appreciation daily. I started by speaking kindly and saying thank you for the little things. I became calm and appreciative of Rajin's presence in my life. I slowly let it sink in that my husband worked so hard so that I didn't have to. He loves and cares for me dearly and, when he is in my presence, he goes out of his way to try to make me comfortable. He was trying in his way to give me the very best. I accepted his apology for the times that he couldn't be with me. I believed him when he said that to him I was the most beautiful person in the world. I found joy in how his face lights up and a lovely smile breaks across his face when I entered the room.

My mum made sure that soothing Indian classical music graced our living space day and night. By deepening her own meditation, she seemed to lift the energy in our home. 'Focus on how kindly Rajin treats you whenever he is in your company', she said. 'You know you mean the world to him'.

'Yes, Mum, you're right'.

'I have so much love and respect for him', she continued. 'He's so humble and treats us with so much care and kindness'.

'That's true. We're so blessed to have him in our lives'.

I joined her in increasing my meditation and sound therapy. As I began to heal emotionally, the joy fluttered into our home like a butterfly taking its first flight. Lightness returned.

When Rajin was home, he displayed more patience, understanding and love. He stopped fuelling my negative talk. He also grew from strength to strength through the support of his caring pharmacy customers. They showered us with prayer, love and advice. They made him feel that they understood his pain, they cried with him and hugged him. They reminded him of his resilience. I believe that our Dalton Pharmacy customers contributed significantly to saving our marriage and renewing our sanity.

If my anger flared, Rajin's insightful kindness would immediately disarm me. Instead of constantly defending himself, he started to apologise for creating situations that created doubt in my mind. It became impossible to fight with him when he refused to get angry. He also helped me to understand my anger better by referring me to a research article titled 'Multiple sclerosis is associated with high trait anger: a case-control study'[13]. This study made me realise that there is far more to MS than the motor problems, fatigue, depression, anxiety and cognitive difficulties. Over time, the extreme episodes of anger and lack of control contribute significantly to mood disorders in MS patients. Understanding the anger better helped, but I had to work harder to figure out how to control it.

8
What is what and which is which?

The arguments started to reduce, but the fatigue, tingling and headaches continued. Even simply touching my head contributed to the overwhelming pain. Placing a pack of frozen sweetcorn under my head helped. I used it all the time – I even slept with it under my head. Nevertheless, my head never actually felt cold; the condition just sucked up the coldness. The air-conditioning was on day and night.

I was hospitalised four times in three months. The symptoms were relentless and debilitating. I had to take a different medication for each symptom and then I had to add more medication to try to manage the side effects of the other drugs. I was swallowing between eighteen and twenty-three tablets at a time, three times a day. But the symptoms just worsened. The neurologist and the rheumatologist were intensively analysing my case, trying to find an immunosuppressant that would cover all my autoimmune conditions. I had already been started on an entry-level immunosuppressant while they made their final decision. Rajin was aware of the medication's toxicity but also horrified at the thought of paralysis setting in or my eye going blind. We didn't seem to have any good options.

My headaches got worse. Even though headaches are not common in MS, they do occur, so I figured it must be the disease. The pain was agonising.

One of my best friends attended a family wedding around this time. A woman seated at her table asked her why she looked so sad.

'My good friend has just been diagnosed with MS and she is in so much pain', my friend explained.

'My mother has also been diagnosed with MS', the woman said. 'She is being treated by a professor in Johannesburg and is doing so much better though'.

'Do you have his details? Mala needs all the professional help she can get to understand what is happening to her'.

'He's very busy, with a long waiting list. But I'll give you my number. Ask your friend to contact me', the woman replied.

My friend visited me after the wedding, optimistic with her new information. It was my umbrella of hope on a stormy day. After I called the woman to get the doctor's details, I called to make an appointment with him. I was told that he had a cancellation and I could come through the following day. Confined to a wheelchair, huddled in pain, I flew up to Johannesburg to meet with the neurology professor. He recommended a nerve block to help lessen the pain. A nerve block procedure involves a local anaesthetic being injected into or near a nerve to stop the flow of nerve impulses that carry the pain signals to the brain and spinal cord. I can vividly remember feeling a bolt of pain and a crushing sensation as the neurologist's needle penetrated my skull. It was so painful, I thought I was going to die. I squeezed the nurse's hand so tight, it discoloured. As soon as I got my breath back, I was told I had to have another injection on the other side of my head. I was terrified. This procedure was repeated the following day. The headaches subsided, but only for a short while. A few weeks later they were back.

I had to deal with the headaches along with many other symptoms. The mere act of moving around required great effort. My legs felt as if they weighed a hundred kilograms each. This didn't help when I was struggling with incontinence and would have liked to be able to react quickly. Though often, after finally reaching the bathroom, I would sit on the toilet and nothing would happen. I knew that I wanted to urinate, but ... nothing. Eventually, just dribbles of urine. More drugs were prescribed to help with these symptoms. One morning the painful constipation glued me to the toilet seat for a long two and a half hours. It was absolute agony.

My tingling body became sensitive to touch. In the past, my husband and I had enjoyed falling asleep cuddled together in classic spooning fashion, with his arms wrapped around me. Now he was terrified to touch me and slept on the edge of the bed. Even though we loved each other deeply, the symptoms made it difficult to share a bed the way we wanted to. Sleeping so far from him hurt – it ripped my heart out. Some nights I heard him crying softly to himself. When I asked him about this, he replied, 'I was wondering how much more pain we have to endure'.

To make matters worse, my muscles, ligaments, and joints were all inflamed and throbbing. On my tenth readmission to hospital, my doctor looked at me in disbelief: 'Mrs Naidoo, you also have fibromyalgia!'

Did somebody just pour petrol on my fire?

I learnt that this chronic pain disorder is sometimes triggered with autoimmune disorders. It is characterised by widespread musculoskeletal pain, stiffness and tenderness of the muscles, tendons and joints, fatigue, restless sleep and insomnia, memory loss, disturbances in bowel function, and anxiety, depression and mood swings. Fibromyalgia also often co-exists with migraines and other types of headaches. The cause remains unknown [51].

For me, it was impossible to know where one condition ended and another began. The symptoms all intermingled with one another as well as the countless side effects of the many medications I was on. Yet another diagnosis didn't provide answers.

Although I now had another diagnosed condition to deal with, I didn't want to drag everyone else down with me. I felt that my family was sacrificing too much in terms of attending outside events, so, when the opportunity to go and watch an exciting rugby game came up, I insisted that Rajin and the boys go, just as we had done in the past.

Rugby is a popular sport in South Africa. Our KwaZulu-Natal provincial team is called the Sharks. On this particular Saturday, they were playing the Stormers from the Western Cape in the Super Rugby tournament in Durban, forty-five minutes from our home. The Sharks had to win in order to make the playoffs.

Both our sons had played school rugby and Tharsheyen had even played provincial rugby in primary school. All four of us are ardent rugby supporters and thoroughly enjoyed the absorbing atmosphere at live games. Even though I couldn't go, I wanted the boys to have some fun for a change. So I asked my husband to take them. 'That is out of the question. I won't leave you alone at home', he responded. My mum was at a family event out of town.

'I'll be fine. Once Beatrice, our housekeeper leaves, I'll take my sleeping pills and enjoy a good night's sleep'.

He relented. 'I'm not comfortable doing this, but I do agree that the boys could do with some cheering up'.

I was delighted. All three of them had been distraught over the last few months, seeing me so ill. They dressed up in their supporters' regalia and headed for the game in anticipation of a Sharks victory. When Beatrice had completed her tasks, I said goodbye to her and went to my bedroom. I hadn't taken any sleeping medication yet. I could feel an uncomfortable sensation in the pit of my tummy. Then, out of the blue, the nausea arrived with a force.

I felt a strong urge to vomit and fortunately made it to the bathroom in time. Sitting on the floor, hugging the toilet bowl, I endured violent bursts of vomiting. But, even after I felt empty, the compulsion to vomit persisted. I went on vomiting and heaving. I could feel myself growing weak. When I tried to pick myself up, I couldn't – my legs were too heavy. I started to cry. I couldn't move and I was nowhere near a telephone.

I placed my head on the bathroom floor and, using my hands as a pillow, I tried to rest. But every ten to fifteen minutes I would have to pick my head up to vomit again. This continued for four long hours. My gut felt raw from throwing up so much.

Finally I could hear Rajin and our sons arrive home, jubilantly discussing the rugby players as they came towards the bedroom.

'Where's Mum?' I heard Tharsheyen ask.

Rajin opened the bathroom door and screamed, 'Boys, come quick, Mum is on the floor!'

As I related what had happened, I watched the joy of the game drain out of their faces. After I showered and dressed, we drove to the emergency room. I was admitted and spent the next five days receiving another dose of the intravenous immunosuppressant together with other medications to try to stop the nausea and vomiting. The vomiting did eventually stop, but the nausea persisted. I battled for the next three months to get rid of it. It was only after a few consultations with my homeopath and using the treatment she recommended that I found some relief. For the rest of that year, the nausea would rear its ugly head at any time of the day or night. Sometimes it would last for weeks. It was yet another thing that was hard for others to understand: my friends and family found it hard to believe that I could experience such a severe bout of nausea for so long.

Despite making some strides forward, the fibromyalgia diagnosis, my relapse and the persistent nausea were all indications that I was not in control of my health at all. MS and my other conditions remained unpredictable. Clearly we had much to learn, and I had to do more to take charge of my well-being.

But I could feel that I had reached a pivotal point. I could choose to continue feeling damaged and spiral down into a life of misery, or I could elect to courageously rediscover myself and start over, looking for answers. It was time to take responsibility for my choices.

9
Time to take back the reins

Sixteen months since I had first been diagnosed, my role as a competent wife and mother was slipping away from me. Tharsheyen was in his final year of high school. I tried hard to be there for him, but I had to rely on our friends to adjust their schedules to drive him to school. Friends, family and pharmacy customers were cooking our meals for us. The support was incredible. In the past, Tharsheyen and I would discuss the learning material together and I would give him a verbal test. Now I just lay there next to him, exhausted all the time, while he studied. Instead of my bringing him a hot meal, he had to bring me my meals. He showed no resentment. He was just so happy to have me there. What he hated was seeing me in hospital, drained by fatigue, with swollen hands, drips in, and the neurologist's helplessness to take the pain away. I longed to be able to provide a mother's comfort to him during this crucial year of his schooling.

The endless visits to the hospital were painful, both physically and emotionally. I was on so much medication that the nurses often battled to find a vein and had to try many times before managing to place a drip. I felt like an animal in a laboratory experiment. On one of these days my brother was with me. Witnessing the numerous failed attempts to find a vein, he burst into tears.

Since the treatment I was receiving was geared at shutting down my immune system, I was terrified of picking up an infection in the hospital. Although attacks from my immune system were being stopped, the treatment wreaked havoc on the rest of my body. Because of the side effects of the medication, I always felt even more ill when I got home from the hospital than before I had gone in. I had to choose between two evils: either live with the debilitating symptoms caused by the autoimmune response or live with the equally unpleasant side effects of the immunosuppressant medication.

I felt like the boiling frog in the nineteenth-century parable. As the story goes, if researchers put a frog in boiling water, it would jump out. However, if the frog were put in lukewarm water that was slowly brought to a boil, the creature would not be alarmed. The hypothesis was that the change in temperature would be so gradual that the frog would not perceive the danger, and thus would boil to death.

The treatment I was receiving was slowly destroying my liver, kidneys, gut, throat, skin and hair – and my mind. When the diseases themselves weren't destroying me, the side effects of the medications were. It wasn't easy, or even possible, to tell the difference between a symptom that was caused by the disease and a symptom that was a side effect of the many drugs I was taking. The question was: Do I behave like the frog and allow myself to slowly deteriorate, knowing and accepting that multiple autoimmune syndrome is defined as a debilitating condition by my doctors? Or do I take notice, acknowledge that funny feeling and get out before it's too late? And, no less challenging: do I have the courage to go against the advice of the people who are trying to help me?

Even though my friends and family reassured me that we were all in it together, I couldn't help feeling like a burden, especially when the symptoms looked likely to be permanent. I needed complex medical care. The responsibility for getting me to my appointments fell on those around me. Having been an independent woman, now robbed of that independence by MS, RA, Hashimoto's and fibromyalgia, I found it difficult to constantly ask for help. Although I had my husband as my personal pharmacist at my side, I still needed to see the neurologist, rheumatologist, physiotherapist, urologist, gynaecologist, ophthalmologist, clinical psychologist, psychiatrist, occupational therapist, speech therapist, pain management specialist, podiatrist, dietician, homeopath and endocrinologist.

Despite all the medical attention and therapies, it was becoming clear that I was not getting better. I could see the helplessness on my husband's face. He was clearly frustrated: he had access to so much medication in the pharmacy, but he was unable to bring me any lasting relief. He needed two pill organisers to pack out my medication for a week. We both felt that the strong prescription medication prescribed for pain and sleep left me even more confused and delirious than I already was. I didn't manage to sleep much either way and was experiencing severe memory loss. The nausea and overall discomfort were also extreme. The high scheduled anti-nausea medication brought no relief.

The events of life cannot be changed, but how we react or respond to them certainly can. Yes, we are all destined to have certain life experiences. These events are not in our hands. But our *response* is. We cannot change the events we are destined to live through, but we can mitigate our suffering. I don't believe that our Creator ever wanted us to suffer. Suffering is a mind-made pain that handicaps us physically, mentally, emotionally and spiritually. When we choose to let go of the suffering as we accept and face our destiny, we experience a new empowered and enlightened version of ourselves. My destiny had just turned up the heat.

I was lying in the foetal position under the covers in bed when my uncle called. He said that a message I had posted online seemed suicidal and asked if I would allow his Christian priest to pray for me over the telephone. Nobody had ever done something like this for me before. I wasn't especially keen, but I didn't want to offend or upset my uncle, so I said yes. Halfway through the priest's prayer I handed the phone to my mum, got out of bed and tried to rush out of the room, but I collapsed and hit the floor. I laughed. I was much too unsteady to act on the sudden surge of positive energy I felt, but something had happened: this stranger's prayer had shaken me out of my negative disposition.

The priest hadn't mentioned it, but something about his prayer reminded me of a famous spiritual poem. The poem came to life for me. I could feel every line. It made so much sense in my present circumstances.

Footprints

One night I dreamed I was walking on the beach with God. Many scenes from my life flashed before me. In each scene I noticed footprints in the sand, sometimes two sets, other times only one.

This bothered me because during the lowest and saddest times in my life, there was only one set of footprints. So I asked God,

"God, you told me when I decided to follow you, that you would walk with me all the way. But I noticed during the most trying times there has only been one set of footprints. Why when I needed you most, were you not there for me?"

God whispered, "My child, I would never ever leave you! During your times of trial and suffering when you saw only one set of footprints it was then that I carried you."

This poem suddenly made everything clear. I am never alone. Nobody is alone. We are all being carried through our difficulties. It felt like an awakening. This is my journey. This is my time to grow internally. My disease is my opportunity to deepen my understanding of and relationship with my inner being. To walk this path with divine awareness is transformational.

I decided to take the reins back from the doctors and do something different. Around the same time, my mum had her routine check-up at her local hospital, which is about seventy-five kilometres from where we live. She insisted that I accompany her. She always valued my opinion in managing her health. Her doctors were investigating a possible

Parkinson's diagnosis. I felt too exhausted to go, but she begged me and refused to go without me. Maybe she wanted her doctor to see what stress she was going through with me being diagnosed with multiple autoimmune syndrome coupled with fibromyalgia.

My brother, Jeevan, drove us there. I prayed and asked God to please let this trip in some way bring me relief, even though it was my mum who was seeing the doctor, not me. I fell asleep in the car. On arrival, I had to use a wheelchair to go in. I fell asleep again in the waiting room. After examining my mum, the neurologist asked about her stress levels. My mum just looked at me as if she was about to burst into tears. I told the doctor that I was her stress and related my painful symptoms to him.

'Did the headaches start with the immunosuppressant?' he casually enquired.

I said I wasn't sure.

When I got back home, I had a look in my diary. I had started the immunosuppressant in hospital upon diagnosis. All the symptoms were intermingled. There was no way of knowing whether a particular symptom was a result of the illness or a side effect of the medication. I discussed this with Rajin and my doctor, and we all agreed to stop the most toxic medication first – the immunosuppressant. It worked. Within a few days the debilitating headaches disappeared. I wanted to leap and dance around like an exultant puppy greeting a much-loved master after a long separation. Like a rainbow after a powerful storm, the colour was back in my world. This was a wake-up call for Rajin and me. We started to intensify our research into reversing and managing all the autoimmune disease symptoms naturally. I started to wean myself off all the pharmaceutical drugs with a high scheduled status that the specialists had prescribed.

The months that followed were filled with both good and bad days. The words uttered over the phone by the priest whom I had never met had shifted something inside me. That awakening, coupled with the realisation that the immunosuppressant had been causing my headaches and our drive to learn more and take back some control, made for a more hopeful outlook. But my uncle had not been wrong when he had seen suicidal thoughts in my words following the diagnosis. And there was no way to simply shake off the depression in one go. I found it difficult to focus on finding ways to manage my physical symptoms when my emotional and mental state harboured irritational thoughts. According to Bill and Denise Code in their book *Winning the Pain Game*, 50 per cent of people diagnosed with MS will develop major depression sometime following diagnosis. The Codes also note that the number one cause of death in people diagnosed with MS is suicide[32]. They point out that those 'most likely to commit suicide are the successful, determined individuals. When they decide to take a course of action, they invariably succeed. Excessive depression can lead to despair, and suicide can present itself as a solution'. My struggles with the depression that had sneaked up on me after the initial diagnosis posed a challenge every day. I often felt that it was somehow my fault that the pharmaceutical drugs couldn't relieve my symptoms. I was not used to failing and didn't know how to handle it.

Now I found myself fluctuating between negative, sad feelings and a new positive, inspired attitude. One minute I felt encouraged to heal myself, but the next thing I knew a dark cloud would engulf me. Just knowing that I had MS already made me despondent. On top of that, the chemical imbalances it caused intensified my down feeling. Mindful of this, I kept bringing myself back into a happy state. I stopped beating myself up every time I had a bad day.

It's not about how many times I fall; it's about how many times I pick myself up.

Initially I felt embarrassed that I couldn't hold my happy space. Now I know how to embrace the sadness and gently return to a state of joy. This process requires a lifestyle change that demands practice and discipline.

In order to minimise the sad moments, I had to learn what triggered them. Just when I felt I had figured out all the triggers, a new one would arrive. The list is long; I will discuss triggers in more detail in Part Two. But, little by little, I managed to make many changes. I felt that I was finally on my way to wellness. At last it had dawned on me that I was responsible for my health. Yes, every cell in my body resonated with an urgency to start the healing process.

Unfortunately, my accelerated healing came to a grinding halt within a few weeks. A kidnapping followed by murder in the family traumatised us all: Rajin lost his brother. They had shared a special bond, which had become even stronger after I was diagnosed. Because Rajin worked out of town, his brother always offered his help and support to us. He even went the extra mile, arranging to have my car windows tinted so as to avoid direct sunlight from triggering my symptoms. He would often visit me in hospital during the day, when Rajin couldn't make it.

With his death, Rajin felt as if his world had just collapsed. Our entire family was in shock and disbelief, and my spirit started to spiral down. The trauma was overwhelming, and the MS relapse was intense. I was hospitalised again. The MRI scan showed both active and new lesions in my brain. The intravenous immunosuppressant I was administered gave me no relief.

Another consultation with my doctor brought further sad news. After examining me, he announced, 'Mrs Naidoo, we could be looking at a more serious stage of MS called secondary-progressive MS'.

With this type of MS, symptoms and disability get steadily worse. I felt crushed. The energy in our home hit rock bottom. It was difficult to motivate myself to use my healing modalities. I didn't have the strength or the energy to be there for my family during this terrible time, and this guilt further fuelled the downward spiral. I learnt from this experience that trauma of this magnitude requires special management for an MS patient.

I wasn't only affected by 'obvious' traumas. Stress triggers could be hidden in unexpected places. My character, my values, my weaknesses and my desires were exposed. I was forced to face the issues that I had tucked away in my mind. There was no more room for pretence. As soon as I felt emotionally hurt or upset, I became physically ill. The moment that I went against my better judgement and tried to please others first, I became physically ill. These challenges were especially unbearable when I also exposed myself to other triggers such as heat and poor diet.

In addition to receiving sad or traumatic news, some of the main triggers were hot weather, unhealthy foods, flashing lights, loud music or noise, lack of meditation and being in the company of people who wanted me to prove how ill I was. Family and friends who didn't understand the condition made comments that felt insensitive and sometimes downright rude.

'Why are you in bed all day? You don't look ill'.

'Join us for just a short while – I'm sure the heat can't be that bad'.

'You're still young. The disease can't be that difficult!'

'I have a friend with MS and she never misses work'.

'You are looking so well, maybe you were misdiagnosed'.

'My cousin had those symptoms and she exercised and now she's cured'.

'You aren't in such bad shape – most MS patients are in wheelchairs'.

'Are you taking enough vitamins?'

I had to learn just to smile when people were insensitive, instead of feeling the sting of their words and letting it hurt me.

The effect that heat can have on me presented both physical and social challenges. An increase in temperature by just a few degrees brings on severe symptoms. My vision becomes blurred due to inflammation of the optic nerve. My entire body starts tingling and the nausea becomes unbearable. My chest feels constricted. Breathing is painful. These symptoms indicate the onset of an MS relapse, for which I have to be rushed to hospital for intravenous treatment. I have missed many important events and family functions because of hot weather. Making the choice to stay home under the air-conditioning has made me somewhat of an outcast among some of my friends and family, but it's a choice I had to learn to exercise for my own well-being.

Besides working on my emotional response and mental state, diet was one of the main issues Rajin and I explored extensively. From our research, we learnt that diet is a key part of the healing process. I started making dramatic changes, as will be detailed in Part Two. Just as with learning how to deal with sadness or certain social issues, it was a process. In the beginning I would still cheat on my diet, which would result in physical pain within a day. Staying in control was a challenge, but bit by bit I learnt to catch myself, gain control and have confidence in my new way of eating and living.

Everything is impossible until someone makes it possible. For years experts said that the human body was simply not capable of running a four-minute mile. They said it was dangerous and impossible. The mile record was pushed to 4:01 and held there for nine years in the 1940s. Athletes struggled to break it and started to believe that the human body had reached its limit. Then, on 6 May 1954, Roger Bannister broke the four-minute barrier by running the distance in 3:59.4. After Bannister's accomplishment, in the same year, Australian runner John Landy also ran a mile in under four minutes. Bannister opened the door for others to follow in his footsteps. Today it's almost routine for athletes. As part of his training, Bannister relentlessly visualised the achievement in his mind and surrounded himself with people who encouraged his dream. Being a doctor, he also used his medical knowledge to create a unique training programme to prepare himself for his barrier-breaking run[88]. Like Roger Bannister, I believe that the human body is capable of accomplishing things that science has labelled impossible.

When a product becomes defective, we intuitively contact the manufacturer after our own attempts to fix it have failed. When our car malfunctions and the dealer cannot help us, we reach out to the manufacturer. So why, when it's our body that is 'broken', are we so accepting of labelling it as a chronic disorder? When are we going to be driven and curious enough to find out why our body, which is such an intricate, complex and elaborate system, has suddenly malfunctioned? We have so much intelligence within the human body, but how often do we ask it for help in the healing process?

To contact our manufacturer, we need to go within. We need to start tuning in to the many messages our body sends us every day. Acknowledging and embracing the divine energy field within us lifts the burden of shouldering the challenge on our own. If we ignore this inner power, we often feel stuck, as if there might be no way forward. Wouldn't it be more productive to acknowledge the divine intelligence within each cell of our body as a masterpiece in itself? Like all the notes played by an orchestra, trillions of these cells are working in harmony to keep us alive. This intelligence has never been replicated by anyone in the entire world.

Furthermore, we need to stop fighting. Our immune system is already at war inside us and then we want to continue battling on the outside too. We have all seen the campaign slogans: 'Fight against autoimmune disease', 'Fight against multiple sclerosis'. When we adopt an attitude of fighting against something, all we are doing is strengthening the opposition, because the mind will attract more of what we are focusing on. Mother Teresa said, 'I will never attend an anti-war rally; if you have a peace rally, invite me'. These are profound words. The problem with the words 'anti-war' is that they keep our thoughts on violence, even though we seek peace. We need to shift our mindset. Nothing good ever comes from fighting; it just creates more resistance. I invite you to put down your ammunition, lower your guard, still the anger in your mind and start to cultivate understanding. Let's cultivate understanding for our circumstances with love and respect, and accept the challenge to change and grow. Let's move into action with integrity and acceptance of the divine will. When you have a rebellious child, you have to work with the child and win the child over. Fighting doesn't win the battle – love does. It's the same principle with a rebellious immune system that is causing autoimmune disease, or any other chronic condition for that matter.

It stands to reason then that we should enhance the body's healing ability instead of trying to take over its healing capability. Chronic conditions are forcing us to change destructive aspects of our lifestyle that we always knew weren't doing us any good. But we have become addicted to the drama that is causing our trauma. If we continue to accept that there aren't any answers for chronic disease, or at least sustainable ways of managing it without knocking out core capabilities in our body, then we will always have chronic diseases. It is only when we are willing to give up this limiting belief and take positive action that our body and mind will start to heal and repair. When we allow the darkness of adversity to become the light of awareness, healing begins. Instead of looking at adversity as something that pulls you down, let it be the portal to higher consciousness, a state where profound healing can unfold.

Part Two
Take Charge of Wellness, Take Charge of Disease

10
Question your beliefs — they can make or break you

Our mind can plunge us into the depths of pain and misery or catapult us to the heights of ecstasy and wellness. The choice is ours as to which end of the spectrum we land on. What goes on in the mind is in our control, whether we are conscious of it or not. The state of our well-being is determined by a dynamic mind-body connection. The mere act of thinking about a traumatic event, elicits the release of stress hormones in our body, changing our physiology. Our daily thoughts and feelings contribute to the way our body functions. Over time, repeated patterns can hardwire us to feel and behave in a certain familiar way, even if it is detrimental to our well-being. Breaking out of our patterns can be challenging: change feels uncomfortable to the mind. When it comes to difficult life circumstances, we often choose to reaffirm a negative emotional state. To disconnect from our outer environment and truly get to know ourselves, we have to brave unexplored, demanding terrain. The unknown feels scary, so we avoid asking questions and unconsciously settle for less.

By becoming conscious and increasing our awareness, we realise that it is our responsibility to make the choice to ask questions.

Frequently we need to surmount some fears before we are willing to take this step. As children, we are naturally curious: during childhood we learn by asking questions. So why, as adults, are we so afraid of asking questions? The Chinese proverb 'He who asks a question is a fool for five minutes; he who does not ask a question remains a fool forever' rings true, and yet we regularly silence our inquisitive minds. Do we believe that we might be judged? Do we think that we are weak and ignorant – not intelligent enough to understand? Are we burdened with sad childhood memories of feeling belittled when we asked a question?

How often have we walked away from a meeting or seminar wishing we had asked our question? How often do we leave the doctor's surgery wishing we had asked more questions? I wanted to know how to interpret my MRI scans better, but I left the doctor's rooms never having asked.

Our intuition as children is correct: asking questions is the most effective way to learn. We see this in many successful people and enterprises. Billionaire Eric Schmidt[24], former CEO of Google and former executive chairman of Alphabet, said, 'We run the company [Google] by questions, not by answers'. He knows that, if you keep asking questions, you keep finding solutions. Or, in the words of Charles Proteus Steinmetz[99], an important contributor to establishing the theoretical basis of alternating current: 'There are no foolish questions and no man becomes a fool until he has stopped asking questions'. Are we perhaps afraid that our questions are going to upset our beliefs and assumptions or the beliefs and assumptions of others? Asking fundamental questions leads to tremendous breakthroughs. Sir Isaac Newton asked himself why an apple falls down from a tree and this prompted thinking that eventually led to the discovery of the universal law of gravity. I believe it's time to let go of apprehension, take the reins and become proactive about our well-being. We need to ask: How am *I* contributing to my illness? What am *I* feeding my body and mind that makes me so ill?

I was diagnosed with four chronic conditions. My immune system was attacking and destroying its own tissues. I kept asking myself why on earth I would want to take such aggressive action against my body on the inside. As much as I was overwhelmed by the diagnoses, I was also intrigued by the idea that my body could actually attack itself. I had to clear up many questions.

Am I going to settle for a life of pain and suffering because of incurable diseases?

Am I writing off the possibility that anything is possible within the human body?

Or what choices can I make to stop the downward spiral?

Once I stopped all conventional medicine and changed my diet, I noticed for the first time that the MS and RA symptoms were less pronounced. I told myself that having multiple autoimmune syndrome is an opportunity to do something different.

I have to take off the blindfolds. Do I join so many other autoimmune patients who are suffering from debilitating symptoms and allow my body and life to decline as prescribed by the medical formula? Or do I start asking questions with positive intention?

What does my mind want?

What does my body want?

What does my heart want?

My poem, 'The Revered Question', is an invitation to trust ourselves enough to find out where to begin when life has thrown us a curve ball. It is a call to open our inner door of wisdom and let the light shine from within.

The Revered Question

When your back is against the rope
   And even those around you have given up hope
When you feel smothered in difficult times
   And there is just no energy to make the climb
Talk to your esteemed self ...
   Ask the question
Don't be afraid
Ask the question with positive intention
   Then pause, wait, let go of supposing
Listen ... the answer will come
   Ask another question
Again pause, wait, let go of assuming
   Just listen ... the answer will astound you
'Hooray!' we echo, 'it's not the end, only a bend'
   Relief leads to belief
Excited, we ask another question
   Feel the power of the question
Ask more questions
   Feel free to ask another question
And another, and another
   The once despair now takes you on the road to repair
Feel the opportunity in the question
   Feel the possibility in the question
Embrace the freedom and joy of asking questions
   Is it the question asked with positive intention that
inspires and stimulates new beginnings?

What's your story?

ANY QUESTIONS

Speaking to a pharmacist friend brought much clarity to my journey. Over the years she and I have shared special moments together, pondering life and asking questions. She has always been encouraging when my plans failed. She would say, 'Don't change your goal, Mala. Change your plans and start again'.

'It's not easy', I would respond. 'My mind and body are so tired of trying. These symptoms seem relentless. Why is it so difficult? Will I ever overcome this illness?'

'Nobody said the path less travelled is easy. Just get back on your horse and ride like the wind. You are blessed with a mind that can see things that nobody else can. You cannot stop now. You and I have studied the placebo effect, which is scientific proof that we have the ability to heal ourselves. Keep questioning your beliefs, Mala'.

Why is it so important to question our beliefs? Because our cells are eavesdropping on our internal convictions and conversations. It is well known in the pharmaceutical industry that a placebo is a substance without medical effects: it makes a person feel better because of their belief that the substance is effective. A nocebo, by contrast, is defined as a substance without medical effects that worsens a person's health status through their negative beliefs and expectations. This is clearly illustrated during medical clinical trials. In clinical trials or pharmaceutical research, researchers are obliged to do a comparative study with the active ingredients in a drug against a placebo before a new drug is introduced to the market. The placebo does not contain the active ingredient; it's usually a sugar pill or a saline injection, made to look like the actual drug. In a study, patients are split into two groups. All the patients are told that they will receive the new drug, which may have certain effects and side effects. Only the researchers and doctors know which group got the actual drug and which group got the placebo. In this way, they can determine the efficacy of the new drug and check for side effects. This is called a single-blind study. In a double-blind study, the experimenters administering the medication also don't know whether they are giving participants the real drug or the placebo, thus cancelling out any influence their behaviour might inadvertently have on the participants and the results.

Logically, doctors and research scientists generally do not expect any change in the participants who take the placebo. However, the scientific community has long been fascinated by the fact that people often do have a response, despite the inactive substance in the placebo. The response may be positive or negative. The person's symptoms may improve, which is the placebo effect, or the person may have what appears to be side effects from the treatment, which is the nocebo effect.

Research into the placebo and nocebo effects has focused on the relationship between the mind and body[57]. A common theory is that the placebo effect can be linked to a person's expectations. When the mind believes that the treatment will make changes in the body, the body's chemistry causes this belief to match what the medication might have caused. The placebo and nocebo effects are a clear indication that the beliefs in our mind can influence our biochemistry and physiology.

In a classic study in which medical students were given a placebo and told that they were receiving a stimulant, the participants' body chemistry changed immediately. After taking the pill, their heart rate and pulse increased and their reaction speeds improved. In the same study, when the students were given a placebo and told that it was sedative, more than two-thirds reported that they felt drowsy, and students who took two pills felt sleepier than those who had taken only one[17]. The authors of the book *Neuroscience*, in which this study is discussed, agree that, the stronger the belief, the more likely it is that the patient taking the placebo will have the desired effect[123]. In some studies, it has been found that the placebo was just as effective as the actual drug[71].

The complex neurobiological reaction between the brain and the body gives much hope that the body can heal itself. The placebo effect is also an indication that people can associate the ritual of taking a pill with positive effects on the body. I'm reminded of the classical conditioning demonstrated by Pavlov's dog experiments. Pavlov discovered that the dogs would salivate even before they were presented with food, because they could hear the assistant's footsteps as he came to feed them. Pavlov then managed to condition the dogs to have this response to other stimuli previously unrelated to being fed, like a ticking metronome[95]. This experiment clearly demonstrates the power of conditioned beliefs and assumptions on our physiology – for the dogs, stimuli entirely unrelated to food caused salivation. In the case of our conditioning, one has to ask the question: How much of the healing does the pill do and how much of the healing is orchestrated by our beliefs and attitudes, based on our respect for the revered research laboratory, pharmaceutical company and doctor?

Personally, I find the nocebo effect most perplexing. For some patients, an inactive pill can bring about negative effects in the body when they are told that it has some side effects. Hence the mere suggestion of a harmful side effect is enough to bring on real symptoms. By extension, I think we should take a moment to think about how our biochemistry might change negatively when a doctor tells us that we have an incurable chronic condition. We put our faith in the doctors' hands and then the news that they cannot help to cure us sends a discouraging message to our cells. This sends our body into a cascade of chemical reactions that enhance the symptoms of the condition. Healing stops.

We must realise that healing is a mind game. It takes great effort to free ourselves from the shackles of conventional medicine when the body refuses to respond positively to pharmaceutical drugs. I believe we often underestimate our inner strength and potential to help ourselves. We have to embrace the challenge of reversing chronic disease with faith and enthusiasm. At a time when information is at our fingertips, we need to seize the opportunity to ask questions.

In my earlier research working with chronic illnesses, I saw a distinct relationship between stress and chronic disease. Let's question why stress is called the 'silent killer'. Let's question the role of stress in unmasking underlying disease and its role in preventing the body from healing. The human body is equipped with two separate systems of protection that are vital to our survival. We have the immune system, which protects us from harmful agents inside the body, and the hypothalamus–pituitary–adrenal axis (HPA axis), which protects us from threats on the outside. The HPA axis is a dynamic system that helps regulate homeostasis in the body and is activated to deal with stress and survival only when we feel threatened.

Our immune system requires a tremendous amount of energy to get its job done. We have all experienced that drained feeling when our body is fighting the flu. The HPA axis also requires a significant amount of energy to be successful. Hence, in order to conserve energy, the body does not run both systems simultaneously. Furthermore, the intelligence of the body reasons that there is no point in focusing on getting rid of pathogens when we are in a physically dangerous or life-threatening situation. It is pivotal for our healing that we acknowledge that our emotional state determines whether our body needs to turn the HPA axis on or off.

When it comes to interpreting emotional experiences, the amygdala in the brain plays a central role in detecting fear, anger, aggression and sadness in order to prepare us for emergency events. It's involved in stimulating the fear response to threats by activating the HPA axis. Whenever our senses detect a change in our surroundings that could be dangerous, the amygdala is responsible for preparing the body to escape or defend itself. However, since the HPA axis requires immense internal energy to function, it's not designed to be continuously activated, but rather only for us to escape the stress of immediate danger. The human body recognises all stress as an immediate physical threat and activates the HPA axis, even if our perceived fear is coming from our negative thoughts about past arguments and situations.

In order to meet this energy demand when we're stressed, the body releases the hormone cortisol, which triggers a cascade of reactions that flood the body with glucose, supplying an immediate energy source to large muscles. When the body is under stress, it is the hippocampus in the brain that monitors the production of cortisol through a negative feedback mechanism. When the body has elevated levels of cortisol, the hippocampus turns off cortisol production. This is the body's intelligent feedback mechanism to turn off its stress or fear mode and return itself to homeostasis and growth. Unfortunately, we seldom take the time to monitor our negative emotions and stress, thus keeping the HPA axis running continuously, which causes us major harm. One of the most interesting observations made by scientists today is that prolonged or chronic stress causes the hippocampus to atrophy or reduce in size, leading to an inability to shut down the HPA axis, which leaves us in persistent fight-flight-freeze mode[3, 81].

Before we lay the blame for our stressful lives on our environment, partner or family, I invite you to pause. Stress is a response created in our minds. It's a response to the happenings on the outside – but the feeling is inside us. We can, however, choose how to manage our feelings. In my stress management workshops, I often give the example of a newlywed couple that I met. They had just returned from a helicopter ride over the breathtakingly beautiful Drakensberg mountains in our country. The new bridegroom had a fear of heights. His body set off a stress response just from this feeling of fear in his mind, and he hated the experience, while his bride was mesmerised by the scenic views and was absolutely euphoric. Same scenario, yet two completely different outcomes. In spite of their feelings of love and joy as newlyweds, the acrophobic partner could not override his fear response.

Stress is a message to our brain that we are in fear mode and a physical threat is imminent. Not many people realise that the negative emotions we create in our minds also place us in fear mode. The body interprets all negative emotions as fear, and it then inappropriately activates the HPA system even though there is no physical danger. In order to conserve energy when the HPA axis mobilises the body for a fight-flight-freeze response, the adrenal hormones directly repress the action of the immune system. The bad news is that this inappropriate stress response, created by our negative attitude, is a significant inhibitor to healing a diseased condition. The absence of the tools and conscious awareness to adjust this inappropriate stress response results in a slow breakdown of the human body and spirit, finally resulting in chronic disease. The good news is that a shift in attitude is a choice that is always within our control.

To fully understand the effect that stress has on the body, it's important to comprehend the nuances of the autonomic nervous system. The human nervous system has a major division between the voluntary nervous system and the involuntary nervous system [94]. The voluntary system is concerned mainly with movement and sensation. The involuntary system regulates the internal organs, instincts and other primal functions typically outside our conscious awareness. This involuntary system is divided further into the sympathetic and parasympathetic nervous systems.

The sympathetic nervous system runs on the neurotransmitter epinephrine, also known as adrenaline. This system activates our fight-flight-freeze mode in a complex set of chemical reactions and places us in hyperarousal. The parasympathetic nervous system is stimulated by the neurotransmitter acetylcholine, which calms the body and helps it to conserve energy. Nourishment, healing and elimination of waste are its main concerns. It's important to note that the sympathetic and parasympathetic nervous systems are antagonistic to each other, meaning that they cannot function simultaneously. When the sympathetic nervous system is active, it is catabolic, meaning that it tears down the body to get the energy it needs to prepare for defence. It tells the heart to beat faster, and it increases blood pressure and boosts blood flow to the muscles, which tense up to guard against injury and pain. The pupils dilate and the mucous membranes dry up. Sweating increases. All this so that we can fight harder, run faster, see better and save ourselves from the physical danger we are faced with.

The problem arises when we activate this system in the absence of physical danger simply by thinking negative thoughts and shifting to a state of hyperarousal. An adrenaline rush can become addictive to the mind. The mind enjoys drama and creates more; it doesn't realise that it's sabotaging itself when it indulges in negative thoughts. Prolonging this stress response in the body with our negative thoughts and feelings creates anxiety and a downward spiral, resulting in the destruction of the human body and mind. Hence: stress, the silent killer.

The continuous release of hormones in times of prolonged stress creates disease. We turn on our survival stress response by thought alone. That means that our thoughts can make us sick. The emotions connected to survival include envy, jealousy, anger, hatred, pain, suffering, aggression, hostility, fear, anxiety, worry, guilt, infatuation, shame and pride. We remember these negative emotions as a survival strategy. That is why we can be showered with compliments all day but just one negative remark will override all the joy.

I had to ask myself some hard questions.

Mala, why on earth would you consciously choose feelings that lead to disease?

I realised that it was my internal environment: my feelings of sadness, anger, bitterness, regret and remorse that was leading to depression and the destruction of my body. With this awareness, I could choose to consciously change how I responded and felt. My thoughts and feelings create my brain chemistry. The key to unlocking the door to wellness is a shift in thought, feelings and attitude. This felt empowering, because it was in my hands to do so, not in the hands of the doctors, pharmaceutical industry, society or my husband.

By becoming conscious of my thoughts and actively trying to stay positive, I started to heal. I wanted to encourage my parasympathetic nervous system to mobilise its rest-digest-repair mode. Pleasant and happy feelings tell the body, 'Okay, you can relax now. There is no danger. You are safe'. The parasympathetic nervous system is anabolic: it is concerned with rebuilding the body. In this mode, the heart rate drops, blood pressure stabilises and a state of calm is initiated in the body and mind. Digestion and elimination are stimulated. Healing and repair are prioritised. Rest, sleep, meditation, relaxation therapies and feelings of being loved are some of the factors that activate this system.

The sympathetic branch powerfully inhibits the parasympathetic system. Only one or the other can be active at any given time. This is such a logical system: if you were camping in the mountains and suffering from a bacterial infection and you then encountered a large wild animal, your brain would have to decide which was the greater threat. It would do your body no good if you conquered the bacteria and let the animal attack you. Your body gathers all the energy it can to flee from the animal by halting certain processes inside itself, including the fight against the bacteria.

With our constant negative thoughts and feelings, our powerful survival mechanisms are stuck in overdrive. In today's world, most of the stress we experience is not from actual physical threats, but rather from worrying about our relationships, jobs, finances, etc. Such worries generally do not threaten our immediate survival, but they nevertheless activate the HPA axis, resulting in chronically elevated stress hormones. It is time we understood that our brain recognises constant negative thoughts and feelings as fear, which it interprets as external danger. We always need to acknowledge that we have a choice when it comes to how we deal with our thoughts and feelings. To promote health and well-being, we have to let go of the drama in our mind in order to keep the HPA axis and sympathetic nervous system in the background and our immune system and parasympathetic nervous system in the foreground. This will allow maximum healing to occur.

The figure below is a simplistic illustration of the biological impact of our choice of thoughts. It shows how the different ways we choose to react can have vastly different consequences.

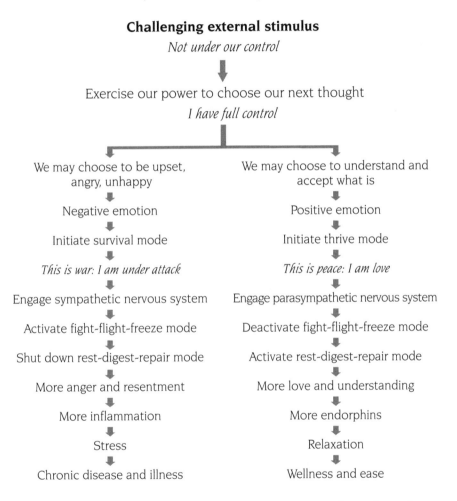

Simplistic illustration of the biological impact of our thoughts

There are twelve cranial nerves that control the autonomic nervous system. Four of them belong to the parasympathetic nervous system. These are the oculomotor, facial, glossopharyngeal and vagus nerves. Of all the parasympathetic cranial nerves, the vagus nerve is the most important, because it contains about 80 per cent of all parasympathetic fibres in the body. The parasympathetic activation of the vagus nerve has a broad range of positive effects on the body that are essential for healing. Among other things, it reduces heart rate and blood pressure, stimulates digestion and encourages anti-inflammatory regulation in the body[15, 19].

The relationship between our belly, body and brain is an important one. It's the vagus nerve that connects the brain to the gut and the brain to the heart[120]. The vagus nerve aids digestion by stimulating the movement of food through the intestines. It's responsible for keeping the larynx open for breathing. Slow, rhythmic, diaphragmatic breathing stimulates and tones the vagus nerve. Humming, splashing cold water on your face, meditation, soothing music and balancing the gut microbiome are ways to start toning the vagus nerve and initiate and promote healing.

Spending a few minutes first thing in the morning to focus on cultivating positive feelings is a powerful way to live life. We can take responsibility for our life's circumstances instead of feeling stuck and disempowered. If we acknowledge that we can steer our well-being, autoimmune disease or other chronic conditions need not be a life sentence. With proper lifestyle changes to heal and repair both our mind and body, we can experience wellness, even when diagnosed with a chronic condition. But first, we need to *believe* that we have the power to ignite wellness with conscious awareness and understanding.

Wellness is an innate process and we have the power to influence it. For many of us a headache means that we have a deficiency of paracetamol in the body. So, we take a tablet. Well, why not? It's what we've been taught is the right thing to do. We ignore how sophisticated the human mind-body system is. A headache should be a strong signal to stop what we're doing and take notice. Our system is telling us that it's under some kind of attack, that it needs a change. The paracetamol can of course give us some relief, so that we may then focus on what caused the pain in the first place and take appropriate positive action. However, in our busy lives, once the pain subsides with medication, we carry on ignoring the early warning sign our body has given us. When the pain returns, we medicate again to suppress the symptom. And, because we experience a bit of relief, we ignore the cause and the cycle continues. Our irresponsible lifestyle choices are keeping us medicated, and then we wonder why the pharmaceutical industry generates such massive profits. Our imprudent behaviour towards ourselves creates the demand and the pharmaceutical industry is happy to supply – in bulk.

Often the body is simply shouting out for some water, rest or freedom from junk food and intoxicants. Instead we medicate to cut the signal and pretend we never received it in the first place. When the body and mind finally give in to disease, we are surprised and shocked. Then we do something most peculiar: we believe that we are clueless about what the body needs and, therefore, hand over our healing to the pharmaceutical giants. The pharmaceutical industry is marvellous when it comes to acute conditions – a broken bone or some cold symptoms, for example. But we are banging on the wrong door when it comes to reversing chronic conditions. I don't subscribe to the belief that Big Pharma does not want to find cures for diseases because they would rather make more money through chronic treatment regimens; I believe that medical science simply isn't up to the challenge of healing from the inside out.

As you are reading this, trillions of chemical reactions are taking place in your body to keep you alive, without your even being conscious of it. The blood racing through your arteries is bringing fresh oxygen and food to your cells. The mitochondria inside every cell are using this food and oxygen to make energy for your survival. Your liver is eliminating toxins from your last meal, from your last in-breath. Your body is repairing itself while still keeping guard and ensuring that, if the situation presents itself, your fight-flight-freeze mechanism can be activated. The human body is one of the most sophisticated, complex and intricate systems on the planet.

It's time to honour this elaborate vehicle we call our body. I have spent most of my adult life in the wellness industry. I'm so grateful for the information and understanding this journey has bestowed on me. I was in my late twenties working half-days in our pharmacy when I was asked to serve on the executive committee of the KwaZulu-Natal Kidney Association. Why this opportunity presented itself was always a mystery to me: there was no one in my family or circle of friends who needed any help with kidney issues. Yet there I was, offering my help. At one of these meetings I was introduced to the story of Morris E. Goodman, 'The Miracle Man' .

My view on healing has never been the same since I saw the video about him. The courage he had to heal himself was awe-inspiring.

He was brought into hospital following a plane crash, so badly injured that the doctors said it was unlikely that he would make it through the night. He had a broken neck and crushed spinal cord, jaw and larynx. He was unable to swallow. His diaphragm was injured and he couldn't breathe. His bowels, bladder and kidneys weren't working.

Goodman defied the odds by surviving a nine-hour operation. Still, his family was told that he wouldn't have any function below his ears. He might be able to hear and see, the doctors said, but he wouldn't be able to talk. He would have no movement from his neck down. Just after the accident, his only means of communication was blinking his eyelids. His sister worked out a chart to help him communicate via blinking. Using this method, he sent a message to his doctors: 'Within a year I will walk out of this hospital and shake your hands'. The doctors believed that Goodman would be a quadriplegic, only able to blink his eyes for the rest of his life. Goodman realised that it didn't matter what they thought. The key thing was what he thought.

Eight months after the crash, Goodman walked out of the hospital in time to be home for Christmas. Today he is a motivational speaker. His inspiration came from Napoleon Hill, who said, 'Whatever the mind of man can conceive and believe, it can achieve'. Goodman set a goal that he would walk out of the hospital without mechanical assistance. My brain initially battled to accept that a human being could defy medical science with such tenacity. Watching this video all those years ago, I became aware of how our need to trust the opinion of medical science with complete faith has made us blind to the body's inborn healing ability. Today I feel that we have moved so far away from true healing that the medical model labels people who have cured themselves of so-called incurable conditions as rare miracles.

We all marvel at people who achieve goals that we thought were impossible. Records are broken almost every year. Cancers are cured. There are so many stories of people reversing disease conditions. Was I going to be the person who applauded on the sideline, or was I going to be the one who crossed the finish line? I wanted to enter the 'miracle race' too. Like any race, I needed preparation as well as dedication and applied effort. I needed to strengthen my mind. I needed to do research and to understand. I also needed to be still and digest this new possibility: my body can and will feel well again.

11
My Take-Charge Wellness Formula

Albert Einstein said that the same level of consciousness that caused a problem cannot solve the problem. There has to be a shift in consciousness. This also applies to limiting beliefs: we have to become aware of them in order to shift our approach. The first step towards change is awareness.

In the 1970s, Noel Burch introduced us to the four stages of learning a skill[1]. I believe that the same four stages can be applied to learning to heal a chronic condition. A shift from being unconsciously incompetent in healing ourselves ('I don't know what I don't know') to being consciously incompetent ('I know what I don't know') about our problem, to becoming consciously competent ('I know what I need to do, but I must concentrate and work hard to do it') and, finally, to being unconsciously competent about healthy lifestyle choices ('I effortlessly act based on what I know'). In order to heal, there has to be a shift in our negative thoughts and beliefs about healing a chronic condition. We need to change the way we think, change the way we speak, change the way we do things.

Investigating the history of multiple sclerosis, I was surprised to learn that a case was first identified in 1822. It appears to have been that of Augustus d'Este, the grandson of George III of England and also Queen Victoria's cousin[80]. According to an article in the *New England*

Journal of Medicine, the first case as a distinct entity was documented as early as 1868, with drawings done from autopsies[125]. A French neurologist and professor at the University of Paris, Jean-Martin Charcot, examined a young woman with a kind of tremor that he had never seen before. He also noted her slurred speech and abnormal eye movements. When she died, he examined her brain and found the characteristic scars or lesions of MS. Charcot was baffled by the cause of MS and frustrated by its resistance to all of his treatments. He wrote a detailed description of the disease and the changes in the brain that accompany it. Much of what he wrote is in alignment with what we know about the condition today[160].

One hundred and fifty years later, medical science is still baffled by the cause of multiple sclerosis and unable to offer a cure. We need to do something different. As author and Olympic torchbearer Courtney Stevens said, 'If nothing changes, nothing changes. If you keep doing what you're doing, you're going to keep getting what you're getting. You want change, make some'. The rapid increase in the number of people suffering from chronic diseases that are plaguing our society is forcing us to move to a new level of thinking.

While medical science is trying desperately to relieve our symptoms, we have a responsibility to stop hurting ourselves over and over again with our poor lifestyle choices. Today we face a global epidemic of chronic disease because of our irresponsible lifestyle habits. Some of us are so locked into a healing paradigm that must be dictated to us by the medical profession that we have forgotten how to listen to our bodies. We continue to deny the fact that we are making ourselves ill with what we eat, what we think and what we do. We need to stop seeing our body, mind and spirit as separate entities and start understanding all aspects of the self as a whole. We have to stop telling ourselves that the plaster healed the cut on our finger. Far more powerful than the plaster are the intricate pathways that the body, mind and spirit employed to knit our skin back together. In the case of autoimmune conditions and other chronic conditions, we have been interfering with the body's natural ability to heal itself on a deep level. For the past one hundred and fifty years, medical science has been trying to solve the MS riddle from the outside and has failed in every way. We have been staring at the closed doors in our doctors' rooms for so long that we have become blind to the many other open doors that we can walk through.

Over the last century we have grown up on a belief that there is no cure for autoimmune conditions. The many disappointments of the pharmaceutical industry to reverse autoimmune diseases have conditioned patients to accept their debilitating circumstances. If I had accepted this belief, I felt that I would be behaving just like a circus elephant. When a baby circus elephant is trained, a rope is used to tie its leg to a small wooden peg in the ground. The baby elephant's many attempts to free itself fails. The pain it feels from pulling makes the elephant realise that it's futile to try to escape. Over time the belief about this limitation becomes stronger and stronger. As an adult, the elephant remains bound to the same small wooden peg. Its early memory of failed attempts has become its self-limiting belief. Even though the elephant, a three-thousand-kilogram powerhouse, can uproot a tree with ease, it remains fettered to a little wooden peg in the ground. How are our beliefs limiting the powerhouse of the human body and mind to heal itself?

It may be that developing MS was an inevitability in my life but, looking back on certain episodes, it would seem that I did delay its onset. I remember at the age of thirty-one, when Rajin and I hosted one of the biggest Drug Wise awareness campaigns in our country, we organised a licensed run to attract people to the event. We had approximately thirteen thousand people at the sports ground, whom we educated about the dangers of substance abuse. I worked so hard during this campaign that by the end of it I had severe numbness, pain and tingling in both my legs. Doctors couldn't find the cause and put it down to burnout and stress. Rajin booked me into Brookdale Health Hydro for five days. I spent most of my time there meditating and doing conscious breathing exercises and visualisations, which are all actions that stimulate the vagus nerve and promote healing. Within a week all the symptoms disappeared, but I'm certain that this was an early warning sign of MS.

When our spa was razed to the ground, I also removed myself from the trauma and focused only on meditation for five days, preventing my body from becoming ill. But, when our house was flooded, I didn't take the time to focus on my meditation and unconsciously allowed the stress of the situation to wreak havoc in my body. I felt that the assessors from the insurance company had declared war on me and I stepped onto the battlefield thinking that my family was counting on me to restore our house without the trauma of another financial shock. I thus kept my HPA system firing continuously for four long months.

I have learnt that in stressful situations we need a time out from the drama. A time out means redirecting our focus to healing modalities like meditation, to encourage the parasympathetic system. In order to protect our body from harm, it's vital that we stabilise our internal environment independent of the outside environment. This allows us to move forward from a space of acceptance and growth. Often our response to stressful life situations creates the final environmental ingredient for gene expression that had been lying dormant. After our house was flooded, the weeks of feeling rage towards the people who were meant to fix it might very well have been the final trigger that the autoimmune gene in my body needed to express itself.

Others have posited similar ideas. In his book *Multiple Sclerosis Mission Remission: Healing MS Against All Odds*, clinical psychologist Steven G. Fox writes about how his childhood trauma made him vulnerable to chronic illness. He also writes about his determination to find a way that would lead to his primary-progressive multiple sclerosis going into remission[53]. Just as I am living proof that taking time out to rest and regroup after a stressful event is vital to prevent the onset of conditions labelled chronic, I am also living proof that prolonged anger is destructive for the body. Being born with an autoimmune gene was not in my control. Giving the gene an opportunity to express itself may very well have been in my control or, more accurately, it was in my control whether or not to respond to trauma with negativity and anger. Now, given that the gene did finally express itself, it's once again up to me how I choose to manage this state of affairs.

In the case of immune-mediated diseases, research by paediatric gastroenterologist Alessio Fasano[48] found that 'less than 10% of those with increased genetic susceptibility progress to clinical disease, suggesting a strong environmental trigger in the pre-disease state'. He also found that, in people who did ultimately develop disease, environmental factors likely affected the outcome of the process and the rate of progression.

From my experience, I believe that a combination of four main factors manifest autoimmune conditions. They are:

- genetic vulnerability
- emotional trauma (which may even be subtle)
- environmental triggers
- a leaky gut caused by poor dietary choices and/or pathogens.

Today medical doctors and research scientists are still investigating the mysterious causes of autoimmune conditions and how to cure them. If I only succeed in making one small contribution with this book, I hope it is to advocate for the idea that a new approach that considers the 'whole' patient is essential. This is what we need in order to advance in our research.

Just as we need to consider the whole patient when we investigate the causes of autoimmune conditions, we also need to keep the whole person in mind when treating these conditions. In my opinion, once the autoimmune gene has been triggered by our emotional trauma, environmental triggers and leaky gut, the body requires a drastic lifestyle change to turn things around. The autoimmune process can be arrested if the interplay between genes and the environmental triggers is prevented by re-establishing intestinal barrier function. We cannot change the past and reverse the trauma that activated the autoimmune gene. We can, however, remove the environmental triggers and heal the leaky gut, since they are the driving forces behind the erupting autoimmune volcano.

With regards to MS and RA, medical science and the pharmaceutical industry are focused on so-called disease-modifying therapies (DMTs) or disease-modifying drugs (DMDs) to manage the disease. The intended outcome of this treatment protocol is not to cure but rather to delay the inevitable. These drugs decrease the rate of disability progression in MS and RA, but with serious side effects. Therapies for MS are predominantly based on immune-modulating or immunosuppressant drugs and do not directly promote repair. DMDs are not a cure for these autoimmune diseases. Taking a disease-modifying drug is like trying to plug a summit crater, which could create a more explosive series of events further down the line.

We are given medication to manage the painful symptoms and more medication to manage the side effects of the first set of drugs. The patient now has two choices: to accept the harsh drugs and succumb to a life of decline and powerlessness, or to step out of the hot lava's path and start paying attention to their inner voice of wisdom, that divine intelligence that permeates every cell of the human body. The second choice allows us to have faith, feel joy again and take positive action. There are already examples that we can look to for inspiration. For instance, George Jelinek, professor and founder of the Neuroepidemiology Unit within the Melbourne School of Population and Global Health at the University of Melbourne, wrote *Overcoming Multiple Sclerosis: The Evidence-Based 7 Step Recovery Program*, which is based on simple lifestyle changes and has helped MS patients around the world live healthy, active lives[73]. Let's muster the courage and faith to do our own research within the laboratory of our body via our lifestyle choices. Let's take a leap of faith and trust in our body's intelligence to heal itself.

My own plan of action involves thinking outside the box, and many people may be sceptical of this approach. With that in mind, I invite you to be cognisant of the fact that the pharmaceutical industry likely cannot give us a complete solution; the patient's active participation is paramount. A radical change in lifestyle cannot be found in a capsule. While I am walking proof that the 'change-in-lifestyle approach' to be outlined here is working, I leave it to you to draw on your intuition and inner wisdom to empower you to think outside the box and try something different. The diagnosis itself is not a tragedy. Tragedy or triumph lies in the conscious choices we make after the diagnosis.

Medical research scientists are starting to agree that, while complete remission in autoimmune disease is possible, the current medical treatment protocol for autoimmune disease does not achieve this [26]. Today, in spite of advancements in the field of immunobiology in autoimmune disease and the discovery of treatments like biologics, both long-lasting remission and a cure remain elusive. While research that is aimed at making the patient comfortable is encouraging, it seems that the burden of aiming high and finding long-term sustainable solutions or a cure is left to the patient.

I first focused my healing journey on finding the triggers that were making me ill and then on ways to heal the damage already caused to my body. During this time, I had three relapses, one of which showed new lesions. I am extremely grateful for the allopathic pharmaceutical medication that complemented my healing regime when these relapses occurred. The relapses taught me about possible triggers, and I intensified my willpower to manage my mind and my body better. When I became diligent about avoiding the triggers that fuelled the inflammation, I could let go of all pharmaceutical medication and use food, breathing, sound, exercise, herbs, conscious visualisation and meditation as my medication.

Our body is the vehicle that carries our essence, our consciousness, our soul. We are excellent at taking care of this vehicle on the outside. We clean it and dress it up. But how about cleaning the engine on the inside and giving this vehicle the right fuel? This body-vehicle is superior to any Ferrari or Maserati. We are so strict about ensuring that our car gets the right fuel, yet we're careless when it comes to supplying the correct fuel for our body-vehicle. In order to heal and stay well, we need to take responsibility for the inside of our body-vehicle.

Unlike a car that we can trade in when it's old and damaged, our body is for life. The exciting thing is that we are upgrading the software and hardware of our body daily. When the upgrade is done consciously, with love and understanding, our body has a better chance of remaining free of damage or disease. If disease does set in, it needn't be a life sentence; it's just an indication that our body is not at ease – physically, emotionally or mentally. Instead of following the socially accepted belief that disease is incurable, we should ask powerful questions. Let's question the many assumptions we have as a society about healing.

- Suppressing a symptom means we have solved the problem.
- Only a pharmaceutical tablet can make us well quickly.
- We are not allowed to listen to our body; only the doctor is allowed to do that.
- Natural medicine is a hoax and that's why the doctor cannot recommend it.
- Medical professionals are highly educated and highly paid, so they must be right all the time.
- When the doctor says there is no cure, there is nowhere else to turn.
- We cannot take responsibility or credit for our healing. We have to hand it over to the professionals.

I had to address my own assumptions about managing and healing four incurable conditions. I kept asking questions. I asked my family, I asked medical professionals, I even asked Google. I used pharmacy journals, PubMed.gov and Google Scholar to search for scientific articles on the latest in multiple autoimmune syndrome research. Night after night, I relearnt biochemistry and neuroimmunology. I made notes on the material I was studying and how I was doing. Rajin asked me to write down:

- what I ate through the day
- what consumed my thoughts for most of the day
- how I felt emotionally
- what activities I did during the day
- whom I interacted with in person and on the phone
- the weather and how it affected me
- the symptoms I was experiencing and their levels of severity.

After months of note-taking, we began to see a clear correlation between the severity of my symptoms and my choice of foods, company and activity, as well as the weather and the quality of my thoughts. We took note of what made the symptoms worse and what made them better. I slowly started to see a picture of wellness emerging as I avoided what made me worse and did more of what made me feel better.

From this experience and my research into chronic and autoimmune conditions, I noticed an interesting pattern that gave birth to an effective formula for a symptom-free life. Every time I challenged the formula, I became ill. Staying true to the formula allowed me to be free of pain and to be confident and happy. My days became symptom-free and like a beautiful sunrise I lovingly rose with the dawn of each new day. My zest for life returned. I welcomed the new me. Even though it wasn't easy, I embraced the change, because I understood why I needed to change. Understanding reaps results. With understanding came the motivation and discipline to implement my formula. I duly discovered that:

having an incurable disease is a matter of *destiny*,

having a relapse in extreme weather is a matter of *nature*,

however, having a positive shift in consciousness is a matter of *choice*.

Even with the best of intentions, most of us will find that the mind resists change. Changing my diet radically, giving up my social life and committing to going to bed early so that I could get up for meditation initially felt difficult, even impossible. In the beginning, it takes great effort and discipline to adopt a new way of being. But, with time, results start showing in ways that might astound us. This becomes the motivation to never give up. Discipline is the driving force that converts our wellness desire into our wellness destiny.

Wellness is more than the opposite of being unwell. The World Health Organization[167] defines health as 'a state of complete physical, mental, and social well-being, and not merely the absence of disease or infirmity'. The National Wellness Institute in the USA[107] considers wellness 'a conscious, self-directed and evolving process of achieving full potential'. The University of California Davis Student Health and Counseling Services[146] describes wellness as 'an active process of becoming aware of and making choices toward a healthy and fulfilling life' and 'more than being free from illness, it is a dynamic process of change and growth'.

I needed to find a method that would lead me back to wellness. The months of research finally gave birth to my comprehensive Take-Charge Wellness Formula.

$$W=L+(\Delta T+\Delta F+A)\times(D+M)-Tr$$

A shift to **W**ellness = uncovering our **L**ove + (change in **T**hought + change in **F**ood + physical **A**ctivity) × (**D**iscipline + **M**otivation) – **T**riggers that cause relapse.

This healing formula can only be effectively applied following a shift in consciousness. New understanding brings the motivation and discipline to ask seven life-changing questions, namely:

1. What am I yearning for that will make my life extraordinary and heal my heart so I feel **loved**? (**L**)

2. How can I change my **thoughts** to make my world more beautiful? (**ΔT**)

3. How can I fuel my body with the most sustaining **food**? (**ΔF**)

4. What physical **activity** can I perform within the limitations of my illness? (**A**)

5. How can I ensure that I remain **disciplined** to continue doing the things that keep me well? (**D**)

6. What keeps me **motivated** to make this radical change? (**M**)

7. What do I need to change to remove the **triggers** that hurt me and cause relapses? (**Tr**)

Finding out how to do this is a personal journey. When all seven steps are implemented simultaneously, the healing can be profound. The most inspiring experience on this journey is rediscovering our true self and what we truly want for ourselves. Many of us avoid answering this question, because the answer will allow our inner light to shine so brightly that we fear the people around us may not accept us. But we need to let go of this fear and acknowledge that this healing journey is our opportunity to live our authentic life. Being true to what brings us joy will ultimately bring us wellness.

Healing a chronic condition has to start with addressing the basic needs of the human body. Simply addressing our intake of appropriate food, water, air and love will force the body to ignite its healing and diminish its pain and inflammation. We have complicated our healing in many ways but, when we get the basic needs right, the body will do the rest to repair, heal and thrive. This process involves action on our part, and we need to take this action with conviction – we usually aren't successful if we try to do something that we don't believe in. Healing a chronic disease means taking responsibility, which is why many people dread it. But we can start by setting small goals and accomplishing micro-missions. The healing journey needn't be complex. Small successes every day will eventually result in the big success of realising our vision of complete wellness. Every time we show positive results, we give other patients permission to also persevere. Our small daily efforts to enter remission can set off a massive domino effect to alleviate symptoms for chronic patients globally.

As I write this, it's four years since I was diagnosed. I have spent the last two years intensifying my research into autoimmune disease. I tried a number of different healing techniques and diet options before I came up with this formula. I made notes daily and spent many hours speaking to my family, fellow patients and medical professionals. Listening to my own body was also an indispensable guide. I had countless insights in the early hours of the morning after my meditation practice. It has become clear to me that, when I pay attention to all seven components of the formula on a given day, the days that follow are pain-free. Telling friends and family about my intentions to stay true to the formula helped with accountability.

In what follows, I will expound each component of the formula in various ways. Beyond further exploration of the mind-body connection and its importance in managing chronic conditions, I offer various avenues for you to consider or techniques for you to try out. I invite you to also take charge. Take charge of your wellness by exploring each component of the formula and finding your path to better health and well-being, whatever your challenges might be.

12
Take charge of love: healing the heart and practising forgiveness

Healing the heart begins by opening up to a lifetime's accumulated, unacknowledged sorrow – both our personal sorrows and the sorrows of the world. Healing the heart is nature's way of encouraging us to stop holding ourselves in the darkness of our past. As Sufi mystic and poet Rumi put it, 'The wound is the place where the light enters you'. When we accept the sorrows of life and let them go, we create a much deeper identity for ourselves as we focus on the good. Once we have acknowledged that life doesn't always go according to our plan and choose the positive, then the feeling of sorrow starts to diminish. We need to heal the relationship we have with ourselves by focusing on what we can do today to get into a better mental state. When we love and respect ourselves enough to take positive action, we unconsciously give everyone around us permission to also love and respect us. For me, it's the energy of self-love and respect, which filters from the heart to the rest of our body, that maintains our wellness.

When the human body is well, it is said to be in a state of homeostasis. That is, the body's internal environment is in a stable, balanced state and every system is able to carry out its functions with ease. It's important to note here that we are not static creatures. We are dynamic beings with our inner and outer worlds in constant flux. Thankfully, the body will always aim to return to its place of equilibrium. However, when the heart is sad, achieving homeostasis is greatly challenged, because negative messages that are sent to the brain set off our stress response and healing stops.

Although the field of biology long held the belief that only the brain instructs the body, science has since started re-examining this. Our heart has a profound impact on our brain. Researchers have for example found that 'coronary artery bypass grafting (CABG) has major effects on neurocognitive functioning'[138] and, in a special issue of the *Netherlands Heart Journal* devoted to the interaction between the heart and the brain, Mat Daemen[35], a professor of pathology, notes that 'neurologists and neuropsychologists also increasingly appreciate the importance of vascular risk factors and cardiovascular diseases on cognitive function'. Science is showing us how physical changes in the heart can affect how our brain functions. Additionally, scientists have found that a prolonged negative emotional state may also physically impact on our heart, and thus this may negatively impact on brain function. In a study published in 2019 in the *Journal of Psychosomatic Research*, the researchers, who worked on a sample group of 2.7 million people, concluded that depression is one of the key factors associated with incidences of acute myocardial infarction and stroke[27]. While medical science continues to learn more about how all the aspects of the mind and body can impact on each other and influence healing, I believe that it's up to the patient to speed up their healing process by healing the heart first.

We all associate our heart with love – even a young child will tell you 'I love you with all my heart'. In the mother's womb, the heart is one of the first organ systems to form in the embryo. We are created out of love. We *are* love. We need to focus on this truth – we are love – in the present. In my research and experience, I found that one of the major causes of disharmony, heartache and physical breakdown is our resistance to accepting the present as it is. I am a firm believer that healing a chronic condition requires healing the heart first in order for our brain to function at its optimum. To heal the heart, we don't have to go looking for love. Looking for love is like a fish in the ocean trying to find water. All we need to do is to find a way to remove everything that is covering up our love.

My urge to control everything and everyone around me was a huge impingement to living in the present from a space of love. My family and friends often describe me as a determined and strong-willed person. It's not that I'm bossy, I just have a better way of doing things! Or so I thought. You may stop laughing now. My need to have every moment unfold according to the plan in my head resulted in much anger building up inside me. This was most strongly evident during the renovations of our home following the flash flood. My foolish attitude, which stemmed from fear and the belief that this present moment is unacceptable if it's not according to my plan, was the final straw that broke the camel's back. My genetic predisposition with multiple sclerosis, rheumatoid arthritis, Hashimoto's and fibromyalgia took me to the edge, but my intense anger and stress response with the flood renovations pushed me over. The anger I created in my mind turned into inflammation in my body. The Buddha said that holding onto anger is like drinking poison and expecting the other person to die. I was the one burning up on the inside, because I had moved away from my space of love.

As I have already related, my anger and desire to control those around me also affected my relationships, especially after I was diagnosed. At the time, the furthest thing from my mind was how the MS and RA would affect Rajin and me as a couple. Living with a chronic illness often has significant marital and psychosocial ramifications. Our relationship took strain. We attended a few counselling sessions – with three different clinical psychologists – but found no help. We both felt that the intervention was not practical for our circumstances. We needed MS-specific coping and communication skills.

According to research published in the *International Journal of MS Care*, women diagnosed with a chronic illness such as MS face a six-fold increase in the risk of divorce[144]. Researching my conditions made me realise that, despite the difficult symptoms I was experiencing, I should also prioritise nurturing and enriching my relationship with my husband. This is something that I felt was worth every bit of my energy. I intensified my self-observation, noticing everything about myself: my thoughts and feelings, my posture, my attitude towards my food, my meditation and my family. I was a spectator watching my every move. This was painful initially. I started to observe habits and things about myself that I did not like and wasn't proud of. But, as soon as I acknowledged that I am responsible for my own joy and happiness, I allowed our relationship to breathe again.

I let go of the sadness and blame I felt towards Rajin for the long hours that he works. When our first son was born, we made the decision together that he would be the breadwinner and I would be the stay-at-home parent. I realised that I was the only one stopping me from getting what I want. When we are not comfortable within ourselves, it becomes difficult to be comfortable with others. I became aware of the light and dark aspects of my personality and started to fully appreciate who I am. I learnt to relate to myself and others with respect and integrity.

Feeling loved and joyful is a choice, not a gift. Rajin and I were both confident that we could use the MS crisis as a turning point to enhance our relationship instead of ruining it. The demand for a 'new normalcy' meant that we had to change our expectations and old ways of doing things. I made it my full-time job to acknowledge the impact that the autoimmune disease was having on my entire family. Knowing that Rajin patiently stood by me as I came to this realisation only deepened my love for him. My desire to keep our marriage strong and our family together fuelled my efforts to stay disciplined with my Take-Charge Wellness Formula. Cheating on my Wellness Formula felt like cheating on my family – they also suffered the impact of my relapses. Staying true to my programme kept me symptom-free, and this lifted my emotional state and created a deep sense of flourishing.

The biggest change happened when Rajin and I started to talk to each other free of blame or guilt. I focused more on giving than wanting and receiving. As I focused more on my meditation and mantras – some of which I'll share in this chapter – our relationship became more loving. By choosing to go within, life became an expression of joyfulness and not a pursuit of happiness.

Together Rajin and I learnt to be pleasant human beings in thought, word and deed. Implementing my formula helped me to stop speaking harshly to my family. The great Rumi has also taught me to raise my words, not my voice, 'for it is rain that grows flowers, not thunder' [68]. Working on myself was the most important job I ever held, as it was the foundation we needed to work on our relationship. Today I see the silver lining in dealing with my MS as partners. It gave us perspective on what's really important and inspired us to take a more soulful approach to living. For the first time we recognised and acknowledged how different and unique we both are. We also laughed more, hugged and kissed longer and simply enjoyed the pleasure of one another's company to the fullest.

While my discussions with Rajin about my past traumas and present fears regarding our relationship had been enlightening and encouraging, I needed to bring this positive approach to other relationships too. I addressed my family about the guilt I felt for being ill and the impact it had on their lives. I also spoke out about the unwarranted anger I harboured towards my father for his neglect of my mother. After this discussion with my mum and siblings, I was surprised at the clarity and understanding that unfolded. Abundant tears, hugs and apologies were followed by a deep renewal. Through all of this, I felt heard and acknowledged. I let go of the isolation, guilt and unworthiness. I had to let go of feeling responsible for the choices others made: their choices were part of their life journey.

I have become increasingly conscious of accepting that everything happens according to the will of our Creator. This new perception allowed me to honour the present moment, free of regrets and judgement. Joy found its way back into my heart. Of course this kind of change doesn't happen in a day, and we can slip at any time: as soon as I stepped outside of the present moment and focused on the past or future, my body would show symptoms. It was clear that the anxiety my mind created when I focused on a past incident or worried about the future was fuel for the inflammation in my body. Pain would increase quickly as well – often within a few hours. Days when I spent most of my time enjoying the present, free of resistance, I experienced the least pain or no pain at all.

Eight years ago, while studying the work of Eckhart Tolle in his book *The Power of Now* [141], I never imagined I would have such a clear life-altering experience with this profound truth: the power is in the now. His work made me realise how often we don't live in this moment but in the self-inflicted stress stories going on in our minds. Tolle says that all negativity is caused by denial of the present and an obsession with the future as an escape from the unsatisfactory present. His work was only theoretical for me until the need for healing arrived. Joy is to be found in the present moment. Healing my heart was easy once I practised staying present as much as possible, remaining free of judgement throughout my day and quietening my mind with daily meditation.

Whenever I slipped into my old habit of reliving an earlier unpleasant conversation, the MS hug – or should I say boa constrictor? – symptom would arrive. My symptoms were demanding that I let go of wanting a better past. I found it intriguing that the agonising pain was focused in my chest and upper back – the very area that houses my heart. Staying in the now and activating love during meditation was the way to heal my heart. I realised that no one around me needed to change so that I could feel more loved. The only person that had to change in order to heal my heart was me.

When I related this observation to my family, Tharsheyen responded with, 'Mum, you're so lucky, so blessed, to have been diagnosed with MS. You have an instant reminder to be present and live your life consciously'.

'Yes, but it's just so challenging with my restless mind that loves attention'.

'Don't get caught up with your random thoughts and allow them to rule you, Mum!' he cautioned.

'But it's so easy for me to slip into a space where I'm listening to the conversation in my head instead of being present in the moment'.

'Stop that movie player in your head, Mum! You're missing out on life. There's so much joy and beauty to take in right here, right now'.

'Yes, there's absolutely nothing I can do about past events, yet I play them in my head constantly', I replied.

'Bring your attention to your breath', he said with a smile.

I burst out laughing. I had such appreciation for his wisdom. 'Thanks for reminding me to walk my talk!'

Today I appreciate that multiple autoimmune syndrome is going to bring out the best in me. I am slowly starting to experience and understand what Eckhart Tolle[143] meant when he wrote, 'You cannot be both unhappy and fully present in the Now'.

I needed to focus on the present to put love and forgiveness into action. For the first time in my life I started to live what my spiritual teacher had been showing me for years: journeying within would bring a deep understanding that I am not the conductor; I am a player in the beautiful symphony of life whose music flows perfectly and effortlessly. My instrument is always in tune. There is no need for me to resist it or tune it. All I need to do is play. The orchestra of life is always in harmony.

I didn't resign myself to the illness; I accepted the diagnosis and made a conscious effort to *lovingly* go beyond the MS, RA, Hashimoto's and fibromyalgia. I let go of all the triggers free of resistance. While many other practices that I will cover in the upcoming chapters each played their part, staying in the present moment free of judgement was healing my heart and filling it with joy and gratitude. My body did the rest of the repair and restoration. I could feel life flowing inside me.

A big part of healing the heart is forgiveness. Feeling bitter interferes with our healing process. Forgiveness isn't about accepting or excusing hurtful behaviour. It's about symbolically releasing the tight grip we insist on keeping on the person who hurt us. Letting go prevents their behaviour from destroying our heart. Forgiveness makes us feel lighter and happier. It's something that uncovers the love that is already there, or, in the eloquent words of Rumi[8], 'Your task is not to seek for love, but merely to seek and find all the barriers within yourself that you have built against it'.

There were many times when my conscious mind failed to see the light, for example when I felt that someone close to me had hurt me. My intense feelings of pain were difficult to let go of, even though

I understood that my response was destructive. It was during these times that I practised a special modality that I designed for myself to shift out of this space, taking Rumi's quote very literally. I would sit in my meditation spot and do the following:

- I close my eyes and breathe only through my nose.

- I visualise a bright white light of love coming from a divine source, entering my body from the top of my head and going all the way down to my toes.

- I stay with this image, imagining the light freely flowing through every cell in my body.

- I then focus on my heart and expand this bright light from my heart to fill the space around me, then the entire room.

- I visualise the earth and expand the light to fill the entire globe.

- Then, I take my attention back to my heart and explode the dark cover around it and shine the light even brighter.

- Next, I visualise the person who I perceive has hurt me and send a white spray of light and love from my heart to them, covering them from head to toe. I see them smiling and thanking me for this love.

- I see their heart exploding its dark cover and shining an intense white light of love.

- I imagine that the light is continuous: the Divine fills me up and I fill the other person with the same divine light of love.

- I continue doing this until I feel the heaviness leave my body.

It works for me every time. This practice helps my brain to understand that, at our core, we are all love. (For some inexplicable reason, I never practised this during the trauma of the flood renovations, when I felt so challenged by our insurance company.)

I sometimes combine the above visualisation with one of three mantras and say it with absolute intent and feeling over and over again.

- 'Thank you, thank you, thank you'.

- 'I'm sorry, please forgive me, I love you, thank you'. This is part of a Hawaiian practice of reconciliation and forgiveness called 'ho'oponopono'.

- When my husband and I have a dispute, my mantra is as follows: 'The universe knows all and sees all. Rajin and I share a kind, loving, respectful, honest, fun, romantic relationship with each other. He enjoys my company and I enjoy his. Everyone is happy with this. The universe knows all and sees all'.

There were many times when we had fought over the phone and tears would be rolling down my cheeks as I sat in this meditation. Within just a few minutes of my practising the above with absolute faith, he would call back to apologise for raising his voice to me and I would immediately apologise for upsetting him. Miraculously, we would both find ourselves agreeing to discuss the issue free of blame and resentment. Even though this is so personal, I had to share it with you. It's simple and it works. The only person who had to change was me. The meditation shifted my resonance with the problem, and this allowed us to see a possible solution.

In *Defy Gravity: Healing Beyond the Bounds of Reason*, Caroline Myss[103] writes: 'Forgiveness is a mystical directive, not a rational one. The impulse to forgive comes from a part of you that often is in direct conflict with how you feel or think about the person in question'. I have found that the meditation and mantras described above can be incredibly helpful in uncovering the love inside me and accessing the part of myself that wants to forgive, going beyond the negative feelings and thoughts I might be struggling with. The next chapter on thought and the mind covers further options for meditation and how powerful changing our perspective can be when we want to restore balance.

13

Take charge of thought: examining beliefs and redirecting intentions

When we change our thoughts, we change our experience of the world around us. We all have thousands upon thousands of thoughts every day. Unfortunately, according to renowned wellness and spiritual teacher Dr Deepak Chopra, about 90 per cent of our thoughts are repetitive and negative in nature, making us victims of the repetition of worn-out memories[29]. The irony is that your tormentor today is your self left over from yesterday. We become so accustomed to this negative state of being, we see it as the norm.

As I have already argued and illustrated through my experience, we can choose to change our thoughts and feelings to change our experience of the world around us. John Kehoe argues in *Mind Power into the 21st Century*, that our thoughts are real forces that influence our reality[78]. Every thought and every act, especially desires and actions that seek self-oriented results, leaves impressions on the individual mind. This storehouse of impressions finds an exact fulfilment by creating the fabric of our future.

Despite some scientists' scepticism, the realisation that our thoughts contribute to our disease state is gaining greater acceptance in the mainstream medical world. Positive thoughts enhance our health and negative thoughts detract from it. The discovery that thoughts influence the immune system via the nervous system has given birth to a relatively new field of study called psychoneuroimmunology. A 2017 paper titled 'Affective immunology: where emotions and the immune response converge'[34], reviews convincing evidence that there is a need to look at 'the immunological basis of mental disorders and the emotional side of immune diseases'. We have to see the whole patient, especially when treating chronic disorders. Researchers found that, when working with HIV-positive patients, negative self-appraisal or blaming oneself for negative events is linked to poorer health outcomes, such as faster rates of CD4 T-cell decline[34]. This science is interpreting the direct effect on our immune system of how we think and what we feel.

While we still need to fill many gaps in our knowledge, common sense and personal experience can become our teachers. We can learn to understand the meaning of the body's signals. For example, have you noticed that, when you are depressed or anxious, you are more likely to catch a cold or the flu? I remember as a young girl in my final year of primary school how a comment from my teacher affected me. The headmaster had told me that I was going to receive an award for coming first in my class as well as the highest accolade a student can achieve in the school, the Student of the Year Award. That year the school decided to change the awards ceremony from an evening function to a day function. At the time, my father worked as a manager on a farm that we lived on, thirty kilometres from my school. He was unable to get time off from work to attend the prize-giving. I understood the situation and had no problem with it.

Then, at the event, my class teacher walked up to me and said, 'Congratulations, young lady'.

'Thank you, ma'am', I replied, beaming with joy.

'Where are your parents?'

'My father couldn't get off from work today, so my parents aren't coming', I replied, still smiling.

'What! That's outrageous! Did you tell them that you are receiving the Student of the Year Award?' she asked.

'Yes, I did', I responded, confused that she was so upset.

'Well, I would never do that to my child', she said, shaking her head. 'It's so sad that your parents don't appreciate your efforts'.

I recall feeling very down. My teacher had torn out all my joy and walked away with my excitement about receiving the award. In my mind, I now felt that my parents weren't there because they didn't love me enough. I'm not good enough for my parents, I thought. I told myself, 'Mala, Mum and Dad love their work more than they love you!' Walking up on stage to collect my awards, I felt empty knowing that the people I wanted most to applaud these achievements were not in the hall. Two days later I came down with a severe bout of flu that kept me out of school for two weeks.

I had always felt loved by my parents. But, listening to my teacher's interpretation of my situation, I allowed myself to think and feel negatively about my life. My destructive thoughts robbed me of the joy of my achievement in the moment. Harbouring the sadness in my mind compromised my immune system and my body became ill. Our choice of thoughts ultimately is the architect of our physiology.

Back then I had no idea about the power of my thoughts. The strong negative feelings towards my parents' work and the fact that it now seemed more important than their love for me became a limiting belief that would play out in my life for years to come. From my teacher's comment, I exaggerated the situation in my mind and wrapped it in strong negative emotions. I sent a clear message to my subconscious mind that I am actually not good enough for the people who say they love me, because they have no time for me.

A few years later my mother opened up a very successful take-away business, and her long hours prevented her from spending much time with me. So my subconscious mind said, 'I told you so!' I then went on to attract and marry a man who built a very successful pharmacy practice and, as I often saw it, his long working hours robbed us of time together. My thoughts became my reality. This is a clear example of how we attract more of what we believe to be true in our subconscious mind. When we resist changing our thoughts and beliefs, we remain stuck in challenging situations. But hardship can force us to re-examine our limiting beliefs, and changing our thoughts and beliefs is the key to changing our world.

Awareness is vital for change to happen in every aspect of our lives. When we become aware of a limiting belief, we can shift it from our subconscious to our conscious mind. It is only in the conscious mind that a limiting belief can be changed. The trouble is that our subconscious mind produces our reality. It does not distinguish the quality of thoughts that are fed to it. Our conscious mind commands, but our subconscious mind simply obeys. So, if you project negative thoughts onto the subconscious mind, it will produce a negative outcome. But, if you send it positive thoughts, it will produce a positive outcome. We are the sum total of our thoughts. As Mikhail Naimy writes in *The Book of Mirdad* [104], 'So think as if your every thought were to be etched in fire upon the sky for all and everything to see. For so, in truth, it is'. The world around us reflects our thoughts. We don't have to tell anyone our incessant thoughts: the life we lead reflects them.

When we become conscious of the quality of our thoughts, we can begin to change the limiting beliefs that we have stored in our subconscious mind. Successful athletes often tell us that they monitor their thoughts and internal dialogue and visualise their goal as if it is actually happening to them in the present moment. They make it real in their mind first with thoughts and emotions and only then do they step up to the challenge of training. They visualise their goal every day and this repetition of conscious positive thoughts creates their reality of success. This daily practice of consciously allowing our mind to think positive thoughts and see a positive outcome is the very instruction our cells need to initiate healing. According to nuclear physicist Amit Goswami [63], 'At the heart of all illness and healing is consciousness'. Instead of the considerable risks that come with some forms of MS treatment, it may thus be worth considering using our thoughts to reprogram the cells in our body.

While destiny plays an integral part in where we are in our lives today, we are still in charge of how we respond to our life's circumstances. I have discovered that, in spite of a challenging diagnosis, I can choose the thoughts that will create exceptional opportunities for positive outcomes. We all have a unique destiny with often extremely difficult and painful challenges. Our negative thoughts and resistance to accepting our current situation keep us stuck in the pain of the challenge. If we don't face the pain, we lose the opportunity of the challenge, that is, to grow and get in touch with our inner strength – a powerful gift from our Creator.

Instead of wasting our energy on negative thoughts and resistance, we need to wisely manage and invest the finite energy allocated to us for each day. Think about your day for a moment. Rushing around, reading traumatic news stories, watching sad or violent TV programmes, getting upset with your spouse, complaining about traffic, worrying about work. When we react negatively to life's events, we lose our balance and harmony. When this happens again and again over a period of time, we become ill. Once we increase our awareness of how we invest our energy for the day and how we address and respond to the stresses in our life, we can set our intention to bring about change.

In the past, Rajin and I consciously set the intention to get our finances back in order with ease and kindness. My mum also used the power of intention in her healing. Intention is not just something inconsequential that we do with our thoughts in our mind. It is an energy, a strong desire that manifests outcomes, because we are the co-creators of our lives. When we embrace and employ the power of positive intention, we radiate an energy of hope and optimism to everyone we encounter, creating a ripple effect of enthusiasm. The opposite is also true. Our intention reflects our attitude. It's an energetic language that speaks louder than words, yet is free of words.

I attended a wellness conference in Sedona, Arizona, in the USA in 2002, where developmental biologist and author Dr Bruce Lipton addressed us on his concept of the biology of belief, as also elucidated in his book by the same name[85]. The implications of his research radically changed my understanding of life. It shows that genes and DNA alone do not control our biology; instead, DNA is controlled by signals from outside the cell. This field of study is referred to as epigenetics. His work has inspired me to question whether the energetic messages emanating from our positive and negative thoughts also impact on our DNA. While we await strong scientific proof confirming the impact of our thoughts on our biology, I set the intention to explore this possibility with my mum when she was diagnosed with lichen planus, and I watched her heal. This was a unique opportunity to experience how changing our thoughts can change our healing experience.

Intention opens us up to new possibilities. When we are clear on what brings meaning to our lives and fills us with confidence and joy, we start to spiral up. Or we can, as in Viktor Frankl's case, find a reason to live even under the direst circumstances. In his book *Man's Search for Meaning*, the Austrian psychiatrist and Holocaust survivor showed how his search for meaning and purpose in his life kept him strong and transformed him despite the hardship and suffering he endured in the Nazi concentration camps[54].

Shifting my attitude to find meaning in the challenges I had to endure was transformational. I had to give my pain my full attention, because, as the American Tibetan Buddhist Pema Chödrön[28] wrote, 'Nothing ever goes away until it has taught us what we need to know'. My mind-body research, tertiary studies, spiritual literature and my children have all hinted at the positive change that comes with the 'gift of pain'. Our way out is to go in. We have to go into ourselves to find that inner strength to understand what we need to let go of, to free ourselves of whatever we have tried to bury. We need to get the message: pain is our final reminder that life is a profound journey of personal growth and transformation. If we can comprehend this, we will embrace pain with thanks and reverence, and we will start living in alignment with what matters most to us. Taking my awareness outside of my place of struggle inspired the poem on the next page.

Pain - Our Determined Messenger

Mr Pain is only the messenger – don't kill the messenger
When Pain comes knocking on our door
Listen to what he has to say
Remember he is only the messenger
Neglect the natural order
And Nature's Intelligence dispatches Mr Pain
to deliver a message
Pain arrives when we have taken a detour
from our essence of being a divine human
Don't kill the messenger
Pain is here to deliver a message
Pain alerts us to danger
Listen to what he has to say
Listen carefully
Pain brings with him a profound message
To stop! To change what we are doing
Ignore the messenger and pain will knock even harder
Pain is relentless with delivering his message
Initially he knocks very gently
But he is persistent
He wants to deliver his message
When pain arrives, pay attention, take time
But Time has no time to listen to messages
'What nonsense is this, take the painkiller,' Time screams
Nature warns: Ignore the message and see what happens
Nature's order will bring you down to your knees
Be it in your finances, health or relationships
To remind you of who you truly are, your divine essence
Pain will leave when right action and positive change arrives
Pain will leave when we are back on the path of love
Love for our spirit, our creative energy, our body
Love for our family, our society, our universe
Pain is only the messenger
Don't kill the messenger
Listen to what needs to be changed

Fretting over the past or future causes tension in our mind. Pain is a strong reminder from our body that we need to stay in the present moment. When I experienced excruciating pain, my thoughts had no choice but to remain in the now, as I was forced to focus on the pain at that moment. I have to thank pain for my awakening to the present and holding me in the now.

Adding to the meditation and mantras introduced in the previous chapter, what follows is a number of techniques I invite you to try out to harness the power of thought. Many of them are forms of meditation or a mix of meditation with other modalities. Perhaps start with whatever version comes most naturally to you and see if it opens up further possibilities as you progress.

Meditation

About eleven years ago, our family and my dad were on our way to Johannesburg. It was a long road trip and the conversation was fascinating. I always enjoyed asking our children deep philosophical questions and relished the wisdom in their simple and practical answers. This journey was no different. The boys were eight and eleven years old at the time. The conversation in the car turned into a discussion about the timeline of the dinosaur era, evolution and the start of humans reaching different parts of the earth. I soon realised that Tharsheyen was very quiet, and just my dad, my husband, Pavesan and I were engaging in conversation.

I turned to Tharsheyen and said, 'You are sitting very quietly. How do you imagine we came to arrive on this planet?'

'Mum, for us to understand that answer, we need to sit and meditate and ask the director. You see, Mum, life is a play, and we are all actors in the play'.

'Really? That's so interesting. Tell me more', I encouraged.

'When we meditate, we have the opportunity to meet the director of the *Play of Life*. We can ask the director about our part here on earth and he can help us change it, if we want. After speaking to the director in our meditation, we will realise that we don't want to change anything in our lives', he said.

'Really!' I responded.

'Yes, Mum, even the robber is playing his role. The robber's light is fused or switched off, but he doesn't know this. We need to help him to switch his light on instead of getting angry with him', Tharsheyen continued.

Rajin and my dad were speechless. I was intrigued by Tharsheyen's answers and wanted to know more. His answer to my next question left me at a loss for words.

'Tell me, who is smarter and more powerful, a man or a woman?' I asked with a teasing smile on my face.

'The one who *meditates*, Mum', he calmly replied.

The greatest gift a person can give him- or herself is meditation. There are many different forms of meditation, depending on our intention. For some people, meditation is a means or a tool to becoming more mindful, while others take it a step further and enjoy its spiritual benefits. Meditation can be used for relaxation, healing[83] and attaining self-realisation and enlightenment. In prayer we ask God for something; in meditation we listen. The letters in the word 'silent' when rearranged spell 'listen'. In meditation we get to be silent and listen to our inner world.

For some of us in the western world, the word meditation conjures up an image of a person somewhere in the Himalayan mountains in an orange robe sitting cross-legged with their eyes closed. But there is so much to meditation that needs to be unwrapped. It is an experience. Words don't do it justice. However, to be able to get into this practice, it does help to satisfy the intellect first. The American molecular biologist and mindfulness proponent Jon Kabat-Zinn has implemented mindfulness-based stress reduction as a core component at the Stress Reduction Clinic, part of the Center for Mindfulness in Medicine, Health Care, and Society at the University of Massachusetts Medical School. The clinic helps people to cope with stress, anxiety, pain and illness. With scientific tools such as fMRI, EEG and others, Kabat-Zinn and his colleagues investigate and develop 'evidence-based mindfulness treatments, grounded in biological mechanisms'[147]. The centre has published a number of papers in neurological, medical and other journals over the past twelve years.

Meditation has long been a part of my life. From the age of five, I watched my parents practising meditation every day. I had the good fortune to be exposed to books and philosophy lectures on the power of meditation from an early age. Today I try my best to make it a daily practice.

Our mind can be our greatest asset and friend or our greatest liability and destroyer. When we are conscious of the impact of our mind on our world, we start to pay attention to the ways in which we can make it an asset. Healing chronic conditions demands a shift in mindset. One has to start with the mind to promote health and treat disease when considering using the body's inherent biological healing mechanism to self-heal.

Meditation is a powerful way to calm our mind, which in turn calms our body and allows us to see our difficult challenges in life as opportunities for extraordinary growth. The body needs the energy of pure consciousness to restore balance. The only way for the body to access this conscious healing is via the quiet and calm mind. We have to practise the art of mindfulness to empty the mind of its overloaded and destructive chatter. Guided relaxation and meditation is a powerful way to empty the negative chatter and quieten the mind.

When the mind is quiet, we have a glimpse of the joy, peace and bliss that are always part of us. We become humble and peaceful. We can have a taste of our true potential. Today, guided relaxation and meditation is fast becoming recognised in medicine as a fundamental part of a healing routine[42].

The internet is full of guided meditations and meditation techniques. I invite you to explore this opportunity, experience the meditations and have a sense for what feels right for you. Some examples you can find online include:

- 'Awakening the mind' by Alan Watts
- 'I am that I am' by Wayne Dyer
- 'Your new now' by Bentinho Massaro
- 'Surrender meditation' by Jason Stephenson

- various guided meditations by Sadhguru
- various guided meditations by Eckhart Tolle
- various guided meditations by Jon Kabat-Zinn
- various guided meditations by Deepak Chopra
- various guided meditations by Abraham Hicks
- meditations based on the ho'oponopono practice.

Some people use a mantra meditation based on sound and light as taught by a perfect living guru. Others might do a simple awareness meditation. Whichever method you choose to pursue, know that the mind will initially resist the conscious focus that meditation practice requires by wandering off. The mind is not in the habit of keeping still. Persevere. Meditation is a practice that allows us to go beyond the mind to pure consciousness. The mind does not want to engage in an activity that is going to surpass it. Persistence is key here. Eventually the mind will give up the fight and calm down completely. Then the real and lasting euphoria bursts into our lives, bringing understanding and solutions that were previously unimaginable.

In the book *Die to Live*, the great mystic Maharaj Charan Singh explains that you cannot change your environment, you cannot change the course of events, and you cannot change the situations you are in[132]. Right now, you might be experiencing some financial difficulties, or you might be going through a tough time with a relationship, or you might be worrying about your child's future. You might be battling a severe illness or you might be having a difficult time at work. Your destiny has brought you into a certain situation, and you have to face it all. It might sometimes seem like too much for one person to take but, if we commit ourselves to daily meditation with love and devotion, we will be given strength, which enables us to be resilient when faced with so many challenges. 'You won't be bothered by them', Maharaj Ji[132] writes. 'Just attend to your meditation'.

Any time is a good time to start our meditation. But the mystics advise us that the early hours of the morning, when the mind is fresh and we are not burdened with responsibility, is best. Before sunrise everything is quiet. There are no phones ringing, no kettles boiling, no televisions babbling, no people chatting – it's a very pure time. There are no distractions. Yogis and mystics explain that, when we start meditating before the sun is up and catch the energy with the rising sun, it's like catching a wave. We rise with the solar energy – nature's powerhouse. When we go surfing and get the timing right and get up on the wave, that's what it means to get up on the *amritvela*, the Punjabi word for the early hours of the morning.

This ambrosial time allows one to drink from the fountain of life. The moment is so sweet, it feels like one is bathing in a pool of golden nectar. This sweet divine bliss is so overwhelming, one is sometimes reduced to tears of joy. The solar energy together with the positive vibrational energy of a mantra or affirmation can get one through the day with absolute ease and joy. I enjoyed a discussion on meditation with a man I met on one of my trips to India, who said that he had been meditating during the early hours of the morning for many years.

'I meet others at seven o'clock, crawling out of bed going for their coffee', he said. 'And then there I am, up since the early hours of the morning, having already been 'surfing' – my energy is pumping! It's fabulous!'

I remember when I was in Sedona, Arizona, I decided to experience the day's energising *amritvela* in the mountains. Sedona has become popular for its enchanting red rock and spiritual energy vortexes. In the early hours of the morning, I headed to Bell Rock for a meditation session. Sitting on my own on the majestic red and orange mountain of sandstone rock, I closed my eyes. A little while later I heard the most beautiful 'Om' sound reverberating all around me. I opened my eyes, thinking that someone was chanting next to me. There was no one in sight. It felt as if the red rocks were doing the chanting. As the sound got louder, I observed a spectacular sunrise with exquisitely intense colours flickering in the sky. A living, breathing work of art. The sounds and sights at that moment sent my senses into a euphoric frenzy. An hour later, on my way down from the majestic mountain, I met a man. I related my experience to him and learnt that he was the one responsible for the sound. He had tears in his eyes, hearing what an impact his toning had had on me during the sacred *amritvela* hours.

Around the world today, millions of people who are saturated with the stress of psychological overload are waking up to the hidden power of meditation to take back control of their health. The greatest challenge most of us experience with meditation is saying no to sleep. We complain that we can't wake up in the morning for meditation – it's just too early. We make excuses. We have to ask ourselves if we really *want* to get up. We can talk about getting up, or we can get up. The thing about getting up early in the morning is that we can't have a discussion with ourselves about it. As soon as you wake up and ponder, 'Should I get up or shouldn't I?', the mind has already won. When your mind directs you to pull the covers over your head, suggesting that you need just five more minutes, it's all over. You are not going to get up. Getting up has to be an automatic situation – you wake up and just get out of bed without thinking.

Mel Robbins, a CNN legal and social commentator and motivational speaker, has a five-second rule[126]. This tool can give us the push we need in the moments when we don't feel like doing something but know that we should. Instead of hesitating and thinking about getting up when the alarm goes off, it's about taking action in five seconds. We need activation energy to start any process of change. She suggests counting down – 5, 4, 3, 2, 1 – and then launching ourselves out of bed. That first push in the right direction is the hardest. Once we get going, it's so much easier. We do certain things without thinking, like brushing our teeth. We don't say, 'Okay now I'm going to brush my teeth – wait, should I brush my teeth? Shouldn't I brush my teeth?' We don't have a mental debate about it, we just do it. It's the same thing when getting up in the morning: you have to decide and commit within yourself and push past your feelings of resistance.

A great way to help ourselves get up early for meditation is to go to bed early. Most of us have created a habit of going to bed too late. Our body needs to rest. Just imagine what life would be like if we had no electricity. When the sun goes down, within the next hour or so, we would go to sleep, because there would be no television, computers, gaming or late-night reading. There would be no electric lights to keep us awake to work into the late hours of the night. We have developed a very artificial lifestyle because of electricity and electronics. All the artificial lighting messes up our internal clock, so we have to make an ardent effort to go to bed early and avoid the abundant stimulation. If we are sincere about changing our lifestyle and healing, then we have to make a choice to restrain ourselves and set priorities in our life.

Melatonin is produced by the pineal gland and has a significant effect on our circadian rhythm, our mood and the quality and quantity of our sleep, which is why it's known as both an anti-stress and anti-aging agent in the body. The production of melatonin is inhibited by light and activated by darkness. Meditation can increase the production of melatonin in the body[145], so it's also a great tool to help us rest better and promote repair in the body.

When we're ill, the mind is consumed with endless perceived problems. Meditation allows a stillness of mind that soon becomes a place of refuge for us. Choosing to meditate is a choice to change the quality of our thoughts. The choice to be content with our life is dependent on the quality of our thoughts. These happy thoughts that we consciously choose send a signal to the heart that all is well, which then sends a signal to the brain to shut down our fight-flight-freeze mode. Now the body is ready to engage in solid, focused healing and repair.

After a period of calm routine, life might hand us yet another perceived challenge. When this happens, we will once again switch on the fight-flight-freeze mode that puts our healing on hold. And, once again, we have to consciously make the decision to calm the mind, choose happy thoughts, switch off the fight-flight-freeze mode and reinstate our healing mode. Daily meditation practice and increasing our awareness of our thoughts throughout the day will redefine the speed at which we heal ourselves.

I have learnt, and continue to remind myself, that I need to take life less seriously and mediation more seriously. For me, meditation means far more than physical benefits. It's a deep spiritual connection and rescue operation. Meditation is like a rescue scuba diver with unlimited oxygen. When I turn away or neglect my meditation, it feels like I'm unable to breathe, drowning and sinking into a dark, dangerous world full of sharks and other predators. But, when I turn towards meditation, I can breathe again and feel the energy lifting me up out of the ocean of turmoil and moving me towards the light of the sun. Then the water isn't scary or dangerous any more. All I see is beauty, colour and light. It's the same water, it's the same world, but the meditation has shifted how I perceive the world.

I have seen many butterflies in my lifetime. They are so beautiful to watch. I have yet to see a butterfly stuck halfway as it attempts to exit the caterpillar's cocoon. The butterfly seems to embrace the struggle and push through. I believe that meditation gives us the strength to embrace our struggle so that we too may push through and fly.

Meditation is the key that unlocked my prison door. It allowed me to walk away from feeling trapped in a body full of painful symptoms and a mind full of anger and hostility. It was through meditation that I understood that, while I cannot change the direction of the wind, I can adjust my sails as I cross the ocean of life. I have realised that sometimes the most productive thing we can do is to be still. When meditation became my medication, illness transformed to wellness.

Resonance Repatterning

I had the good fortune of being introduced to Resonance Repatterning approximately twenty years ago. It was the initial breakthrough in my personal transformation. I was so intrigued by this discipline that I enrolled to study it. I had the privilege of studying under its founder, Chloe Faith Wordsworth, in South Africa and the USA.

Resonance Repatterning is a system of identifying limiting beliefs and unconscious patterns that are hindering our health, finances and relationships. Instead of feeling constricted and restrained and resisting positive change, I was schooled to constantly look for the opportunity in the problem. Resonance Repatterning helped me to resonate with or tune in to my true strengths and gifts. Problems can serve as a motivating force to help us change direction in life.

Over the years, as a Resonance Repatterning practitioner, I had many clients who experienced this positive shift. They were in awe of the process, whether the shift for them had been low-key or profound. This system deepened my understanding of the subtle human qualities and natural flow of energy through our chakras and meridians. We exist in a field of energy. What we resonate with in this field of frequencies determines what we experience. When we are tuned in to hurt and hate, we experience more of this from the field of energy. In the same light, when we are tuned in to love and understanding, we experience more of this from the field of energy. The good and bad, positive and negative, are all available for the taking. We get to choose how we want to feel at any given moment or in any given circumstance and this choice unfolds our way forward. The challenge is that we often become addicted to our choices in life, especially the drama. Resonance Repatterning provides the tools to identify and stop our addiction to negative emotional drama.

While studying Resonance Repatterning, I was introduced to the healing impact of laughter. Back in the 1960s, Norman Cousins used bouts of belly-rippling laughter for pain relief from the chronic disease, ankylosing spondylitis. He went on to publish the extraordinary book, *Anatomy of an Illness* [33]. I have always enjoyed comedy shows and movies and I found them most therapeutic, especially when the pain felt persistent. Sometimes I would also just stand in front of the mirror and laugh. It felt so refreshing. I noticed how the energy in our home lifted when my family heard my laughter. Smiling and laughing causes the brain to release dopamine, a neurotransmitter that produces feelings of lightness, joy and happiness [161]. This is a wonderful way to switch our body to the parasympathetic healing and repair mode. And deliberately bringing smiles and laughter into our life is a great way to tune in to pleasant feelings that help to pave a positive way forward.

Using Sound With Music and Vocal Toning

I have already introduced some of the potential benefits of listening to Indian classical music as I experienced it in both my mother's journey and my journey to betterment. Emeritus Professor Nigel Osborne is a British composer who uses music, including Indian classical music, to help people affected by trauma, such as war veterans and children who are victims of conflict. Osborne[36] finds that 'Indian classical music is particularly powerful in therapeutic processes because in my opinion it encompasses the whole human evolution and the whole of our personal development in it, in the way the raga is developed'. He goes on to say that rhythm in Indian classical music 'excites the most primitive as well as higher cognitive areas in the brain and stimulates the motor cortex'. I believe that Indian classical music can act as a soothing balm to the wounded hearts and tired nerves of those who struggle with the heavy burden of life.

Our Hindu scriptures, the Vedas, teach us the concept of *nada brahma*, which translates as 'the world is sound'. The ancient yogis who spent most of their time in meditation were able to listen to the celestial sound current – the *shabd* – within the human body. They saw the power and value in this music and brought it to the places of worship to remind us of the inner sound that resonates in all of us. We can also find the importance of sound in the Bible: 'In the beginning was the Word'. I understand the human body to be an ocean of vibrating frequencies that is positively influenced by the vibrating frequency of sound. When I listen to Indian classical music, I feel as though it penetrates my whole being.

When I was pregnant with our younger son, I exclusively listened to Indian classical music. We even played it during his wonderful water birth. Afterwards, whenever he would cry or struggle to fall asleep, I would put the music on. It instantly soothed him and helped him to fall asleep.

When I realised that the pharmaceutical industry had no answers for me, I turned to Indian classical music, where I found solace. I felt joy and a deep connection with my inner being, which facilitated healing my heart and deepening my meditation. I could hear my inner voice, a voice of reason, which knew right from wrong in my choice of thoughts, words and actions. We all have this voice of reason built into our hearts. Multiple autoimmune syndrome might have taken me ten steps back, but once I tuned in to myself, I could use it to catapult me a hundred steps forward.

Growing my desire for more spiritual alone time by listening to Indian classical music let a hypnotising peace and calm unfold within me. It transported me to a place of gratitude and forgiveness. I managed to stop sabotaging my relationships. Slowly my entire world changed. Listening to soothing and relaxing music with intention and focus is a powerful way to realign ourselves with our truth and replace judgement with kindness in our heart and mind.

We can also enjoy sound by producing it through singing, chanting, humming to music, playing musical instruments and toning, all of which are activities being studied for their potential to induce positive brainwaves and alter our mood and biochemistry[21]. Part of the reason some of these modalities may be beneficial goes back to the parasympathetic nervous system discussed earlier. The vagus nerve can be engaged to bring about positive effects. In fact, treatments for certain conditions using an implanted device to stimulate the vagus nerve are already in use and more applications are being studied[75]. But we needn't wait for devices: it appears that we have the possibility to naturally access some of the benefits of improving 'vagal tone' through yoga and meditation, and related activities such as deep breathing, along with practices that relate to sound and music[149].

We can think of vocal toning as a massage for the body and mind from the inside out. It has a positive impact on our mind, feelings and physical body. The human voice carries something in its vibration that makes it more powerful than any musical instrument: consciousness. Vocal toning helps us to focus and relax, release negative emotions, reduce stress and improve stamina and concentration. Dr Alfred A. Tomatis, a researcher in the field of auditory and vocal problems and their broader effects, discovered that high frequency vocal sounds recharge the brain through direct bone conduction[69]. We don't need anything fancy – no melody, no words, no rhythm, no harmony – we just need the sound of the vibrating breath.

Sound vibrations and toning are also central to nāda yoga. Practitioners extend vocal sounds on a single vowel in order to experience the sound and its effects in other parts of the body. The power of toning lies in the vowels: OO – OH – AH – EH – EE. The vowels can also be followed by MM or humming with lips closed. Humming and toning vibrate the larynx or voice box, from where the sound is transmitted, and the vibrations travel to the cervical bones of the spine, just behind the larynx. Our bones then conduct the vibration throughout the body, restoring balance and harmony. I sometimes choose to tone just one vowel sound or all five in one session.

There is no right way or wrong way to tone. Your way is the right way for you. Your sound is unique, and the experience is uniquely yours. So my way is just one of the ways to do it. I start by letting my intuition choose a vowel for me. I may lie on my back, stand, or sit up with my spine extended vertically. I then smile. I breathe in generously, and as I breathe out I allow the sound to come through, lasting for the length of the out-breath. I try to elongate the vowel. I try to do this at moderate volume and without straining.

I then sit in silence and explore the sensations of each of these vowels and their total effect on my body and mind. I pay attention to everything the vibrations may be awakening in me. I am conscious not to judge myself. Depending on my mood and stress levels, some tones seem to come more easily than others. It's important to explore those where we feel discomfort. They signal that there is an imbalance somewhere in the body and mind. I acknowledge the imbalance free of judgement and then tone some more. I allow my voice and tone to bring me into the present moment. When I am toning, I feel a sensation of depth in my body – the vibration becomes pronounced in my head and chest area and then my entire spine. I embrace the pleasant, heartfelt emotions that surface. A calmness and mental clarity pervade. I feel grounded.

A little can go a long way with toning. I found that it's more beneficial to tone more frequently for shorter periods. I experience the best results when I tone daily for a few minutes at a time. I must concur with the research that toning can contribute to shifts in attention, awareness and consciousness[134].

To get started with toning, you can take a look at online resources like Jonathan Goldman's video *The 7 Vowel Sounds* [60] or Jill Purce's videos on overtone chanting[121, 122]. I have also summarised the basic steps below.

1. Toning can be done while sitting, lying down, walking, working, driving, etc.
2. Take a deep breath in and become aware of lengthening your spine. Breathe out and relax.
3. Breathe in. Then, as you breathe out, use the breath to elongate the sound of the vowel.
4. Relax and breathe in again.
5. Repeat: breathe out and elongate the sound of the same vowel or a different one. Enjoy the relaxation and sensation of letting go as you tone.
6. After toning for a few minutes, just sit quietly and allow your body and mind to integrate this simple yet profound sound experience.
7. Remember: the point of toning is not the quality of the sound but rather the experience of the vibration it produces. No two people experience toning in the same way, so honour and trust your own experience.

Affirmations and Visualisation With Sound

I have combined some of the sound therapy described above with visualisations and affirmations. Visualisation with affirmation is a mental technique to harness the power of the subconscious mind. Try this experiment – do it slowly. Close your eyes and imagine yourself picking a bright-yellow lemon from a tree in a garden. Take the lemon to your kitchen. Then cut the juicy fruit in half and bring it to your mouth. Now open your eyes and notice the saliva that has built up in your mouth: your mind has sent a message that food is on its way, so the digestive process has started.

Energy goes where thought goes. This is a powerful way to harness the power of the mind to heal the body. Our repeated thought impulses, which get stored in our subconscious mind, form the mechanism through which our reality manifests. I took these facts into consideration and decided to help my body turn off its HPA axis and redirect its focus and energy into healing. Meditation is a potent way of achieving this outcome, and combining affirmation and visualisation is a form of meditation. The combination makes use of the mind's faculty to see and hear, thereby affirming what we want by presenting it to ourselves as if we actually have it.

When it comes to visualisations and affirmations, three ingredients are essential:

1. Choose concise, positive words in the present tense. Example: 'I am well' instead of 'I will be well'. Personally, I avoid sentences like 'I am going to fight MS, RA and Hashimoto's'. I prefer positive statements like 'I understand MS, RA and Hashimoto's, and I am letting them go'.

2. Imagine a clear picture of the positive desired outcome. Allow your mind to see yourself achieving the results and enjoying them. For example, although I could barely walk, I visualised myself dancing with Rajin.

3. Feel the positive emotion of the desired outcome. Your imagination must be so clear that the joy and satisfaction should feel almost overwhelming. It should leave you euphoric. Make it as real as possible.

Visualisation is a form of meditation that has been around for thousands of years. It can be found in the Hindu Vedic scriptures of India. Regularly practising visualisation can make the subconscious mind believe that we have already achieved our goal. This makes the actual manifestation of what we are visualising seem much more attainable, even inevitable.

Visualisation has been a part of my world from an early age. I practised it intuitively, even before I read about it. It was during my university years that I used it the most. I was six months into my medical science master's degree and all my laboratory results were unsuccessful. Naturally, I started to panic. I was researching the effect of apolipoprotein E allele distribution on the lipid profile of pre- and post-menopausal woman in the South African Indian population[14, 64]. The methods we were using to extract the DNA and conduct the genotyping yielded no results. I kept finding dead ends. To make matters worse, my supervisor resigned. At the time, DNA research was fairly new. I was assigned a brilliant replacement supervisor, but she was unfortunately inexperienced in this field. I was left all on my own.

Every night before falling asleep, I would visualise my graduation and hear my name being announced followed by 'degree obtained *cum laude*'. I did this every night without fail. Then, very systematically, I started the project over from scratch. Within a few weeks, I started seeing results. When I had completed my thesis, I was told that the external examiner assigned to me was a drill sergeant. He was very strict, and the thesis would be scrutinised in detail. I was told I would probably have to resubmit many times. I handed it in and continued my visualisation. The thesis came back faultless and I was awarded my degree *cum laude*. My professor said that in the department's 150 years, it was the first time a master's degree had been awarded *cum laude*. I remember being simply stunned with the result. It took a few days before I managed to accept that I could actually manifest what I truly believed in, even if others around me thought it was impossible.

I had another profound experience with visualisation about six years ago. A patient who was diabetic came to me for help with her diagnosis of Charcot foot. Charcot arthropathy is the neuropathic progressive degeneration of a weight-bearing joint. Her foot had significant nerve damage and the bones had weakened and were disintegrating. Her doctor thought that the best way forward for her would be to have the foot amputated. She came to me desperate to save her leg. We worked together every day for two weeks.

As part of the Resonance Repatterning consultations, I introduced her to Indian classical music and asked her to visualise running on the beach with her family. This was her favourite activity. Three weeks later, when her doctor examined her, he was expecting to see gangrene, but instead he found that the bones were regenerating. He operated on the foot and told her that she would have to be in a cast for a few months, because her body wouldn't be able to heal easily, due to her diabetes. She continued with her sound therapy and harnessed the healing power of her subconscious mind with her visualisation. Six weeks later, the doctor removed the cast. Her foot was well, and she is still walking on it today.

For my purposes, I created two visualisations: a primary and a secondary visualisation, both with affirmations. The primary visualisation addresses my ultimate goal of healing. The secondary visualisation helps me to overcome emotional triggers as they surface.

For the primary visualisation, I lie in bed, tune in to the soothing sounds of Indian classical flute music, close my eyes and visualise the sound waves entering my brain. I create a picture in my mind of what my damaged nerve cells look like. I imagine the neurons as thick electrical wiring that needs new insulation. I remove the old insulation, the scar tissue. I visualise the new myelin as a super strong insulation tape that reinsulates the neuron. I carefully wrap all the neurons. The new myelin is indestructible. I then take my attention down my spine and do the same.

I see my gut as a long pool pipe in my body. I flood it with white light from my inner divine source. I zoom in to the wall of my gut and see its rounded bricks. I visualise the bricks moving closer together and tightening up. I then secure them with white light super glue.

I move my attention to my immune system. I visualise the power of the Divine turning on a fire extinguisher of white light inside me, stopping the inflammation, calming my immune system and nourishing my body. I see my immune system like little soldiers in my body: they lay down their weapons, hold their hands in a prayer position and apologise for their hostile behaviour towards me. We forgive each other and order is restored in the kingdom of my body. I then imagine all the cells in my body smiling and echoing that all is forgiven and all is well. I see my cells and myself dancing joyously. My affirmation, which I say out loud during this visualisation, is: 'My body is healed, strong, balanced and joyful. I love and respect myself. Thank you, thank you, thank you'. I enjoy the process and relish the feeling of contentment from contributing to my healing with my positive thoughts and intentions. I am very clear in my mind that this 'reprogramming' exercise is powerful, beautiful and productive.

When I initially turned to this practice, I would do it for many hours a day. I enjoyed the process and fell in love with my body's cellular intelligence. After applying my Take-Charge Wellness Formula, including six weeks of visualisation practice, my next MRI showed a halt in lesion progression in my brain. This was great news! The report from the radiologist stated: 'The previously noted enhancing periventricular lesions do not demonstrate enhancement on this study'. Upon diagnosis, the prognosis had been dire, and the persistent symptoms pointed towards secondary-progressive MS, meaning disability would most likely steadily increase. You can imagine the look of joy and surprise on the neurologist's face when he realised that I was showing signs of improvement free of immunosuppressant drugs.

I had harnessed the power of visualisation to potentiate brain activity, which manifested a positive physiological response in my body. According to Harvard University professor Rudolph E. Tanzi and doctor and alternative medicine advocate Deepak Chopra in their book *Super Brain: Unleashing the Explosive Power of Your Mind to Maximize Health, Happiness, and Spiritual Well-Being* [30], 'Everything hinges on how you relate to your brain. By setting higher expectations, you enter a phase of higher functioning. One of the unique things about the human brain is that it can do only what it thinks it can do'. It was this understanding that catapulted me into believing that I could alter the pattern of my disease.

Ultimately, I think I just had an experience of neuroplasticity. My brain took instructions from me and started to make changes. Neuroplasticity is the brain's ability to form and restructure its neural connections [130]. Our adult brain is not hardwired with fixed neural circuits. It is, in fact, constantly changing. Neuroscience research has found that our brain cells can be altered throughout our lives and neurons that fire together wire together [124]. I believe my brain is able to repair itself – it just needs a little bit of my help.

I use my secondary visualisation with affirmation whenever something happens that makes me sad or upset. I lie in bed, tune in to the soothing sounds of the flute, close my eyes and visualise the sound waves entering my body. I see them healing my heart and my brain. I become aware of the voice in my head. 'What story do I want to feed my body?' I ask myself. I then repeat the words: 'The infinite intelligence of my subconscious mind knows all and sees all. Everything is perfect and as it should be in this moment. Thank you, thank you, thank you'. I stay with the visualisation until I can see myself happy and accepting of what is, free of hurt or judgement.

In his books *The Brain That Changes Itself* [37] and *The Brain's Way of Healing* [38], the distinguished psychiatrist, psychoanalyst and author Dr Norman Doidge draws attention to the fact that the brain is capable of much more significant self-repair and healing than previously thought by the medical profession. Furthermore, his work shows that the brain can 'rewire' itself when we make conscious habits of certain thoughts and actions. A variety of techniques to stimulate the brain's innate plasticity is being explored and employed.[1]

Through my visualisation with affirmation practice and my research, I realised that my positive belief and intention to reverse the effects of the autoimmune conditions were vital to my process. My brain's neural pathways could be changed with the thoughts in my mind. Below I have included a step-by-step guided relaxation in the form of visualisation with affirmation for you to try out. I had to practise it many times before my mind eased into the process. I always allow myself as much time in this happy place as possible. Only I can take myself there. I deserve it – and you deserve it too! We all have the power to choose to create a happy moment amidst the chaos. Start by turning your cell phone to flight mode and ensure that you are not disturbed while doing this exercise.

- Find a comfortable, safe, quiet place.
- Put on soft soothing instrumental music or listen to the sounds of nature.
- Find a comfortable position, either lying down or sitting.
- Take three deep breaths.
- Gently close your eyes.

---

1. Doidge[37] examined the way a device, called a Portable Neuromodulation Stimulator (PoNS device), when applied to the tongue to cause vibration, helped an opera singer with MS to regain his voice. He saw positive changes in all MS patients that he worked with. Even patients confined to a wheelchair started showing marked improvement. He is also doing further work on sound healing. A research article confirmed Doidge's findings and suggested the need for a larger study group that balances disease duration across groups [38].

- Repeat the words, 'Thank you ... thank you ... thank you ...' a few times, taking a moment to pause between each 'thank you'.

- Focus on your breathing. Breathe in deeply through your nose and expand your tummy and diaphragm. Then breathe out deeply through your nose, relaxing the tummy muscles.

- Scan your body, starting at your feet and going all the way up to your head. Use your breath to let go of any tension that you pick up with this scan.

- Smile. Keep smiling even if you have to fake it.

- Now think of a place in nature that appeals to you. It could be a gorgeous beach, some majestic mountains, a beautiful garden ...

- It's early morning and the sky is alive with expectation. The sun is about to rise. Make it real.

- Once again repeat the words, 'Thank you ... thank you ... thank you ...'.

- Feel yourself present in this place of nature. Hear the sounds around you. Breathe in the colours around you. Notice how everything is calm and as it should be. Honour the opportunity to embrace this beautiful creation.

- Now, turn your attention to the horizon. The morning sky is bursting with colour. Notice the colours: the blues, pinks and oranges blurred together in a glittering mist.

- Feel the energy of expectation from nature. Something great is arriving: it's the dawn of a new day. The ball of fiery energy is peeking in.

- Feel the excitement and hope of new beginnings all around you. Breathe it in.

- The sun's gentle morning rays are starting to caress you now. The sun is sending you a clear message of hope and joy. Allow this hope and joy to filter into your body.

- As you breathe in the majestic orange sun rays, take your attention to your heart centre and feel that you are also breathing in love, hope and understanding. Imagine that your heart is smiling. It is full of love.

- Hear both your mind and heart echoing the words, 'Thank you ... thank you ...'.
- Feel the ease with which your body is accepting this new beginning.
- Take a few minutes and stay in this place of joy.
- When you are ready, open your eyes to a new moment.
- Allow a few seconds for your body and mind to digest this experience. Notice the calmness that has come over you.

Breath and Colour

You may already have noticed that breath and colour featured in some of the exercises above. I'd like to focus on them especially in this final section on the Thought aspect of my Take-Charge Wellness Formula.

We human beings are blessed with a built-in destress button: the breath. It's simple, free and literally right under our nose. It's such a vital part of being human, yet so little emphasis is placed on it. Focusing on our breathing is like charging our batteries. I always make sure that my phone battery is charged, but then I make excuses that I have no time to charge my inner battery. Can you relate?

Breathing is so much more than an action performed by the respiratory system. In *The Breathing Book*, Donna Farhi[46] writes, 'Breathing affects your respiratory, cardiovascular, neurological, gastrointestinal, muscular, and psychic systems, and also has a general effect on your sleep, memory, ability to concentrate, and your energy levels'. Breathing can also be essential in making the connection between the conscious and unconscious mind, acting as a key to entering the dimension of presence or the now[141].

Today, more and more people are discovering conscious breathing or breathing exercises as a tool to promote good health in body and mind. Despite this, some of us are so focused on wanting to pay for wellness that, when it's free, we battle to believe that it can be a powerful healing tool. And yet it's so simple: a calm mind and an energised body is as close as your next breath. Breathing requires no equipment and can be done anywhere. Vietnamese Buddhist monk and spiritual teacher Thích Nhât Hạnh[108] puts it simply, 'Breathing in, I calm body and mind. Breathing out, I smile. Dwelling in the present moment, I know this is the only moment'. I find these words both empowering and comforting.

Some people, in an attempt to boast a flat tummy, have unconsciously restricted their breathing to shallow 'chest breathing', which increases tension and anxiety. Shallow breathing limits the diaphragm's range of motion. When we breathe deeply, the air coming in through the nose fills our lungs fully and the lower belly rises to accommodate the diaphragm, which gives way to expand our lungs to their full capacity. Deep diaphragmatic breathing for a few minutes is one way to turn off our fight-flight-freeze mode[87]. With a few deep in-breaths followed by long exhalations, you can stimulate the vagus nerve, which then releases the neurotransmitter acetylcholine. This substance causes a reduction in heart rate and blood pressure, contributing to a state of inner calm[15].

You could try a short, simple breathing exercise. Either lie on your back with your spine as straight as possible or sit upright with your spine erect so that your lungs can expand freely. Become aware of the coolness of the in-breath and the warmth of the out-breath. Allow your tummy to expand as your diaphragm pushes down to open up the lungs. Experience the pleasure of your lungs expanding as you breathe in. Smile. Notice the calmness of your body as you breathe out. Relax your eyes. Become aware of the vitality of your body as your torso expands and relaxes. Think of the life-giving oxygen being delivered to your cells. Sense how happy you are in your awareness of your breath. Something as simple as becoming aware of your in-breath and out-breath can instantly elevate your mood. Tell yourself, 'Just for this moment, I am going to smile and pay attention to my breathing – just for this moment'.

I invite you to tell yourself, 'Just this moment ...' every fifteen minutes throughout your day. Soon you will be smiling all day. Wellness is a full-time responsibility.

Another potent breathing exercise to improve well-being is alternate nostril breathing, or *nadi shodhana*. It is considered the king of all breaths in Ayurvedic medicine. 'Nadi' means channel and 'shodhana'

166

means cleansing or purifying. This breath is able to bring balance to our physical, emotional and mental well-being by harmonising the two hemispheres of the brain[139]. Its ability to activate the parasympathetic nervous system and reduce blood pressure makes this modality a gift to wellness. It can ease racing thoughts that cause anxiety and stress and can help relieve insomnia[76]. I have integrated alternate nostril breathing into my daily routine and it's my go-to tool for calming my emotions. It can also be a wonderful precursor to meditation.

You can prepare for a brief alternate nostril breathing exercise by sitting in a comfortable position. Keep the spine straight and relax. Lift ever so slightly from the crown of the head to elongate your spine. This posture gives the lungs room to expand. Breathe in deeply a few times. You are now going to breathe in and out through your nose using one nostril at a time. If you are right-handed, relax your left hand in your lap.

Close your eyes. Using the right thumb, softly close the right nostril and inhale slowly through the left nostril for a count of four. Then close both nostrils with the thumb and ring finger of your right hand. Hold the breath for a count of sixteen. Keeping the left nostril closed with your ring finger, release the thumb and breathe out through the right nostril for a count of eight. With the right nostril open, inhale slowly for a count of four and then close it with the thumb. Hold for a count of sixteen. Release the ring finger and exhale through the left nostril for a count of eight. This is one cycle. Repeat this pattern five times, allowing the mind to follow the in-breath and out-breath. Once this is complete, relax and allow your breath to flow easily and enjoy the new you. Open your eyes to a new moment.

When white light passes through a prism, it breaks up into the colours of the rainbow: red, orange, yellow, green, blue, indigo and violet. What I find most interesting is that the seven energy centres of the human body in traditional Asian religions, also called chakras, are associated with the exact order of the colours that make up white light. When we breathe in white light, we allow our chakra energy centres to balance themselves with colour.

To share with you the method I use to incorporate colour into my daily healing process, I invite you to employ the powers of visualisation and imagination. Imagine you are breathing like a dolphin. Before you inhale, place your tongue on the roof of your mouth just behind your front teeth. Imagine you are inhaling and exhaling through the top of your head. Breathe in through your nose and imagine the white light energy and breath coming into your body from the top of your head and moving all the way down your spine. Breathe out and relax. Practise this a few times.

Ancient Celts and Greeks and many other cultures have associated dolphins with unique divine powers; some even regard them as guardians. You may be familiar with recordings of dolphins and whales that are used for relaxation. Dolphins are seen as joyful creatures that spend most of their day playing. For me, combining breathing with the imagery of dolphins definitely augments the relaxation process.

I now invite you to expand on the above breath with the popular 4-7-8 ancient Vedic technique of breathing. This pattern was popularised by Dr Andrew Weil[159], who describes it as a 'natural tranquiliser for the nervous system'. First, breathe out and empty the lungs. Now breathe in for a count of four, hold the breath in for a count of seven, then blow out through the mouth for a count of eight, making a 'whoosh' sound as you do. Inhale – hold – exhale. That's one cycle. Do four cycles in total.

First practise 4-7-8 breathing a few times, then combine it with the white light visualisation. As you breathe in for four counts, imagine you are breathing in white light through the top of your head. As you hold for seven counts, take the white light from your crown to the bottom of your spine. When you blow out for the count of eight, visualise the white light shooting out from the top of your head just as the air shoots out from a dolphin's head.

This breathing pattern involves breathing in quietly through the nose and breathing out audibly through the mouth. Exhalation takes twice as long as inhalation. This breathing exercise is subtle in the beginning, but it gains power with repetition and practice. The wonderful surge of oxygen rushing through your body will sometimes make you feel light-headed. This will pass. After a month, increase from four to eight cycles. This breathing exercise will push the reset button and leave you feeling recentred.

I practise this technique throughout my day, especially when I am aware of internal tension and stress. I also do it first thing in the morning before meditation and as my last activity before bedtime. I continue with the visualisation until I fall asleep. I combine this visualisation breathing technique with Indian classical music.

The starting point of all achievement is desire. How badly do we want to get well? Weak desire brings weak results. A home generator is too weak to power up a city. We need more energy. We can hold a desire only when we believe that we will feel better when we achieve it. A powerful desire fuelled by daily practice will reap results. The secret here is practice, practice, practice. We have to consciously integrate good practices into our daily routine. It's a simple yet potent way to facilitate healing the body and mind. Remember to smile and relax your eyes while doing all of the above. As you continue the practice, your ability to remain calm and controlled in stressful situations will also be enhanced.

14
Take charge of food: fixing a leaky gut and halting inflammation with nutrition

Food is medicine. It's the hidden remedy for reversing chronic disease. We pick up our prescription in the kitchen. Over the years, science has come to learn that there is so much more to the human gut or gastrointestinal tract than a simple pipeline that absorbs nutrients and eliminates waste. In my research and experience, I have found that the gut-brain connection – yet another connection between mind and body that is tied up with the vagus nerve – is a major doorway to wellness, especially when we are faced with chronic disease. Our gastrointestinal tract is more than a simple pipeline because of its many tiny citizens, a plethora of good bacteria that help us to break down our food – more than four hundred species have been identified to date[62]. These microbiota are a sea of microorganisms that reside all over the human body. The trillions of good bacteria present are integral to countless processes in our body and paramount to our survival. The largest microbiome lies in our gut.

A good balance of healthy bacteria is key to ensuring proper digestive functioning. The microbiome helps the body to digest certain foods that the stomach and small intestine cannot digest on their own. Gut bacteria are also known to synthesize vitamins, meaning that some of the vitamins your body needs do not come directly from the food you eat – they are produced by the bacteria in your gut[127]. Vitamin K, for example, which is necessary for effective blood clotting, is provided mainly by gut bacteria[100]. Gut microbiota also produce B-group vitamins[127]. Beyond normal gastrointestinal function, well-balanced gut flora provides protection from infection, regulates metabolism and plays a key role in the complex mechanisms of immunoregulation, that is, keeping the immune system in homeostasis. The gut houses the largest number of immune cells in the body, comprising 70 per cent of the cells that make up the immune system[91, 150]. Hence, for me, it made sense to focus my research on the gut microbes' immune-modulating capacities to enhance regulatory responses rather than suppress total immunity with medication.

Serotonin, one of the 'happy' chemicals I mentioned previously, also has an important relationship with the gut, since gut bacteria are involved in its production[168]. As a brain neurotransmitter, it affects emotions and behaviour. It regulates anxiety, happiness and mood. Low levels of serotonin are associated with depression. Research shows that therapeutic targeting of the gut microbiota might be a viable treatment option for serotonin-related disorders[110]. In my case, correcting my gut flora played a pivotal role in lifting my depression. Who would have thought that my relationship with my husband was in the hands of microscopic bacteria.

There are thus many important connections between our gut health and our overall well-being. At the interface of the 'microbiota-gut-brain axis' is the vagus nerve. Research is now shedding new light on the important role of the vagus nerve in gut health: it's involved in decreasing intestinal permeability, modulating the microbiota composition and reducing inflammation. In an article titled: 'The vagus nerve at the interface of the microbiota-gut-brain axis', the researchers concluded that a reduction in vagal tone implies a disorder of the autonomic nervous system that is characterised by a leaky gut and microbial imbalance or dysbiosis[18]. They also state that 'complementary medicine [like hypnosis and meditation], cognitive behavioral therapies, deep breathing, and moderate and sustainable physical activity would be of interest to restore a homeostatic microbiota-gut-brain axis'.

This study helps us to appreciate the huge responsibility we have when it comes to managing autoimmune conditions. Hence, these are not things that can simply be fixed by swallowing a pill.

It's in fact often through swallowing pills that we disrupt the intricate workings of our gut. Dysbiosis – an imbalance between beneficial and harmful bacteria in the gut – can be brought on by medication. Many of us are now familiar with the fact that we need to replenish gut bacteria when we take antibiotics. However, our microbiome is also compromised by medicines that contain codeine and non-steroidal anti-inflammatory drugs (NSAIDs). The continuous use of NSAIDs for pain and inflammation may eventually lead to holes in the gut, commonly referred to as ulcers. We sometimes fail to realise that most medication can disrupt our gut microbiome. If you carefully read the package insert, you will very often find a warning that the drug 'may cause gastric disturbance'. This means the medication might upset your gut microbiome, which can have painful consequences, including diarrhoea, constipation, nausea, vomiting, stomach cramps, acid reflux, bloating and flatulence.

The other major disservice we do our gastrointestinal system is related to our modern lifestyle. Diets high in refined carbohydrates, sugar, gluten and processed foods significantly contribute to the destruction of our microbiome. Stress also impacts on our microbiome negatively and scientists are now investigating how the gut microbiome might influence the neurobiology of stress[52]. In my research it has become abundantly clear to me that, when we have chronic pain, inflammation, fatigue or depression, we need to start by healing the gut[133].

Gut health is a hot topic in all chronic conditions today. The body has an intricate system of allowing just the perfect-sized molecules to pass from the gut into the bloodstream to become the building blocks for our survival. The gut prevents toxins, pathogens and undigested food particles from entering the bloodstream. In order to achieve this, the gut wall epithelial cells, which are only a single layer of cells, form a barrier. The spaces between the cells are referred to as 'tight junctions'. These tight junctions play an intricate role in the permeability of the gut wall.

The intestinal permeability goes out of balance when these tight junctions are no longer tight, causing undigested food particles, toxic waste products and bacteria to leak through the gut wall and flood the bloodstream. Hence the term 'leaky gut'. This 'illegal' entry of large protein molecules into the bloodstream sets off the immune system, which attempts to destroy the foreign particles. As is customary, our immune system opens its attack on foreign particles with intense inflammation. Prolonged entry of these foreign substances into our bloodstream signals the immune system to keep up inflammation. This excessive inflammation in the body causes pain and lack of functionality and may manifest as a number of disease states, including autoimmune disease.

Understanding what causes the gut to malfunction is key for wellness. Research scientists have identified a type of protein, called zonulin, that increases the spaces between tight junctions in the intestinal lining[49]. When there is too much zonulin in the gut, it causes intestinal hyperpermeability, or a leaky gut. Gliadin, a protein component of gluten, is one example of a substance that triggers zonulin production, widening the spaces in the intestinal wall and causing food particles and bacteria to escape from the gut. The havoc a leaky gut causes is compounded when the microvilli that line the intestines and absorb nutrients also become damaged, leading to nutrient deficiencies. When we understand that the foods we eat play a major role in gut health, we have the opportunity via our choice of food to contribute to immune modulation at the gastrointestinal level. We also need to nurture beneficial microbes in our gut, because they hold the key to our health and happiness.

Presenting with four chronic conditions meant that my body was riddled with inflammation. I had inflammation in my brain, my spinal cord, my joints, my muscles and my thyroid gland. Fire was blazing inside me. Anti-inflammatory drugs gave me temporary relief, but I had to take high doses for any respite.

When I was newly diagnosed and flooded with medication, I experienced the dreaded side effects of anti-inflammatory and immunosuppressant drugs. As far as my digestive system was concerned, these included severe heartburn, stomach pain, diarrhoea, constipation, nausea and vomiting. The lines were blurred as to what caused these symptoms – the medication or the illness. The entry-level immunosuppressant never agreed with me, so I refused to consider any of the other MS and RA disease-modifying drugs on the market to suppress my immune system.

I had to find an alternative anti-inflammatory solution. While I found the answer in a number of healing modalities, food was the most prominent. Addressing the body's basic needs, I questioned the fuel I was giving my body. I began to search for foods with anti-inflammatory properties and was delighted to find many. It was after all the father of medicine, Hippocrates, who said, 'Let food be thy medicine and medicine be thy food'. I find it difficult to understand why our medical model struggles to properly recognise and emphasise the massive impact that food – the body's energy source – has on the human body. The body starts to break down with the incorrect nutrition. This manifests as illness but, instead of changing what we eat, we medicate to suppress the symptoms. The solution to so many health problems in our society may very well be in taking a closer look at what we choose to nourish our bodies with. I strongly believe that our wellness is in large part governed by our food choices.

Foods to Avoid and the Struggle to Change

When our body is in a compromised state, that is, when disease has set in, choosing a nutritionally dense diet is a logical decision to help the body return to homeostasis. The trillions of chemical reactions taking place in our body to keep us alive are either enhanced or hindered by our choice of food. We might all do well to eat less of some things and more of others. Those of us battling chronic conditions are required to be even more mindful of our food choices.

Although I was vegetarian before the diagnosis, the food I consumed was mostly processed and curried with lots of potatoes, grains and legumes – all the ingredients for a leaky gut. I neglected to nourish my body adequately with fresh fruit and vegetables. Although reducing

174

or giving up the consumption of meat and other animal products may still be contentious in many cultures and societies, it's definitely worth at least considering if you are interested in better managing your health. Ask yourself this: What harm could it do to give vegetarianism or veganism a try?

Often the response is, 'But where will I get my protein?' or 'Won't I become protein deficient?' Well, let's take a cow as an example. A cow is a huge, strong beast. Where does it get its protein from? Grass! Protein is broken down into twenty amino acids that our body needs as building blocks to grow and repair. Of these, nine amino acids are essential, meaning that the body can't make them – we have to get them from our food. All nine of these essential amino acids are present in plants. They are histidine, isoleucine, leucine, lysine, methionine, phenylalanine, threonine, tryptophan and valine. A plant-based diet provides all the minerals and nutrients for our bodies to flourish – and it's wrapped with love from nature. Even vitamin B12, often considered to be the sole vitamin that is absent from plant-derived food sources, is found in high quantities in the seaweed known as nori, which is used in sushi[157]. I have my sushi with nori, avocado and cucumber, and instead of rice I have millet. Apart from the fact that we can get all the nutrients we need from a plant-based diet, it's also worth considering what science is saying about the potential benefits of restricting meat consumption [12] as well as the potential hazards of eating meat[163].

I also draw inspiration from yogis, who have proven for centuries that if we want to quieten the mind, we have to adopt a vegetarian diet. Since healing starts in the mind, keeping our meals light keeps the mind calmer and more focused. Whatever your opinion of meat and animal products might be, simply remember that it can't hurt to experiment with a different approach.

Processed food challenges our bodies because we have been designed to thrive on food in its natural form. For most people, this realisation is quite an inconvenience. Nowadays we are living to eat instead of eating to live. We forget to appreciate the colour, texture, shape, aroma and flavour of natural, healthy foods.

I believe that conscious eating will catapult us forward in healing our body and mind. We are all familiar with the adage 'an apple a day keeps the doctor away', but it should actually be 'fresh, unprocessed food all day keeps the doctor away'.

Today, with the overwhelming amount of data generated by diet books and the media, many people are left feeling that choosing a healthy eating plan is akin to describing the intricacies of particle physics. In our quest to save time, we compromise on quality, freshness and nutrient value and go for processed foods instead. It's unfortunate that we have complicated something that is so simple and easily available. I too battled to get my diet right. I didn't want to believe that my favourite foods were causing inflammation in my body. I kept testing the system. I sometimes hid from my family and snacked on a piece of garlic bread or chocolate cake. Within twenty-four hours my joints would become inflamed and the tingling and prickling pain arrived.

There were times when I felt so well with correct eating that I believed I had earned the right to go back to my old eating habits. This ridiculous attitude took me right back to hospital. At times like these, I was grateful for the allopathic medication that brings immediate relief from my acute pain. But I am also thankful for the knowledge that this is not a permanent solution. I cheated on my diet many times before I finally got the memo: my poor food choices were hurting my body.

I had to choose to change from eating on autopilot and start consciously eating food that is nourishing. I had to get outside my comfort zone and force myself to eat correctly and create new eating habits. We live in a world overflowing with food products that are scientifically engineered to be addictive. I needed to remove the burden to say 'no' to foods that were compounding my illness. In order to stop being seduced by processed and other forbidden foods, I had to remove them from my environment. It's hard to stay consistent with the right food choices in a poorly designed environment, especially in the initial stages. Willpower and motivation are not enough to sustain healthy eating habits. Creating an environment that supports our goals is the key ingredient that shapes our behaviour and nudges us towards success. We have to change our environment to work for us instead of against us.

I also had to watch my mood and my mind. I learnt to forego immediate pleasure in exchange for long-term self-respect and wellness. I noticed that, when I was happy, my new eating habits were easy. When I was unhappy, it was difficult to follow my new way of healthy eating. I would crave sugary and processed snacks and other foods forbidden for my conditions. Success in the kitchen, I learnt, is achieved by making the effort to remove the temptation. Even though I primed myself before entering the kitchen or eating out by placing notes with strong messages all around the dining room and kitchen, I experienced the best results when my environment was free of temptation.

On days that I did cheat, my sons hit upon the idea of cutting up my fresh vegetables into the shapes of tablets and capsules. That way, they reasoned, my brain would maybe acknowledge that food was my medicine.

'Perhaps if the fresh vegetables took the shape of pills you wouldn't feel the need to cheat, Mum!' they explained.

'I'm sorry, boys'. I'm not sure if I responded more with astonishment at their unique idea or embarrassment that my behaviour had led them to this thinking.

'Don't let that tiny muscle in your mouth manipulate and ruin your body and your life. Be strong, Mum', Pavesan pleaded.

'Be honest, Mum', Tharsheyen said. 'How badly do you want this change? Your actions *must* reflect your desire'.

'There is no excuse for my behaviour, boys. Thank you for showing me how foolish I've been'.

Surrounded by so much love, I couldn't give up. I learnt that my choice of food was an important cause of inflammation in my body. I learnt from each failed attempt with my diet. I used failure as a solid foundation for success in the kitchen. I kept moving forward, determined to find the foods that made me feel ill. I had been a lacto-vegetarian for about thirty-six years. Even though this might have included many choices generally considered healthy, my diet was inappropriate for healing a leaky gut in an autoimmune patient. I already did not consume meat or alcohol, which can damage the gut lining. But there were many other inflammatory foods I would need to consider eliminating, including:

- foods that contain gluten, like wheat, rye and barley
- dairy
- processed foods and refined sugar
- rice
- vegetables from the nightshade family
- legumes (including peanuts) and dried beans
- refined vegetable oils.

It became clear to me that our simple food choices can support healing and help maintain gut health. While it's generally accepted that healthy food choices are recommended for everyone, they are even more applicable to someone struggling with an inflammatory disorder. From my experience, paying attention to my nutrition became more pertinent than medicine. In light of my multiple autoimmune syndrome, I even had to re-examine what would generally be considered healthy food options for most people.

Dairy is an especially interesting problem in the case of autoimmunity[89]. If dairy casein and other animal protein particles enter the bloodstream via a leaky gut, the body recognises them as foreign, because they are. The body then makes antibodies against these foreign proteins, but it doesn't just stop there. Being a mammal just like humans, the cow shares certain protein structures with us. In its quest to destroy the foreign animal protein, the immune system recognises similar segments of proteins or amino acid sequences in our own tissues. It incorrectly recognises our tissues as foreign cow protein and attacks them. This is referred to as 'cross-reactivity' or 'molecular mimicry'[116, 152].

When it comes to MS, scientists are studying one dairy protein in particular, namely butyrophilin. This dairy protein is very similar in structure to the proteins that make up the myelin sheath. Butyrophilin protein molecules mimic myelin protein molecules, causing the immune system to cross-react. A study titled: 'Antibody cross-reactivity between myelin oligodendrocyte glycoprotein and the milk protein butyrophilin in multiple sclerosis' showed that milk and milk products can influence the autoimmune response in MS[66]. In other studies, butyrophilin was injected into mice, which then exhibited MS symptoms[111, 137]. As a research scientist, I found these articles convincing enough to remove dairy from my diet and would recommend that MS patients and people with leaky gut symptoms consider the impact dairy and other animal products might be having on them.

It was interesting to note that certain foods, like rice and potatoes, brought on mainly my RA symptoms. Rajin had repeatedly suggested that rice could be a trigger, but I had stubbornly ignored the idea for a long time. The slight RA pain in my ankle and shoulder joint after dancing disappeared completely once I had eliminated rice from my diet. Processed foods and foods containing gluten triggered my MS symptoms, which would start with the tingling of my tongue, followed by the painful MS hug, persistent nausea, brain fog and fatigue. There were times when these symptoms brought on by my food choices were so severe that I had to be hospitalised.

Although I would generally recommend looking into the benefits of a plant-based diet, it might be that some plants cause problems for people with autoimmune or other conditions. So, once again, some experimentation is required. Plant 'toxins' are natural compounds produced by a number of plants, including many that we grow as crops. Their effects within our bodies can be subtle and hard to recognise. In most cases, these toxins are defence mechanisms the plant produces to protect itself from being eaten by insects and animals in its environment. Nightshades, plants of the Solanaceae family, produce high levels of toxins. The commonest nightshades include potatoes, tomatoes, aubergines, goji berries and peppers – both spicy types and bell peppers.

Nightshades contain compounds such as lectins and saponins, and, in particular, glycoalkaloids, which may potentially cause damage to the intestinal lining when consumed by humans. Legumes also contain lectins. There are many different types of lectins and not all of them are harmful to the body. The two types of lectins that are known to cause problems in humans are agglutinins and prolamins. Lectins and saponins disrupt the functioning of the epithelium, the thin layer of cells lining our gut that keeps undigested food from slipping into our bloodstream. Over time, lectins and glycoalkaloids in the diet can create holes in the epithelium, contributing to leaky gut syndrome [114].

Agglutinins and glycoalkaloids are natural pesticides produced by plants and can be an aggravating factor in autoimmune disease. They are there to defend the plant against bacteria, fungi, viruses, insects and animals. Glycoalkaloids act as invisible weapons: they bind strongly to the cholesterol in the cell membranes of predators, and, in so doing, they disrupt the structure of those membranes, causing cells to leak or burst open[56, 154].

Glycoalkaloids in foods are low-grade neurotoxins[39]. They block cholinesterase, an enzyme that is responsible for breaking down acetylcholine, a vital neurotransmitter that carries signals between nerve and muscle cells (acetylcholine is both excitatory and inhibitory depending upon the receptor). When this important enzyme is blocked, acetylcholine can accumulate and electrically overstimulate the predator's muscle cells. This can lead to paralysis, convulsions, respiratory arrest and death.

It's interesting to note that, for those people not facing a chronic inflammatory disease, plant toxins go unnoticed and are considered harmless. However, for those of us with an autoimmune condition, their effects become more pronounced. The glycoalkaloid in nightshades may cause paralytic-like muscle spasms, abdominal pain, headaches, fatigue, joint pain and inflammation, morning stiffness, muscle pain, soft tissue calcification around joints, and nausea [96]. The best way to test yourself for sensitivity would be to try an elimination diet for thirty days. Then reintroduce the nightshades or legumes one at a time and wait a few days to see if you have any sensitivities before reintroducing the next one.

Something that I am in total control of, that is, the choice of food I put into my mouth, was fuelling the inflammation in my body and producing painful symptoms. I had to appeal to my intelligence and willpower.

Come on, Mala, surely you are smart enough to put a stop to this destructive dietary habit.

We need to remove all the food that is hurting the gut wall, escaping via the leaky gut and fuelling inflammation in the body. We need to consume probiotic and prebiotic foods that support the gut microbiome. Our body is constantly replacing its cells with new ones. Our gut lining is replaced every three to seven days. When we correct our choice of food, we can heal the gut and start to reverse autoimmune symptoms. It's a challenge, but it is possible.

I have been inspired by other MS patients in my quest to get my diet right. Dr Terry Wahls, a clinical professor of medicine at the Iowa Carver College of Medicine in the USA, reversed her severe MS symptoms with food and lifestyle change. In one year, with her own version of the paleo diet, she went from having to sit in a tilt-recline wheelchair to actively participating in sports. Her TEDx Talk, *Minding your mitochondria* [153], was my first introduction to proof that change in my diet was a vital part of my healing process. Ann Boroch, a nutritional consultant, in her book *Healing Multiple Sclerosis: Diet, Detox & Nutritional Makeover for Total Recovery*, outlines how she has been symptom-free for twenty-one years after making lifestyle changes and sticking to them [20].

In my case, as a vegetarian, legumes and nightshades, like potatoes, were a staple part of my 'heathy' diet. Removing them brought immediate relief to my joints. The pain, inflammation and redness disappeared.

It became clear to me that a diet of fresh fruit and vegetables, free of all processed foods and sugar, gluten-containing grains, dairy, nightshades and legumes, is my healthy eating plan for wellness and freedom from pain and inflammation. I have no doubt that all patients with a chronic disease should be motivated and educated to change their eating habits. Dietary intervention is not only affordable and accessible but also highly effective in reducing disease symptoms [79].

After working out my various sensitivities, I then focused on nutrient-rich options to reverse the damage caused by the foods that were harmful to me. My research pointed to green juicing as a great option for accelerating repair at the cellular level. I also looked into the benefits of superfoods – including pawpaw and its seeds – and explored water fasting as a way to occasionally hit the 'reset' button.

Juicing, Superfoods and Water Fasting for Wellness

Green juicing creates a concentrated nutrient-rich juice from fruits and vegetables that is low in sugar and high in chlorophyll. Green juices do not contain insoluble fibre, so they are highly absorbable, providing an immediate influx of energising nutrients to our cells. Our bodies live and die at the cellular level. Green juicing is a great way to give your cells a rich dose of amino acids, minerals, vitamins, antioxidants, phytochemicals and other essential nutrients, which we need to improve and maintain our overall health. These healing and protective nutrients help to boost cognitive and immune functions, cleanse the blood, detox the tissues and balance the body's delicate pH.

The potential of hydrogen or pH is the measurement of the alkalinity or acidity of a substance. It ranges on a scale from 0 to 14, with 7 being neutral. A pH below 7 is considered acidic and above 7 is alkaline or basic. The human body requires a tightly controlled pH level, around 7.4 in our blood serum, to survive. The body automatically regulates acidity via its acid-base buffer system. We can give it the right fuel and avoid harmful foods or stressful behaviours to help it with this process. If we consume too few alkaline foods, such as fruit and vegetables, and too many acid-forming foods, such as meat, dairy, sugar, processed foods, alcohol and coffee, our body pH becomes acidic. The body tries to protect itself from the heavy acid burden. It then needs to work harder, by leaching calcium and other minerals and electrolytes from our bones, teeth and tissue, to neutralise the acid and balance its pH levels. Stress also puts strain on the body, because an increase in cortisol levels causes an increase in acidity. Our lifestyle choices can thus either deplete our pH balance or help to preserve it, and ultimately exacerbate or prevent the development of diseases like osteoporosis, gout, kidney disease and RA. When we drink enough water, eat enough fresh fruit and vegetables and manage our stress levels, we can make it much easier for our body to maintain its balance[92, 98, 129].

A body that has to fight to keep its pH balance is a breeding ground for disease. When the body is compromised, green juice is like a downpour on drought-parched land. The alkalising ingredients in green juice are a powerful blast of instantly absorbable nutrition and energy that brings our cells to life.

The intention of juicing is not to replace all meals. When I juice, I still have a wholesome meal a few hours later, thereby ensuring that I have sufficient fibre, essential fats and protein. While medical science awaits published research that supports the safety and efficacy of juicing, more and more people are finding that it helps to restore balance and health in their bodies.

I was exposed to juicing at the age of eight. Being so young, I had no appreciation for its powerful nutritional value; all I remember is thinking that it looked, tasted and smelled yuck! Today I start to salivate when my husband is making my green juice. That's the power of the human mind: I have seen what green juicing can do. Rajin and I have been juicing daily for the last six years. Two years before I was diagnosed, we embarked on an experimental journey with juicing to help Rajin lose his excess weight. We had no idea how important this decision would turn out to be for my well-being.

It's interesting to note that, even though I was juicing at the time of the diagnosis, it wasn't enough to prevent the illness. I had to work on many other factors – it all works together. I shudder to think how much worse my body would have been if I hadn't been juicing when I was diagnosed. While juicing is excellent for health, it's not a panacea for all the factors that cause the problems leading to autoimmune disease. In my case, the benefits of juicing could be seen only after I removed all the foods that were contributing to a leaky gut.

One particularly beneficial ingredient in my green juice is kale. From reducing the risk of cardiovascular disease and controlling blood sugar levels to being an anti-inflammatory agent, enhancing oxygen transport and aiding cancer-preventive activity, kale is now recognised as one of the healthiest vegetables on the planet. Curly kale is a nutritional powerhouse. According to research, it is best to consume kale raw or with very little cooking[131], so using it in green juice is ideal.

ORAC, which stands for oxygen radical absorbance capacity, measures a food's ability to scavenge free radicals. Free radicals are unstable molecules that can cause damage to our body at the cellular level, resulting in a wide range of diseases. As a result of its high antioxidant content, kale has one of the highest ORAC ratings.

Phytochemicals such as glucosinolates and isothiocyanates, together with betacarotene, vitamin C and polyphenols, have popularised kale for its antioxidant and anti-cancer properties [74]. They also play a preventative role in assisting the body in fending off a variety of neurodegenerative diseases[5]. Kale is high in lutein, which is a carotenoid best known for its supportive role in eye health. This is essential for an MS patient like me, because my optic nerve is often a target for inflammation. The high iron content in kale is essential for the formation of haemoglobin and hence the transportation of oxygen to various parts of the body. Including kale in my diet was paramount in combatting the fatigue I was experiencing.

The distinct dark-green colour of kale is attributed to its generous chlorophyll content. Chlorophyll has a cleansing effect on the blood and purifies the lymph and liver through its ability to remove toxic substances from the body. Chlorophyll also acts as a prebiotic in the gut. Our friendly intestinal flora feast on the chlorophyll in our diet, which in turn supports the growth of these advantageous bacteria. Chlorophyll-rich foods also help to alkalise the body's pH, thereby reducing high acid levels.

The Flaming Challenge Green Juice

Here is a list of the ingredients for my powerhouse anti-inflammatory green juice, including the most important nutrients and their benefits. To make two litres of this cocktail, I use six apples, two beetroots, one head of broccoli comprising six to eight florets, six carrots, one bunch of celery comprising six to eight stalks, one cucumber, two thumb-sized pieces of ginger, ten kale leaves, two lemons, four radishes, and four thumb-sized pieces of turmeric root.

My Flaming Challenge Green Juice Cocktail is made fresh every morning at five o'clock by my husband. We both have 500 millilitres immediately. I consume the other litre through the course of the day. Fruit and vegetables used to make up the Flaming Challenge Green Juice are rich in a wide range of phytonutrients, vitamins and minerals, some of which are highlighted below.

- **Apple.** Source of pectin and soluble fibre as well as vitamins A and C, calcium, iron, phosphorus, potassium and phytonutrients. Best source of malic acid for improving muscle performance and reversing muscle tiredness. Quercetin is a powerful antioxidant compound found abundantly in apples.

- **Beetroot.** Packed with a range of vitamins including A, B6, C and folate. Rich in iron and magnesium. High nitrate content increases oxygen uptake. Antioxidant properties. Good source of carbohydrates and energy for prolonged sporting activities. Best source of detoxification for liver health.

- **Broccoli.** Is said to pack a powerful nutritional punch. Contains sulphoraphane, which has potent antioxidant and anti-inflammatory properties. Contains kaempferol and quercetin flavonoids that fight free-radical damage. Contains vitamins A, C, K, B-complex, betacarotene, folic acid, phosphorous and potassium. High fibre content.

- **Celery.** Packed with phytonutrients and an excellent source of vitamins B1, B2, B6, C, K and folate. Rich supply of calcium, iron, magnesium, potassium, phosphorus, sodium and amino acids. Regulates blood pressure and reduces inflammation. Neutralises acidity.

- **Carrot.** Vitamins A, B1, B2, C, D and E. Good source of magnesium, potassium and calcium. Betacarotene and lutein improve eyesight and strengthen the immune system. Helps to cleanse and detoxify the kidneys and liver.

- **Cucumber.** Diuretic. Improves kidney health. Hydrates the body and flushes out toxins. Stabilises blood pressure. Contains vitamins A, B, C and K. Boosts immunity.

- **Ginger.** Contains gingerol, which has powerful medicinal properties. Helps with digestion and is effective in reducing nausea. Reduces muscle pain and soreness. Powerful anti-inflammatory properties.

- **Spinach and kale.** Rich source of chlorophyll for the gut microbiome. High in vitamins A, B1, B2, B6, C, E and K. A great source of iron, magnesium, calcium, copper and manganese.

- **Lemon.** Helps to balance the body's pH. A rich source of vitamin C. Anti-inflammatory. Contains the neuroprotective phytonutrient tangeretin as well as limonene, which promotes weight loss and slows down cancer growth. Contains the bioflavonoid rutin, which strengthens blood vessels.

- **Radish.** Packed with vitamins A, B6, C, D and K. Source of calcium, iron and magnesium. Powerful detoxifier with antimicrobial and antibacterial properties. Aids in digestion, urinary disorders, constipation and weight loss.

- **Turmeric.** Curcumin is the main active ingredient with powerful anti-inflammatory and antioxidant effects. Speeds up healing. Used in Chinese and Ayurvedic medicine as a treatment for chronic pain, inflammation and depression. Natural antiseptic and antibacterial agent.

My Raw Superfoods Breakfast

Today superfoods are a major focal point of nutrition, because they are raw nutrient-dense foods that correct imbalances and readily deliver energy to our cells. That's exactly what I needed – all raw, vegan and gluten-free nutrition to quickly boost my nutrient levels. Around eleven o'clock in the morning I blend my superfood smoothie using the ingredients and quantities listed below with either banana or pineapple as the base. This smoothie always leaves me feeling full.

One important step in making the smoothie must be taken care of the night before. Raw nuts and seeds are a nutritious and tasty way to get high-quality protein via smoothies. They do, however, contain the enzyme inhibitor phytic acid, which serves to protect them until the right conditions for germination are present. Phytic acid is useful for safeguarding seeds until germination but, when we eat it, it binds to minerals in the gastrointestinal tract, causing irritation and nutrient deficiencies. Phytic acid may not be entirely bad, but the dose makes the poison. That's why the nuts and seeds must be soaked overnight in warm water and salt to reduce the enzyme inhibitors and stimulate the early germination and sprouting process. Soaking is essential for proper digestion and increasing the bioavailability of nutrients[45].

- **Almonds (ten).** High in fibre, protein and magnesium. Rich in antioxidants and vitamin E, which helps to protect cells from oxidative damage.

- **Banana (one), [otherwise pineapple (half)].** Contains high levels of tryptophan, which is converted to serotonin. Good source of energy to sustain blood sugar levels. High in potassium, vitamin B6 and magnesium. Rich in pectin, which aids digestion.

- **Cacao powder (two teaspoons).** High in magnesium, which supports cardiovascular health. Super rich in antioxidant flavonols. Contains phenylethylamine, which increases the activity of the neurotransmitter anandamide, known as the 'bliss chemical', because it's released when we feel great. Energy-boosting and natural antidepressant.

- **Chia seeds (one teaspoon).** One of the richest plant-based sources of omega-3 essential fatty acids (EFAs). Great anti-inflammatory food. High levels of antioxidants and EFAs help to maintain flexibility in joints. Contains nineteen amino acids – high in protein. Bulks up meals and keeps blood sugar stable. Contains five times more calcium than milk. Also contains boron, a trace mineral that helps transfer calcium into bones.

- **Flaxseeds, freshly ground (two teaspoons).** Also called linseeds. Great source of dietary fibre, omega-3 alpha-linolenic acid (ALA) and antioxidant lignans. Reduces inflammation.

- **Hemp seeds (one teaspoon).** Contains all twenty amino acids, the building blocks of protein. Contains significant amounts of omega-3 EFAs. A good source of lecithin, which is essential in maintaining brain and nerve function and supports the liver.

- **Pecan nuts (four).** Contains fibre and vitamins A, B and E, iron, folic acid, calcium, magnesium, phosphorus, potassium and zinc.

- **Pineapple (half), [otherwise banana (one)].** Contains high amounts of the enzyme bromelain, which reduces swelling, pain and bruising. Suppresses inflammation. High in vitamin C, betacarotene, copper, zinc and folate. Regulates the immune system.

- **Pumpkin seeds (two teaspoons).** Good source of magnesium, manganese, copper, zinc and protein. Rich source of tryptophan, the precursor to serotonin and melatonin. Exhibits anti-inflammatory effects.

- **Sunflower seeds (two teaspoons).** Good source of magnesium and selenium. Anti-inflammatory with high vitamin E content. Also rich in B-complex vitamins.

Every morning around 8 a.m. I eat a large bowl of pawpaw (or papaya), including a teaspoon of its crushed seeds. I then wait two to three hours before eating again. The nutrients found in pawpaw have a wide range of health benefits. Zeaxanthin, an antioxidant found in pawpaw, is thought to help prevent macular degeneration in the eyes. It's also beneficial in managing diabetes, cancer, digestive problems and heart disease, and it promotes bone health. It's an excellent source of vitamins A, C and folate, magnesium, copper, and fibre. Choline, which is similar to the B vitamins, is present in pawpaw and helps to reduce fatigue and chronic inflammation[156]. Eating pawpaw regularly promotes liver and kidney health.

Having a leaky gut means that I'm more susceptible to parasitic and intestinal infections. I was pleased to learn that pawpaw seeds contain anti-helminthic and anti-amoebic properties, with no side effects. They also contain high levels of the proteolytic enzyme papain and an alkaloid called carpaine, which have strong anti-parasitic properties and help to rid the body of parasites[109].

Water Fasting

Water fasting is a type of fasting in which one consumes only water for a set period of time. It's different from starvation: while starvation is harmful to the body, water fasting has amazing therapeutic benefits. During a water fast, we take in no calories, allowing the body to focus on repair instead of digestion. In Ayurvedic medicine and naturopathy, water fasting has been employed for centuries as a means to cleanse and rejuvenate the human body. Some people do it for religious or spiritual reasons: water fasting is believed to promote greater intuitive powers and deep spiritual insights. It has been described as food for the soul. But water fasting isn't just a way to demonstrate faith and devotion – it has health benefits too.

When we take food away from a sick person, we don't starve the sick person, we starve the disease. Digesting food is one of the hardest jobs our body has to do. We snack constantly and never give the body a break. Water fasting allows the body to finally rest and heal. In my days as a racehorse owner, I was always intrigued on race day when Rajin wanted to know from the trainer, 'Did the horse eat up?' I quickly learnt that this was an indication of the wellness of the horse. Animals do not eat when they are unwell. They simply hydrate and allow the body to heal itself. And, as evidence would suggest[67], we should be doing the same. Water has the power to restore vigour.

Water fasting has been shown to promote potent changes in metabolic pathways and cellular processes as well as reduce oxidative damage and inflammation[86]. This process helps the body reach ketogenesis more quickly than dieting. Ketosis is a state in which our body uses energy from our internal fat stores instead of food. This makes it an attractive option for those wanting to lose weight. Fasting in cancer patients and hypertensive patients, for example, is showing positive results[119]. In a study carried out on the MS model using mice, scientists found intermittent fasting to have potent immunomodulatory effects[31].

I strongly felt that a water fast would be a useful way for my body to reset. In my diseased state, I sensed that food was slowing down my healing process. Eighteen months after I was diagnosed, I attempted my first water fast. My body welcomed it. I drank approximately three litres of water a day. I fasted for four days. During a water fast, the pace needs to slow down. It was a wonderful time just to focus on my breathing and meditation. My mind became clear and focused during the fast. Water fasting gave me an amazing opportunity for emotional and spiritual introspection. It felt like I had better control over my thoughts.

At the end of the four days, my joints were pain-free. The swelling had disappeared. My mind felt clearer and more creative. The water fast allowed my body to focus on healing without having to spend any energy on digesting food. The depression had lifted and I felt exhilarated. This water fast gave me hope that my body could heal itself and that I was going to be okay. I broke the fast by having green juice for the day. On the second day I ate fruit only. The following day I introduced more solids.

This is my go-to healing modality when I feel my body needs a reset. I do a forty-eight-hour fast to recharge my body and feel rejuvenated once again.

15
Take charge of activity: finding an enjoyable mode of movement

Physical activity not only changes our body, it also changes our mind, our attitude and our mood. It boosts our vitality and energy, and our passion for life. The human body is designed to move. We are strengthened with movement. When we physically move, our physiology changes. Movement enhances growth and repair and creates balance in body, mind and spirit. Our muscles, tendons, ligaments and joints become strong and flexible with movement. What often goes unnoticed is the emotional upliftment that movement brings about. We are happier when we move more. A research article published in the *British Journal of Pharmacology* in 2012 found that exercise can be so effective in treating various conditions that we should consider it as a drug[151]. Regular exercise does a lot more than just burn calories. It has been shown to increase our levels of endorphins, serotonin and dopamine, which are the neurotransmitters that regulate our mood and make us feel happier. This is a great way to treat depression and anxiety naturally. An endorphin boost has also been shown to reduce pain[136].

In people who experience chronic stress and anxiety, cortisol and norepinephrine are continuously over-produced, keeping them in fight-flight-freeze mode. The body's cortisol receptors become resistant to cortisol signals and the HPA axis becomes desensitised to the body's negative feedback to stop it. Dancing is a form of exercise that can reset the HPA axis so that it can become more responsive, thus improving cortisol balance.

I had my own interesting experience with the benefits of dance in the early 2000s. I paired up with a professional dancer to conduct corporate wellness programmes. We presented stress management workshops and seminars called Wellness in Motion. While I gave the presentation on stress as a silent killer in our lives and highlighted the physical and emotional impact of dance movements as a form of exercise, she demonstrated beautiful dance moves that always rocketed the energy in the room and put a smile on everyone's face. I have no doubt about the importance of exercise and movement for wellness. Physical movement creates the momentum for change in our minds. In my case, it enabled a profound shift in my mental state when I needed it most.

I have always enjoyed exercise. In the past I enjoyed cardio workouts, weight training, qi gong, tai chi, Nia dance, Tae Bo and yoga. I learnt from other MS patients that exercise tended to improve their symptoms. The most popular activities among the MS patients I talked to were cycling and yoga. However, with multiple autoimmune syndrome, this type of exercise was not suitable for me. Although there certainly are others, neither my neurologist, nor my rheumatologist nor I have ever met another patient who has been diagnosed with the combination of MS, RA and Hashimoto's thyroiditis. I had no one to talk to about tips for suitable exercise. Besides the types of exercise already mentioned, before the diagnosis, I was also a fan of resistance training at the gym. But, with my combination of conditions, this became a challenge for me. I noticed that my symptoms would intensify after a few hours of exercising. As for the exercise recommended by other MS patients, my joints were too sore for yoga poses and stationary cycling increased my core temperature too much. This increase in body temperature caused severe pain and aggravated my symptoms, especially fatigue and joint pain, the following day.

I did not give up on trying to find a suitable exercise routine though. The image of a healthy person in my mind has always been one of someone who exercises and looks toned and happy. In the past, exercise improved my mood and made me feel more confident. Being able to exercise would be a clear indication that my body was moving in the direction of wellness, so I persevered.

It became clear that I needed to be more selective with my choice of exercise. Then something wonderful happened. Rajin agreed to take me dancing, even though it's not his favourite activity. I couldn't believe that he was prepared to do this late in the evening activity with me in spite of his long and busy days. I only learnt later that he had read a research article on how important it is for MS patients to engage in movement. According to what he had learnt, he told me that forcing the brain to learn a new dance step would create new neural pathways. This kind of continuous stimulation of the brain improves cognitive, tactile and motor performance in MS patients[59]. I later found the very same thing in an article that tested a newly designed dance training programme for seniors. The authors found that constantly learning new movement patterns was superior to conventional fitness activities with repetitive exercises in terms of promoting neuroplasticity[101].

I had always wanted to learn social ballroom and Latin American dancing. A friend of mine introduced us to Ben Brandon, a professional dance instructor whose studio was down the road from our house. Ben's Dance Studio soon became our haven. Ben is patient, fun and passionate about teaching dance. He has participated as a professional in the popular Playhouse Theatre production *Shall We Dance*, and it is an absolute pleasure to watch as he untangles complicated dance routines for us to learn. As a member of the World Dance Council, Ben's standards are world class. I would sit out the dances that involved fast twirling, because this disorientated me. Even though I cancelled many dance lessons because of severe fatigue, he kept encouraging us to come back. Furthermore, the well-ventilated dance studio together with short dance routines ensures that this activity does not act as a heat trigger.

When I felt clumsy and awkward on the dance floor, Ben would encourage me to continue. 'Mala, we're going strong. You're doing great. The steps will eventually feel easier. I promise'.

Although Ben is meticulous in his teaching methods, he also displayed volumes of empathy. He modified most of the dance routines to accommodate my MS and RA symptoms. He has taught me to fall in love with my body and to appreciate the joy of movement again. He taught me the difference between Rajin dancing *to* the music as he leads, and me dancing *with* the music as I follow.

Dancing became therapeutic for us on many levels. We call it our date night, because it's so light-hearted and fun. The body heals with play while the mind heals with laughter. Even though we often mess up the steps, we laugh so much. Rajin tried incredibly hard to switch from his usual logical left-brain way of doing things to flowing with his creative right brain – it was hilarious to watch. For me, the brain fog and poor concentration left me confused on the dance floor. I decided to go for extra one-on-one lessons with Ben to force my brain to remember the steps, and it worked. After the diagnosis, my confidence had taken a beating, because I felt like an outcast. Remembering and following the complex dance steps and moving to the precise beat of the music renewed my confidence both on the dance floor and outside the dance class. My balance improved. The mood swings lifted. I could feel the joy bouncing back into my life.

When I dance, I feel like a paintbrush in motion, bringing a blank canvas to life. It's entrancing. When dancing with a partner, one has to keep a slight tension in the arms in order to give and receive the lead. Just as I feel the slight tension in the dance hold, so too I feel this tension in my challenging life circumstances, which remind me that it is the divine Creator who is leading me in the dance of life. When we don't know the steps, we feel confused but, if we trust the lead, everything works out beautifully. This realisation inspired my poem, 'The Dance of Life'.

The Dance of Life

The Master Creator lovingly held out his hand, looked my soul in the eye and said,
'They are playing our song; would you like to do The Dance of Life?'
'Oh yes,' my soul responded jumping with joy.
The soul took on the body – the dancing shoes of life.

In the womb the Master said,
'Remember, in this dance, I lead and you follow.
It doesn't matter how difficult the dance steps may become,
focus on the music, hear the melodious sound, lean into me and trust my lead.'
'I will, I promise.'
Then I took birth, grew up and forgot my promise.

I was distracted on the dance floor of life,
by all the other dancers who moved differently to me.
I wanted to copy them, to be like them, so I decided to take the lead.
I stumbled, I fell, I bruised myself, I felt pain...
Only then did I remember my promise.

I leaned in and felt my Master, who never once let go of my hand.
He gently lifted me off the floor and propelled me into the air,
reminding me to stay connected to my exceptional choreography.
With renewed trust in the arms of my Master, feeling the Divine chemistry,
I gracefully dance my unique Dance of Life, allowing Him to lead as I follow.
Respecting the lead, I seamlessly step in time, knowing that I am a perpetual student.
The Dance of Life is team effort – it takes two to tango.

The difference dancing made was clear to both of us.

'It's so encouraging to watch how your energy and mood lift on the dance floor', Rajin remarked. 'You look so happy when we're dancing, especially when we both remember the routine'.

'I'm glad you noticed it, because I really feel it'.

Even though we're still in the early stages with our dance lessons, we both feel we have found our bonding activity and we hope to dance for the rest of our lives. Often, people look at dancing as just a physical activity, but for us it was more than that. It connected us on an emotional level in a way that we didn't even know was possible. Doing the cha-cha-cha allowed me to flirt with Rajin on the dance floor. Dancing rekindled our romance and our passion for life. The non-verbal communication on the dance floor spilt over into our daily lives. We began to embrace life with renewed zest. Nothing brings a couple together like the vibrant and playful tango, both on and off the dance floor.

This has been a welcome change from the early days after I was diagnosed, and all I could think about was possibly becoming disabled. I watched music videos over and over again, wondering if I would someday dance to the songs. I was dreading the day – perhaps all too soon – that my legs might not work the way they used to. Luckily, through our dance classes and the other components in my Take-Charge Wellness Formula, we've come to a place that is so beautiful and filled with hope.

Another form of movement that I enjoy, which I was initially introduced to while studying Resonance Repatterning, is katsugen. It's a healing art form that invites spontaneous movement from within oneself. Katsugen was developed by a Japanese healer, Haruchika Noguchi, as a part of his seitai concept – the well-coordinated body. One has to simply allow the body to move in any way it wants to with the understanding that the body-mind system knows what it needs for self-correction and alignment.

Katsugen movements balance the energy in our body to enhance confidence, physical strength and coordination. It can be done with or without music. The founder of Resonance Repatterning, Chloe Faith Wordsworth, describes katsugen movements as a release of physical and emotional toxins, leading to a sense of freedom, fulfilment and well-being[164].

Doing katsugen movements is one of my favourite parts of the day. I relish the idea that the movements are uniquely mine. I have found them to be an expression of my pain and my joy. I start by standing still, closing my eyes and focusing my attention on my body. I pay attention: my body decides when it wants to start the movement. Then, with my eyes either closed or open, I allow my body to move freely in any way it wants, free of resistance and without trying to force a certain action. Giving my body the freedom to move as it pleases feels soothing and calming. When I stop moving, I feel peace and joy emanating deep within my body. The best way to understand it is to just experience it.

16
Take charge of discipline and motivation: establishing a routine and sticking with it

The time is now! Let's make the choice to say goodbye to a life of disability, pain and suffering. The greatest gift we can give ourselves after being labelled with an 'incurable' disease is to challenge ourselves to reverse it. If there is one thing that all successful patients have in common when it comes to managing their condition well, it's the combination of unwavering faith, discipline and motivation. The question is: How badly do you want your health back? The depth of our desire for wellness will determine the rate of our success. We have to ask ourselves: How far am I willing to go to get back my health?

Dealing with a chronic condition leaves no room for negligence: self-control, discipline and one-pointed focus are the order of the day. It's the most rewarding challenge we will ever encounter. Wellness demands effort. We must take responsibility for the process, we must take action. Reversing the disease is our new priority. Game on!

It's hard enough for those who are disease-free to adopt a healthy eating habit, exercise regularly and do their daily meditation. For us autoimmune patients it's hell. The secret is to take it one step at a time and never ever give up, because you will get stronger – I did. The fruit of everything good in life begins with a challenge. I had to look at my body and see what nobody else could see and have the discipline to do what nobody thought I could. I had to believe that it's possible. It's like a block of marble: give it to someone who can't see its potential, and you end up with the same block of marble but, put it in the hands of a master sculptor, and that very same block can be transformed into a masterpiece. Every sculptor looks at his block of marble with an artist's eye. Committed to the discipline of his craft, slowly and surely, he chisels, shapes and polishes the stone until the lifeless block is transformed into an object of beauty.

A few things can fuel a person's commitment, and among them is one's dedication to excellence. The desire for excellence is what carried Michelangelo through to complete the Sistine Chapel. That same desire is what drove Thomas Edison to persist until he finally created the light bulb. The one vital ingredient necessary to maintain this superior level of commitment, while in pursuit of excellence in health, is discipline. Discipline is self-love. Discipline is your superpower to seeing the bigger picture. I realised that, if I wanted to be happy, I needed discipline in my behaviour. No more excuses. I realised that excuses sound best to the person who is making them. I became conscious of choosing behaviour directed towards myself that was loving and nourishing for my body, mind and spirit. For the first time in my life, I put my needs first.

It's my responsibility to fix my body. Yes, I am worn out and sick of the grind. But I must do it anyway. There are no shortcuts to greatness. I have to put in the effort. The formula works. On the other side is wellness. Neglecting to follow what I know works because I don't feel like it is not an option for me. I have to have discipline and be consistent every day. I have to feel confident putting in the hard work, knowing that it's the only thing that will dismantle that guillotine hovering over my legs. I have to believe without a shadow of doubt that I can do it.

I remember Pavesan's first win on the golf course. He was fourteen years old and during the school holidays he participated in tournaments hosted by the South African Junior Golf Foundation. This was a very special time for Pavesan and me. He played on some of the most beautiful courses in our province and I got to chauffeur him around. On this particular day, he was his normal self and approached the first tee full of hope as usual. I wished him well and watched him tee off for the first time at the beautiful Kloof Country Club. Later that morning I watched him sink his putt on the ninth green and move towards the clubhouse full of smiles.

He approached me oozing with confidence. 'Mum, I think I got this one', he said.

'That's awesome! Nine more holes to go. Stay focused, my boy'.

I had taken my son to many golf tournaments in the past and this was the first time he showed such confidence. At the end of eighteen holes he had the best scorecard and brought home the trophy. The level of confidence and belief in himself that he displayed was exactly what I needed: absolute unshakable confidence in my ability to achieve anything I put my mind to.

First, we need our mind to fully understand the new way of healing. The body will only achieve what the mind can conceive. I spent months reading, learning and empowering my mind about the possibility of complete remission and healing. This action gave me understanding and removed all doubt and, as in a game of poker, I was all in. We have the power to surround ourselves with people who will support our goals and improve our odds of success. I did this. Our healing is a life-changing journey, and discipline and commitment is the vehicle that keeps us going in the right direction. We have applied discipline and commitment to all our achievements in our careers and passions. Now it's time to apply it to our health. We have to choose between what we want now and what we want most of all. Self-discipline is doing what we need to do even though we don't feel like doing it. Discipline is not punishment; discipline is our friend, our saviour. It doesn't matter whose fault it is that we are in this condition. What matters is that it's our responsibility to fix it.

Rajin often says, 'Discipline is one-pointed focus. Human beings are the most resilient creatures on the planet. If we can just keep our focused attention one-pointed, everything is possible'. After our spa burnt down and our finances hit rock bottom, Rajin kept his focus on the prize: getting our financial strength back. He went to work every day without any doubt that it would be busier than the day before. And it was. When he started his raw food diet to keep himself well after I was diagnosed, again he kept his one-pointed focus on his goal. The stress and trauma of our past had resulted in his becoming extremely overweight and unwell. He weighed 126 kilograms and his blood pressure averaged $^{200}/_{120}$ mmHg with medication.

'I have neglected my body for so long while I focused on getting our finances on track', he said. 'You need me now, Mala, so I have to start taking better care of myself as well. Just imagine the trauma our family will have to experience if I too get ill'.

'What do you have in mind?' I asked.

'I want to lose fifty kilograms before my fiftieth birthday to bring back my wellness. I have nine months to achieve this goal'.

During these nine months he lost weight consistently but was unable to drop it below eighty kilograms. He decided not to weigh himself in the month of August until his birthday. On the morning of his fiftieth birthday, Rajin stepped onto the scale and started whooping for joy. The scale read 74.9 kilograms. With a huge smile on his face, he proudly announced that he had gone beyond his target and lost a whopping 51.1 kilograms. Wow! Armed with the motivation to stay healthy to be able to support me and our family and equipped with his strong self-discipline, he had achieved an incredible feat. Once he had made his decision to start his raw food lifestyle, he never allowed his mind to deviate and have a cheat day. He believes that, when you have the discipline to do the things you really don't feel like doing, you earn the right to have the things you really want. He planned his day meticulously. He strongly believes that, when we fail to plan, we are planning to fail. He taught me to plan my meals for the week in advance and not to leave it to the moment when hunger sets in. Planning my meals encouraged the discipline to stick to foods that would heal my body.

Rajin is ruthless with discipline. When he puts his mind to something, you can consider it done. I remember the day when he gave up alcohol. He had often consumed alcohol during his four years at university and his internship. He enjoyed it. On completion of his internship, he bought his pharmacy. Stepping into his own business, he made the decision that he would like to stop drinking alcohol in order to maintain his professional image at all times.

'I never want to drink alcohol again', he said. 'I want to be certain that I never say or do anything irresponsible like I have done in the past when I was under the influence as a student'.

'I'm so proud of your decision, Raj', my twenty-one-year-old self responded encouragingly, even though I didn't believe he could do it.

But I was wrong. Without any outside help, he achieved his goal. With just his willpower and single-pointed focus, he has been able to maintain his sobriety to this day.

When I look at my husband, I see discipline personified. I, on the other hand, have no personal discipline stories to share. I find it difficult to see things through.

He often teases me. 'When God was handing out discipline, I think you were playing with marbles'.

'No, Raj, I think you used your charming smile and those gorgeous brown eyes and stole my share'.

Diagnosed as I am with conditions that demand discipline in order for me to stay well, I feel fortunate to have the chief whip of discipline right beside me. Even though I lacked discipline in the past, today I welcome the opportunity to be disciplined in order to maintain my wellness. I had to constantly address what moved me out of my wellness routine. I kept falling into the trap of trying to meet other people's needs and expectations, and this often left me feeling overwhelmed, because I didn't have the time to complete all aspects of the Wellness Formula.

Discipline and motivation go hand in hand on this wellness journey. A change in lifestyle is no easy task. Discipline is saying 'yes' to the one and 'no' to the ninety-nine. It's a huge sacrifice. It's only when we focus on the one that we can achieve success. It's relentless faith and belief in ourselves. By believing in yourself, you will find the courage to take immediate action on your goals to reverse the condition. It requires extraordinary self-discipline and sacrifice to break old habits and change our life-depleting beliefs about healing. Our mind resists change.

That's why it's important that we help the mind to understand why we want to change our lifestyle. The answer to the 'why' may sound logical at first. But, if we're not clear about why we should make a particular change, the mind will resist it and change becomes difficult, if not impossible. Once we establish the 'why', next we need to decide on the 'how' and the 'what'.

Putting pen to paper is powerful. I found that writing down why a particular change in lifestyle will work for me helped me to stay on track. I have notes all around my house as reminders of why my behaviour, thoughts or choice of food has changed.

Are you going to let food be your medicine or your poison, Mala? That tasty cheat meal is going to give you pain for weeks to come. For crying out loud – do the right thing!

When are you going to let go of the past? It's hurting this present moment. We all deserve a second chance. You can't go through another painful relapse. Change your thoughts now.

Keep the vision, Mala. Make it happen. No matter how hard it gets, you're going to make it, girl!

I find I need to be a little strict in my tone – it helps me to stay conscious and disciplined with my new way of being. Furthermore, the cathartic experience of putting pen to paper cannot be overstated. The act of actually writing down my goals made them more achievable. Seeing my goals every morning in large print across my dining room wall kept my eye on the prize.

My brain resisted change many times. I faltered. I felt disappointed in myself for not keeping my word and not following through on what I said I would do. *Just because I failed, it doesn't make me a failure.* I forgave myself and started again. Change in lifestyle is no easy task, especially when one is battling fatigue, pain and discomfort. Had I given in to the fear of failure, this book would not be in your hands today. I would reward my small efforts with positive self-talk and by congratulating myself on a job well done. Removing all temptations and distractions from my environment was a crucial first step when working to improve my self-discipline. Our environment is one of the most important factors influencing behaviour in our lives. It's subtle but incredibly powerful.

Managing the complexity of multiple autoimmune syndrome demands discipline. Well done on taking the high road. Dig deeper for that inner strength. You are not alone. Baba Ji is with you. Look how far you have come.

I would bask in the glory of achieving my goal. Focusing and lingering on positive emotions for most of my day helped my mind to accept that this new way of being not only is good for me but also brings me tremendous joy.

Even if we sometimes find it hard to make progress, we have to celebrate the small victories and believe that we can achieve more. We need to believe in ourselves and have faith. I remember a time when my faith and belief reached a zenith. Tharsheyen was just two years old when I left both our children with my parents and joined Rajin on a work trip to Namibia. It was there that I convinced him to join me on a tandem skydiving experience. The thrill of the danger involved seemed to heighten the experience. I remember sitting on the edge of the open aeroplane with my legs dangling out approximately four thousand metres from the ground, about to jump. Unquestioning faith that my parachute would open on time calmed the fear and let the endorphin floodgates open. Free falling was such a rush. I felt free like an eagle. I was gliding through the air in absolute bliss.

Once the parachute opened, my tandem partner yelled in my ear, 'So when last did you touch a cloud?'

'Oh wow', I heard myself say. I remember how cold it was as we moved through the cloud. I was lost in the experience of euphoria encapsulated with trust and faith. We had a perfect landing and then out of the blue the thought popped into my head, 'I'm a terrible mum! What if the landing had been fatal? What would've happened to my children? They need their mother'. I then burst out laughing. There I was, safely back on the ground, and my brain was still calculating possible dangers. Stepping away from conventional thinking and taking responsibility to manage an autoimmune disease is also a leap – an adventure in faith, the faith that we can come out of our comfort zone of familiar pain and experience new joys.

Our destiny with chronic disease is here to help us find our strengths. We are all born with unique strengths. Take the leap of faith to move away from all the negative talk about your disease and embrace the challenge to discover your uniqueness as you gravitate towards wellness. Your job is to believe and have faith that life is going to get better for you. You have to plan and work at it every day. Let your every action reflect your positive beliefs. For example, I stopped watching television at night. I broke the habit of going to bed late so that I feel refreshed when I get up in the morning. You see, the morning meditation process starts the night before. I have set an alarm for bedtime and called it 'Medicinal meditation in progress'. Don't give yourself permission to make excuses.

I also continue to work on breaking my old habit of negative thinking. Every day I spend time reading inspirational literature or watching motivational videos online. I'm learning that integrating a higher state of well-being takes constant conscious effort. It takes hard work and dedication every single day to discipline the mind. I have to remind myself that it's the difference between a debilitating life and a vibrant, active life. Instead of triggering symptoms, let our actions trigger love and wellness. We must keep our motivation front of mind and take the necessary action in a disciplined manner.

Damn the status quo, full speed ahead!

Remember we are going against the practices of the medical books, pharmaceutical industry and some of our doctors, family and friends with our new way of thinking and acting. We have to stay focused. Only we know the depth of our pain and misery. We deserve to give ourselves a winning chance. I could only do this when I got out of my comfort zone, wiped away my tears, looked at myself in the mirror and said with conviction, 'Dear Lord, I know it's hard, but I'm up for the challenge!' With focus and discipline, I have no doubt that we can achieve great things with our healing. There is nothing small about us. We are powerful beings. Challenge yourself to do more and believe that you can reverse your condition. Make this Flaming Challenge the greatest gift you can give yourself and take it on with faith, hope, confidence and ruthless tenacity.

Energy flows where thought goes. Being conscious of this, I changed my morning behaviour. I stopped checking my phone first thing in the morning. When we look at our phone the second we wake up, we are training our mind to react. I have to say 'no' to that which is a distraction and 'yes' to that which is a decision. We need to retrain our mind to be still. Our morning time is sacred and the perfect opportunity to do this. We command respect throughout our day when we respect ourselves enough to take some personal time upon rising. I am learning to be selective with my energy distribution for the day.

I am up fairly early and have structured my morning routine to support my wellness goals. Working out a solid routine for the morning when we are free of disturbance, when the demands of the world around us haven't kicked in yet, is a great way to stay disciplined and achieve our aims. To reach our goals we have to apply discipline and consistency every day. The mere act of always honouring my first commitment gave me the courage to say 'no' to my old way of being for the rest of the day.

This is my morning routine:

1. Meditation.
2. Alternate nostril breathing.
3. Gratitude journal. Smiling while listing five things that I am grateful for this morning.
4. Katsugen movements.
5. Sound bath: toning the vowel sounds.
6. Enjoying a mug of green juice, freshly made by my husband.

Throughout our day we need to ensure that the conversations we have in person – and on the phone – do not trigger our fight-flight-freeze response. It's also important to monitor the impact of subliminal communication: Are we unconsciously comparing our lives to other people on social media? We have a responsibility to ourselves to be discriminating in what we expose ourselves to. Do we really want to start our day by listening to the news and moving into survival mode?

We have the power to choose a gratitude meditation and start our day in thrive mode. When we set ourselves up with the right morning rituals, we consciously set ourselves up for an incredible day.

We have the power to decide what we want to expose our energy to for the day. We have power and influence over our thoughts and beliefs. Many of us don't realise the depth of this power that we hold. We deny our awesomeness and hand over our power to those around us. Then we foolishly blame them for making us take a negative stance on life and making us take actions that leave us feeling exhausted and unwell. A positive morning routine prepares us to be more conscious throughout the day of the quality of our thoughts and choice of our actions. Our mind is eavesdropping on our self-talk and the information we imbibe. When we focus our thoughts on sadness and fear, we move out of the healing space. We have to adopt positive and empowering beliefs to help our nervous system function at its optimum.

If we know our motivations, our why, we can push ourselves to be disciplined and take positive action. Our actions have to reflect our desire to heal. We have to wake up five minutes earlier every day until we reach our target of one hour or more of morning me-time. The psychological benefit of a morning empowerment routine is like putting on shoes instead of trying to pull out every thorn our bare feet pick up on the road of life. Morning me-time is the armour we need to face our day.

17
Take charge of triggers: knowing what to avoid

A trigger is an external or internal stimulation that brings on symptoms or worsens the current symptoms. All chronic illnesses are aggravated by triggers. In order to manage any chronic disease, it is paramount that you identify the triggers that worsen your condition, and eliminate them. While there may be similarities with some of the triggers that cause flare-ups, MS affects each person differently. Common triggers include dietary aspects, changes in temperature, physical and emotional stress and trauma, smoking, bright flickering lights, fatigue, lack of sleep and infection. With my formula, I want to draw attention to the importance of figuring out individual triggers and how to manage or avoid them. If we use the means available in any given situation to manage triggers, we create more opportunities for other wellness-promoting behaviours to have a positive effect. Turning a blind eye to our triggers is like throwing a burning match into a petrol tank – it will produce an explosive reaction. The body can only stop the burning inflammation on the inside when we stop reigniting it. Removing triggers is an integral part of the Take-Charge Wellness Formula, in order to achieve and maintain wellness.

We cannot control external traumas, but how we manage our response to them could determine whether we experience a relapse or not. We had learnt from my brother-in-law's passing that the tragic news of death is a blow for my condition. Rajin and I consciously decided to manage this type of trauma differently. When another unfortunate death in the family occurred, I knew I needed to minimise my exposure to the grief-stricken environment and be at home surrounded with Indian classical music and the company of supportive friends. I also intensified my meditation.

In terms of physical triggers, heat is a significant trigger for me. Just a slight increase in temperature creates symptoms. In hot weather, I have often found myself trapped under the air-conditioning. A short walk from our house to the car is all it takes to bring on symptoms and make me ill. I have found that heat immediately produces muscle spasms. The painful MS hug is first to arrive. This is sometimes followed by nausea, fatigue and tingling, prickling, or a numb sensation throughout my body. It can last for a few minutes or several weeks.

I finally stopped challenging the heat and learnt to respect it. My social life was and often still is tested in summer. Initially, not many people understood or believed me when I explained to them how much it hurt after I exposed myself to heat. The crippling pain from the squeeze of death is invisible.

Most MS patients will bear testimony to the negative impact of heat on the body. In my case, cold can also cause symptoms to flare up: the rheumatoid arthritis symptoms become unbearable in extreme cold. I've had to find the middle ground to manage both weather extremes.

Food, which I've already covered, is another massive trigger not just in MS but in all autoimmune and many chronic conditions. We have to realise that food is health care whereas medicine is sick care. As I cleaned up my diet, the symptoms from all four chronic conditions started to disappear. Food was and remains a major pillar of my formula.

We have to acknowledge the control we have over triggers. Of course, the amount of control varies – we can choose our food more easily than the weather or external events – but some aspects of our response are always a choice. What the medical books do not tell us is that the initial relapsing-remitting stage of MS occurs when we trigger the body by disrespecting the condition. Then we are forced to medicate to try to reduce the inflammation, and so the cycle continues.

Even though the autoimmune gene has been expressed and the condition has manifested, the body does not relapse unless we trigger it. Hence, treatment without prevention of triggers is simply unsustainable.

I believe that healthcare workers should encourage patients with autoimmune conditions to figure out their triggers instead of being told that there is no other solution but to use toxic immunosuppressant drugs for the rest of their lives. In this way, patients will take more responsibility for their wellness. When an MS patient continues to trigger symptoms with poor lifestyle choices, the disease is more likely to move on to the next stage. Ignoring triggers in the long term creates a self-inflicted disability sentence.

For a patient, acknowledging the triggers, whether obvious or hidden, is not an easy task. This is especially true of emotional triggers. I needed to identify the triggers that disrupted my wellness frequency and compromised my body and mind before other modalities could be successful. Trying to force positive change while one is still weighed down by the negative effects of triggers is like trying to make a mobile call when there is no signal. It doesn't matter how many times you turn the phone off and on again, it will not pick up a signal if you are out of range. If we want to make a call, we need to move into a space where we can be connected. Healing is the same: I needed to move out of my low-frequency diseased space to pick up a well-connected, uninterrupted high-frequency wellness signal.

Letting go of denial is crucial when identifying triggers. Obvious triggers are simpler to acknowledge, but less obvious destructive triggers may take time to recognise and adapt to. For me, they included fatigue from attending functions, engaging in too much conversation and trying to make people understand my silent symptoms. I noticed how I triggered my fight-flight-freeze response when I was at war with what is.

As I described in Part One, it was a challenge to watch my friends make arrangements for events I couldn't attend, but fortunately they were wonderful in accommodating me by moving their discussions to another WhatsApp group, so that I wouldn't feel left out.

'We have to redefine our rules of engagement to enhance your healing', one of my friends said.

When I felt better, I said yes to a number of events, but unfortunately I often couldn't make it on the day, because the symptoms would suddenly flare up and become intolerable. My friends and I finally learnt how unpredictable MS can be.

In the first year of dealing with the disease, when I did go out, even though people around me tried to be tactful, I felt that symptoms like my head tremors and slurred speech were being judged. I seemed slightly inebriated from the medication and I often wondered whether my verbal responses in a group were coherent or whether I was embarrassing myself. The brain fog was exaggerated in a group setting when many people were talking at once. By the time I got home, more symptoms would arrive, and I would regret having left the house and often burst into tears. I now know that group outings are challenging for me: I feel more coherent and comfortable when it's just one-on-one.

Often the answer is simply more quiet and stillness[142]. In the first year after the diagnosis, my nausea was either triggered or amplified whenever I was in a moving vehicle. I have learnt to avoid travelling at the slightest hint of that queasy feeling. Although I felt that the MS, RA, Hashimoto's and fibromyalgia robbed me of so many opportunities to have fun, I now realise that I'm not giving something up; rather, I'm moving towards something more profound and very special. The disease is channelling me in the direction I always wanted to go, that is, to calm the mind with meditation and serene activities. I've come a long way since some of the more dramatic relapse episodes my family and I had to endure initially.

I remember an incident that happened during the festive period, barely three months after the diagnosis, when my behaviour left Rajin at a total loss for words. At this point in my illness, we didn't have the Wellness Formula to work with. I was extremely ill and spent most of my day in bed. At this time of year we always held a staff Christmas party. For the past twenty-five years it had been my responsibility to organise the pharmacy staff party, because I was the 'party animal' in the team. This year Rajin had to coordinate the event on his own.

He decided that he was unable to celebrate knowing how ill I was, lying in bed alone, so he didn't want to attend. But I encouraged him to go and give his traditional thank-you speech, and he agreed. He kissed me goodbye before he left for the party and said, 'I'll be back in thirty minutes. I'll give a quick speech and then we can enjoy some alone time'.

'Sounds perfect', I replied. 'I'll watch a movie while I wait for you'.

I felt so happy that he wanted to spend some quality time with me. In my mind, I planned to surprise him with a romantic scene when he returned. But then, just minutes after he had left the house with our sons, I felt a hollowness in the pit of my stomach. I felt sorry for myself for not being able to go to our staff party. My sadness intensified when I remembered that I had also declined the invitation to my group of girlfriends' Christmas party that very night. So many people who were close to me were at a party, while I had to stay home. Filled with self-pity, I decided to take my prescribed pain and sleeping medication and go to bed.

We had underestimated the negative impact of the chemically imbalanced MS mind. I was unable to see things from a clear perspective. I lost all discretion and the ability to be rational, especially when Rajin was involved. I dipped into a deep hollow feeling that I was missing out on fun times because of the disease. I was hankering for attention and unable to rationalise that my sad state in that moment was created in my mind. I became my worst enemy. Rajin left for the party only because I had insisted. Now I was upset that he had gone without me. I sent him a nasty text message.

He arrived home and came to my bedside confused, wanting to hold me. I was having none of it.

'I felt you were gone for so long. Why didn't you call and let me know that you were on your way back?' I demanded.

'Sorry, I didn't want to disturb you', he said, still trying to figure out why I was so upset.

He then showed me a text message that my friends had sent him, asking him to please bring me to their Christmas party, even if only for a few minutes. He knew how much I loved to dance and party.

'You look so sad, Mala. Please, can we go to your friends' party? They'll be so happy to see you, and you could do with some cheering up now. Please, let's go', he begged. By this stage the medication I had taken had made me very drowsy, but I decided to go.

The rest of the evening was a total blur. The medication took my memory away. I recall nothing of what happened. The next morning when Rajin showed me the photographs he had taken, I was shocked and confused. I had no memory of putting on leather pants and a sexy top that I had last worn fifteen years ago on our wedding anniversary.

'Last night when you got out of bed and stood up, I realised how ill and drowsy you were. I suggested that we should cancel going to the party', he said. 'But this just infuriated you. You insisted on going even though you could barely walk. I had to carry you into the party. As we reached the door, your friends rushed to welcome us. They were so happy to see us. You insisted on dancing. I whispered to your friend to hold your hands tightly on the dance floor'.

I listened in disbelief to my behaviour.

He continued: 'You couldn't stand up on your own and I could hear that your speech was slurred and your conversation was incoherent. You looked drunk. After one dance, I encouraged your friends to persuade you to go home. Almost half the people at the party walked you to our car. That was before you insisted on a group photo'.

'I'm so sorry for putting you in such an uncomfortable position', I said.

In my depressed and medicated state, it was clear that I had become unreasonable. I felt that the MS and the medication prescribed for me were isolating me. After this incident, he decided never to leave me home alone again in order to attend a function.

Four years down the line, I see my situation with a different pair of eyes. I treasure and value my alone time and see it as an opportunity to focus within myself. Instead of feeling sorry for myself, I am now grateful for the opportunity the disease has given me to turn my attention inwards and focus on my spiritual bliss. What a blessing in disguise. But, before coming to this realisation, I would test the MS a few more times.

I was so desperate to be 'normal' again. I wanted to prove to myself that the autoimmune disease was not going to stop me from enjoying my life the way I used to. Just over a year after the diagnosis, in the weeks leading up to my birthday, I felt that the symptoms were in remission following my change in diet and months of rest. It was my forty-sixth birthday and I wanted to do something that reminded me of my youth – a time when I felt full of life – exploding with energy.

Since I love to dance and party with friends, I asked Rajin to please humour me with this request: 'Raj, I would like to celebrate my birthday this year with a few friends at a night club'.

'I think we're a bit too old for that now', he said, smiling.

But I begged and pleaded, and finally he said yes.

He found a nightclub in Durban that would accommodate our requests. After a few meetings with the owners, he secured private use of the club on a Friday night until eleven p.m. The music would be focused on an eighties theme. We invited thirty guests and bussed them down to the club. This journey itself was a party on wheels. I wasn't the only one feeling twenty-one again. My guests let their hair down and forgot the demands of work and everyday life. I was filled with excitement that my legs were functional and that I had the energy to party. I entered the nightclub trying to convince myself that I was free of the dreaded diseases. I was starting to feel better and thoroughly enjoyed moving on the dance floor. After eleven, when the doors were opened to the public, a younger crowd poured into the club and the music changed to a much more intense hip-hop vibe. We left shortly afterwards and headed for home. But my birthday party didn't end there. All my guests and their children were invited to our home to continue the celebrations the following day.

The Rugby World Cup was on at the time. South Africa was playing Scotland that Saturday. Having lost their opening game to Japan, it was a must-win game for the Springboks to make the quarter-finals. Rajin converted our garden into our own fan park. He erected two wooden poles and used a sheet as a big screen on which we projected the live rugby game. It was a beautiful evening. The children played in the pool while some guests relaxed in the jacuzzi, from where they watched the game. South Africa won convincingly, 34 – 16. Even though I felt exhausted, I was in my element, celebrating my birthday and the Springboks' win with my friends and family.

Sadly, the exhilaration was short-lived. I realised that MS symptoms don't always arrive at the same time as they are triggered. The following week, they flared up with a vengeance. I was exhausted and drained of energy. Feeling disoriented and unsteady, I found it difficult to walk. I bumped into walls at home. My tongue was tingling and burning. I battled to urinate. My entire body felt so sore – almost as if I had received a beating. My ankle and wrist joints were inflamed. My head felt too heavy for my shoulders and started to tremor. I had disrespected the disease and now I was miserable.

I was slowly learning that I was not the same person I had been before the diagnosis. The autoimmune condition was far more complicated than I had imagined, and I needed to do much more research to try to understand how to keep myself well. I needed to change and adapt to a new way of being. My energy levels needed to be respected and not tested. Loud music and bright flashing lights are triggers for my condition. I thought that I was giving myself a birthday treat by eating the foods I was meant to avoid, only to discover that they contributed to my debilitating symptoms. Through my Wellness Formula, I now understand the need to maintain the changes in order to live a symptom-free life. If I go back to doing things the way I did before, I go back to being the ill person I was. My mind got this message, but my heart wanted more. It craved a hearty laugh.

My favourite genre in entertainment is comedy. In my world, nothing beats a hearty belly laugh. The popular show *Kings and Queens of Comedy* was on again.

'I know how much you'll enjoy this show', my husband said. 'Do you think you'll be able to manage?'

I lit up. 'Yes! Yes! Yes! Please let's go', I pleaded.

Rajin went ahead and bought tickets for the show, which was in Durban, and booked us into the Hilton Hotel next to the venue to minimise travelling, which often aggravates my nausea.

By this stage we had already figured out that loud sounds and flashing lights bring on nausea, vomiting, headaches and tingling. At home, when watching TV with company, I would place headphones over my ears to dampen the volume. I avoided bright flashing lights by using sunglasses.

I entered the venue armed with my headphones and dark glasses. It was a three-hour show; I lasted barely twenty-five minutes. The energy of the massive crowd, the thundering applause and roaring laughter – which in the past would have got my endorphins flowing – set off an intense sensation of nausea. With tears in my eyes, I left the show feeling disoriented as I headed for the nearest bathroom. We went back to the hotel and I rested. I was in no state to travel. The following day we headed home.

This time I refused to go into hospital. I switched on my Indian classical music and practised meditation and visualisation with intent and focus. I did my breathing exercises and followed my eating programme diligently. Within a few weeks the symptoms disappeared.

We are dynamic beings, changing and evolving every second. A new day brings new challenges and these challenges allow us to grow internally – if we choose to. When we let go of fighting our issues, we find within ourselves a strength we didn't know existed. This hidden strength, once discovered, changes everything about us. When we resonate with acceptance, forgiveness and trust, challenges in life give us the opportunity to redefine ourselves and appreciate our blessings.

I am slowly learning to get up every morning and say 'thank you' to the Creator for the gift of this day and to spend it in a way that expresses my gratitude. I have learnt to be grateful that I have legs that still allow me to walk. I intentionally choose to embrace the new opportunities that come with every sunrise. It's an opportunity to start fresh every morning. I have to consciously choose positive thoughts and adjust my attitude. I have finally grasped what I always preached but never experienced so profoundly: I am defined by the quality of my thoughts. The limitations presented by the triggers are no more than an opportunity to expand my consciousness, awareness and wellness.

18
Mala Naidoo's Take-Charge Wellness Formula at a glance

Consciously choosing to repair from the inside out.

This is nature's template for renewed wellness in chronic disease. It's about gently treating the whole patient to manifest a symptom-free life.

Take-Charge Wellness Formula
$$W = L + (\Delta T + \Delta F + A) \times (D + M) - Tr$$

Love (L): We choose our feelings. It's safe to take control of how we feel. Consciously choose to feel loved, no matter what your circumstance may be. Believe that you are a beautiful person, that you are love. Be kind and gentle to yourself. Use only loving words even when you feel like crying. Become obsessed with showing gratitude. Smile.

Change in Thought (ΔT): Start every morning with twenty minutes of meditation and visualisation. Recommended affirmation to go with it: 'My body is strong and healthy. Thank you for my healing. Thank you, thank you, thank you'. (Say it with conviction.) Do four rounds of alternate nostril breathing and the 4-7-8 breathing exercise. Listen to Indian classical music. Pay attention to keeping your thoughts in the present moment – the now.

Change in Food (ΔF): If you have an autoimmune condition, strongly consider eliminating foods that damage the gut lining: processed foods, gluten, meat, alcohol, dairy, refined sugar, refined vegetable oils, legumes (including peanuts) and vegetables from the nightshade family. (For RA, also consider eliminating rice.) Include lots of fresh fruit and vegetables. Try green juicing and superfood smoothies. Experience a forty-eight-hour water fast.

Activity (A): Movement positively impacts on our physiology. Have fun moving your body. Do at least thirty minutes of suitable exercise every day.

Discipline (D): Plan. Take the programme one day at a time. Focus on doing what needs to be done even if you don't feel like it. Put up reminders all around your living and working space, highlighting the actions you need to take today in order to enhance your wellness.

Motivation (M): Get ready to be different. Embrace the challenge to positively turn your life around. Motivate yourself before going to bed. Remember you are the most important person in your life. Write, write, write. Write down what the pain and discomfort feels like and why you need to make massive lifestyle changes.

Triggers (Tr): Commit to working out your triggers. Make a list of the following for a number of days or weeks:

1. Which symptoms you experienced and how severe they were.
2. What activities you did.
3. What foods you consumed.
4. Where you focused your thoughts for the day.
5. What weather conditions and temperatures you experienced.
6. Whom you interacted with.

Generate your personalised list of triggers that make you feel worse and make the choice to remove them or consciously adjust to them. Respect the triggers and embrace your new world.

In the end you will be well and, if you still have symptoms, know that it's not the end.

Celebrate your daily successes: remember, you are going where no pharmaceutical giant has gone before.

19
When you need to treat

Just as it's futile to try to force positive change when the negative effects of triggers have got us trapped in a hole, without any signal to connect to wellness, it can be hard to implement healing modalities when we are simply too ill. Sometimes allopathic medication is necessary, and sometimes alternative treatments might be helpful. Supplements could also help to support our body, and, at times – when we're really stuck and unwell – we might need to think outside the box.

Although allopathic medication did not present a long-term solution for me, on the odd occasion when I inadvertently trigger RA symptoms with my food choices, especially when I eat out, I take a single dose of an anti-inflammatory, followed by many glasses of water. I also apply an essential oil embrocation that Rajin makes up for external use to help with joint pain. It immediately soothes my aches.

Upon my initial diagnosis, in order to assist my body in regaining its balance, I took Calciferol (vitamin D), A. Vogel Multiforce Alkaline Powder, A. Vogel Molkosan (prebiotic), Neurobion (vitamin B complex), Vita-Thion Energy Tonic, Himalaya Mucuna nervine tonic, flaxseed (omega 3), curcumin and homeopathic medication. Now, because I strictly adhere to my Wellness Formula, which includes my green juice and superfood smoothie that give me all the vitamins and nutrients I need, supplementation is no longer necessary.

Addressing My Fatigue

In my search for answers, six months after the diagnosis, I had a bio-energetic stress test (BEST) to investigate possible pathogens that could be contributing to the violent immune system response in my body. This bio-energetic testing of organs and systems, including the lymphatic, digestive and endocrine systems, uses acupressure points on the fingers and toes to give an overall assessment of the body's health. Here I was informed about the presence of the Epstein-Barr virus (EBV) in my body.

EBV, also known as human herpesvirus 4, is one of the commonest human viruses. It is found all over the world. Most people are infected with EBV at some point in their lives. Some of the commoner symptoms of an EBV infection are fatigue, sore muscles, severe weakness, dizziness, fever, headache, rash, sore throat and swollen lymph nodes.

After receiving the result, I took another look at my recent hospital blood test results and found that EBV had been detected. The medical team had informed me that in their books EBV wasn't treatable. I immediately turned to homeopathy and was treated accordingly. Within days of my using the homeopathic EBV preparation, the fatigue lifted completely. I completed the course and I could feel the positive shift in my body.

I now had energy to start my research and make decisions. I learnt that some scientific laboratories are investigating whether EBV infection of the brain is a necessary prerequisite for MS pathology[115]. A 2016 study published in the *Journal of the Neurological Sciences* also stated that EBV may be involved in the pathogenesis of the disease and is possibly a prerequisite for the development of MS. The study went on to state that MS patients might have a deficient capacity to eliminate EBV infection in the central nervous system[50]. In my opinion, the wisdom of homeopathy and its respect for the body is often underestimated by our conventional medical model. I'm thankful for the relief the treatment offered from the EBV symptoms. It felt so good to finally wake up feeling more energised. My family was amazed by the shift. They found it hard to believe the extent to which the extreme fatigue had kept me trapped physically and emotionally.

An Uncomfortable Treatment Decision

Cannabis. The mere word conjures up images related to drug addicts and drug abuse. For me, growing up in South Africa, that's the association I was programmed to receive. Cannabis or marijuana, also called dagga or weed in our country, was and often still is considered an addictive psychoactive drug that one must avoid at all costs. It took a dreaded debilitating disease to wake me up: there might be more to cannabis than this.

The obliteration I experienced when the MS-induced chemical imbalances in my body and mind were combined with trauma and tragedy made it a massive challenge to engage with all the healing modalities that I had learnt over the years. Logically I knew what needed to be done to facilitate healing, but my system was so run-down that I had no motivation to even consider trying. Ultimately, I was faced with two choices: either take the extremely toxic biological disease-modifying drugs, which have devastating side effects, or turn to a plant that could offer some relief, although it was a banned substance.

I had spent years fighting substances of abuse, including the use of cannabis. We were in our early twenties when Rajin joined the Pharmacists Against Drug Abuse campaign in South Africa. He was saddened by the substance abuse problem in our society and wanted to understand it better. While couples our age were partying on a Friday night, we attended Narcotics Anonymous and Alcoholics Anonymous support meetings at Talbot House, an in-patient drug and alcohol rehabilitation facility on a farm outside Pietermaritzburg, which was run by Father Reg and a dedicated team of volunteers. We learnt so much about addiction and rehabilitation. Despite not having alcohol or drug addiction problems on either side of our family, we wanted to learn more. I wrote booklets, ran awareness programmes and delivered many talks to school children on the dangers of substance abuse. Our passion to help children say 'no' to substances of abuse led us to host one of the largest Drug Wise campaigns in the country in the nineties.

Today, with the new information available on the miracle of cannabis, I am left with no choice but to watch my words go up in smoke. Just as in the use and abuse of pharmaceutical drugs, cannabis has two sides to it:

a recreational side and a medicinal side. I had allowed myself to accept society's opinions about cannabis without investigating for myself.

The human body's endocannabinoid system, named after the plant that helped discover it, holds therapeutic promise for treating a wide range of pathological conditions. These include mood and anxiety disorders; movement disorders like epilepsy, Parkinson's and Huntington's disease; neuropathic pain; fibromyalgia; multiple sclerosis; motor neuron diseases; spinal cord injury; cancer; atherosclerosis; myocardial infarction; stroke; hypertension; glaucoma; obesity and osteoporosis. Scientists discovered that the human body actually produces its own cannabinoids, called endogenous cannabinoids or endocannabinoids. These chemicals are otherwise unique to the cannabis plant[118].

In 1992, the chemist Dr Raphael Mechoulam's investigations into the effect of the cannabis plant on the human body and mind led to the discovery of our endocannabinoid system. Today, science is exploring the key role this physiologic system plays in establishing and maintaining human health[112].

Endocannabinoids and their receptors are found throughout the body, including the brain, organs, connective tissue, glands and immune cells [7]. In each type of tissue, the endocannabinoid system performs different tasks, but the primary goal is always the same: homeostasis – the maintenance of a stable internal environment despite fluctuations in the external environment.

CB1 and CB2 are two major endocannabinoid receptors that have been discovered in the body. They are the primary mediators of the effects of endocannabinoids. CB1 receptors are found primarily in the brain and spinal cord, whereas CB2 receptors are concentrated in connective tissue, glands, organs and the immune system, where they aid reduction in inflammation. Both of these receptors are responsible for regulating a wide range of biological functions including pain, appetite, neuroprotection, cardiovascular function, digestion, reproduction, movement, mood, memory and learning, metabolism, and sleep.

Our body produces endocannabinoids to stimulate the CB1 and CB2 receptors. The most studied endocannabinoids are the neurotransmitters anandamide and 2-arachidonoylglycerol (2-AG). The name anandamide is derived from the Sanskrit word *ananda*, meaning bliss and joy, and it is referred to as the 'bliss molecule' for its ability to induce a sense of happiness and mental well-being. While these cannabinoids are distinct from those produced in the cannabis plant, they interact via the same pathways in the brain and body, so they share many similar properties and effects.

Cannabinoids bind to cannabinoid receptors as a key fits into a lock. Unlocking the receptor causes changes in how cells function, leading to different healing effects in the body.

Our body communicates via neurotransmitters that move from one neuron, called the presynaptic cell, to the next, called the postsynaptic cell. This spurs the receiving neuron into action, triggering a cascade of events that allows the message to be passed along. The endocannabinoid system, however, works in reverse, which is referred to as retrograde neurotransmission signaling [169]. The cannabinoids move on demand from the postsynaptic cell to the presynaptic cell. This is important, as it allows for control of the amount of neurotransmitters that are released, which in turn affects how messages are sent, received and processed by the cell. Speaking to a master's student currently conducting research into the pharmaceutical benefit of cannabinoids, I also learnt that both CB1 and CB2 cannabinoid receptors are G protein-coupled receptors, which detect molecules outside the cell and activate internal signaling, thus enhancing neurotransmission from the brain to the point of execution.

With their complex actions in our immune system, nervous system, and virtually all of the body's organs, cannabinoids function as a bridge between body and mind and are believed to hold promise for treating many diseases. The ubiquitous presence of the endogenous cannabinoid system correlates with its role as a modulator of multiple physiological processes. This has prompted scientists to reconsider the way we understand healing in the body.

There are two ways of targeting the endocannabinoid system to promote wellness, namely medical cannabis and synthetic cannabinoids. The cannabis plant makes phytocannabinoids that bind to the same receptors as the endocannabinoids made by the body. Active compounds in the cannabis plant, including delta-9-tetrahydrocannabinol (THC) and cannabidiol (CBD), interact with the endocannabinoid system to produce therapeutic effects. THC is psychoactive, whereas CBD is non-psychoactive.

Cannabis is one of the oldest known natural medicines, dating back five thousand years, but sadly it has been a source of controversy throughout its history and still remains one today, though legislative changes for its medicinal use are now under way[22]. Despite its legal battles, this plant is finding its way into the healing cabinet of many patients diagnosed with so-called incurable and debilitating diseases. Positive results are flooding in. Scientists in a number of countries are investigating the plant's ability to help alleviate the symptoms of MS and other diseases[72]. This is an area of hope, but more research still has to be done.

As I mentioned before, just six months after the diagnosis, the shock of my brother-in-law's death caused a massive relapse. The MS and RA symptoms consumed me as my body and mind were unable to watch the deep sadness and hurt Rajin was experiencing. The MRI scan showed new lesions in my cerebellum. The neurologist suggested that I reconsider my decision regarding the use of biological disease-modifying drugs. The immunosuppressant that he proposed would increase my risk of contracting encephalitis or meningitis, which, in turn, carried their own risks. This treatment could also increase my risk of cancer. Between the risks and my experience with the excruciating headaches caused by the entry-level immunosuppressant, I had to ask: How can this be our choice of treatment? Riddled with anxiety, pain, discomfort, disability and depression, I battled to reach for the healing modalities like sound, meditation and breathing. Added to that, my husband, the main pillar in my support structure, was crumbling. I was back in hospital on antidepressants and the maximum dose of intravenous immunosuppressant medication. Nothing worked. I was so defeated, I couldn't even muster the energy or desire to pray.

Tharsheyen approached me with tears in his eyes and begged me to look into medicinal cannabis. I refused. He then intensified his research on the web, looking into options to help me get well. It was his matric year and, from the research he had done, he even presented an oral on the therapeutic benefits of medicinal cannabis and some of the complexities associated with using it as a treatment. We began to have many discussions and debates about the role of medicinal cannabis. The controversies surrounding ethical, legal and societal implications associated with its use made our conversations difficult. Speaking to university lecturers, Rajin learnt that this medicinal plant was gaining much attention in the pharmaceutical industry and that it had been introduced into the pharmacy curriculum.

After months of research and debate on medicinal cannabis, Rajin called a family meeting.

Tharsheyen started: 'Mum, nothing is working to make you better. It hurts to watch you battling your disease. We are so unhappy looking at you in so much discomfort and pain every day'.

I burst into tears.

'People who haven't walked in your shoes and felt your pain and hopelessness will judge you for using medicinal cannabis. And that's okay', Rajin argued. 'You have to accept that you are the only one who knows the depth of your pain. You can barely get out of bed. You're so weak, so ill'. I looked down at my painful hands as he spoke, and he followed my gaze.

'Just look at how swollen your hands are from all the drips inserted in hospital'.

He continued: 'Please, Mala, you have to give cannabis a try. You wouldn't be using it recreationally, you wouldn't be chasing a high, you wouldn't be chasing a mind-altering experience. You would be trying to ensure basic functionality to do the simple things for yourself'. He had tears in his eyes. 'When you are medicated with prescription drugs, you are so confused – you can't remember your conversations with us. You are unsteady and you walk into walls in the house. These drugs shouldn't be your only option'.

I sat in silence. I felt like a criminal – the jury was out and a final decision had to be made. I felt angry that my condition had come down to making a choice that went against the law of our country and my spiritual beliefs.

My silence seemed to crush my husband and son's hopes. It broke my heart to see them feel helpless because of my condition. My situation was causing my family so much pain. The thought of the MS causing permanent disability was overwhelming. The thought of becoming a burden to my family as a result of this disability was devastating. The MS didn't just affect me – my entire family was being crippled.

A few weeks after having this discussion, I attended a meeting at the KwaZulu-Natal MS Society with my brother, Jeevan, where a presentation on medicinal cannabis was given. I reconsidered. My family and I intensified our scientific research. Rajin started to point out how irrational my decision was to pick the mind-bending pharmaceutical drugs over cannabis.

'The schedule 5 and 6 drugs, like opioids, antidepressants and benzodiazepines, that have been prescribed for you also cross the blood-brain barrier and impact on the brain and spinal cord, so they're also mind-altering. You're so disorientated, dizzy and confused – and not forgetting your memory impairment – with these pharmaceutical drugs. They cause dependency and, if you use them long-term, your kidneys and liver may become compromised. When the benzodiazepines are combined with opioids for strong pain relief, these side effects are amplified', Rajin explained.

'I'm in so much pain and discomfort, Raj. I don't know what is the right way forward. All I know is that I want this torture to end!'

'The cannabis plant has molecules that are recognised by our body and it enhances healing without damage to the kidneys and liver. With micro-dosing we can eliminate the mind-altering effects of THC. And there's the fact that none of the pharmaceutical drugs are giving you any relief anyway, so maybe we should try the cannabis. I am going to investigate a pure source so I have it available if you choose to go ahead', he said.

'Okay, Raj'.

'Millions of people are dying from adverse drug interactions, but there is not a single recorded case of death from cannabis overdose. I definitely think it's the safer and more effective form of treatment for you'.

Rajin knew what he was talking about. According to Harvard University's Edmond J. Safra Center for Ethics, systematic reviews of hospital charts found that even properly prescribed pharmaceutical drugs cause about 1.9 million hospitalisations per year and about 128 000 people die from drugs prescribed to them[84].

Nevertheless, I had my doubts and fears. 'I feel that, whatever choice I make, I am going to be either physically, emotionally or spiritually crushed', I said to Rajin.

'We have done the research. You are so ill. The boys and I can't bear to see you suffer any longer and we strongly feel that cannabis could help. But, at the end of the day, the choice is yours and it's a decision that you have to live with'.

After eighteen months of researching, debating and challenging our belief system, I made my choice. 'Okay, I'll try it', I told Rajin, 'even though I don't feel comfortable using it'.

I was still terribly ill and had started experiencing pain and vision difficulties in my right eye again. But, this time, instead of rushing to the emergency room as I had done on many occasions in the past, with trepidation, I decided to try the cannabis.

Suddenly Rajin became the sceptical one. 'You could lose your eye, Mala. Your optic nerve is inflamed. We've got to go to hospital right now! Let's try the cannabis after the hospital treatment has calmed the relapse'.

'I want to try the cannabis now!' I responded, worried that I might lose the courage to use it.

'Okay, I'm giving it one hour. If you feel the same, we're going to hospital'.

Without medical science presenting me with what I deemed viable options for treatment, I felt cornered into using cannabis. As it turned out, the micro-dose was faster and more effective than I could've ever imagined. My eye symptoms cleared within thirty minutes. I continued using cannabis twice a day. In just three days, I started to notice my symptoms disappearing. I found the cannabis heightening the here and now by making my senses more intense. It would exaggerate my current symptoms for a few minutes, forcing me to keep my attention and thoughts in the present where healing happens and relief finally flows from. In spite of my depressed state of mind, once I used the cannabis, I experienced no mental strain from negative thoughts about the past or future worries. Like the sun at the crack of dawn, my happy feeling was re-emerging.

Treating my acute flare-up with cannabis required both THC and CBD. THC served as my analgesic and antidepressant by changing my thoughts and mood, whereas CBD assimilated essential nutrients and created a healing environment. Both served as strong anti-inflammatories for me. If we go back to my Wellness Formula, we can see how a change in thought (ΔT) is key in the healing process. The bitterness, anger, sadness and pity that I felt for myself all disappeared.

Conventional antidepressants take weeks if not months to correct the chemical imbalance that causes depression. The cannabis plant works much faster. And it needn't produce mind-altering states: micro-dosing works. Until one has experienced the continuous wrath of physical pain and the depths of a dark downward spiral into depression as a result of a chemical imbalance, it's unfair to pass judgement on the use of medicinal cannabis. Multiple autoimmune syndrome not only affected my physical health profoundly, it also took a serious toll on my mental health. I was grieving for the loss of a normal life until I was introduced to medicinal cannabis. When I felt trapped in a fog of irreversible decline, cannabis helped me to climb out of the black hole. Now I could focus on implementing other positive changes.

Together with the right foods (ΔF), I went from being dysfunctional, pain-ridden, depressed and suicidal to walking, driving and taking care of my family. I was able to refocus on my meditation practice. I became functional and independent again. I believe that cannabis nullifies the fight-flight-freeze response and initiates the much-needed rest-digest-repair response in the body. It is most effective in combination with a diet that provides all the necessary nutrients to further support these processes.

Rajin was amazed and relieved. 'Your emotional stability on the medicinal cannabis is unbelievable! You are your kind, gentle, happy self again'.

'Yes, I feel it too. That dark ominous cloud has disappeared. It's simply mind-blowing how much physical and mental relief I've experienced'.

He could only agree. 'I applaud your decision to use it'.

Cannabis is definitely providing relief where other pharmaceutical drugs have failed. However, despite its efficacy, because of the fact that it was entirely illegal in our country and is prohibited by my spiritual teacher, I made the decision to stop using it. Although it had provided relief, making the decision to stop using it was also a relief. I will always be grateful for the healing it brought at a time when nothing else worked. It gave me the window of opportunity to become functional enough to remove my stress triggers and get back on track with my other healing modalities to strengthen my body and mind. I renewed my passion and optimism for life.

While cannabis is excellent for the body, its effects on the mind and human psyche are still contentious and could therefore be a possible hinderance for spiritual growth and transformation. Shortly before this book went to print, on Tharsheyen's twentieth birthday, South Africa's highest court decriminalised the use of cannabis by adults at home[111]. I agree that cannabis may be thrown out for its mind-altering psychoactive effects when taken recreationally in high doses. But I also agree that this plant's fast-acting efficacy in hopeless, debilitating medical conditions demands respect and is worthy of being considered in micro-doses.

A Favourite Remedy From Nature

Rajin and I studied and completed a course on Bach Flower Remedies in 1998. When I was initially diagnosed, I unfortunately forgot about this potent remedy. It would probably have been a valuable aid at the time.

Bach Flower Remedies are used to treat a person's emotional state. They serve as a natural method of healing that gently restores the balance between mind and body by casting out negative emotions[158].

The Welsh physician Dr Edward Bach first created these remedies of spring water infused with the essence of wild flowers in the 1920s [6]. Trained in conventional allopathic medicine, he observed that his patients' recovery seemed to have as much to do with their emotional health as it did with any physical condition. Those in a positive emotional state recovered more quickly. Dr Bach found that his flower remedies allow peace and happiness to return to the patient so that the body is free to heal itself. He was inspired by the work of Dr Samuel Hahnemann, the founder of homeopathic medicine, who emphasised treating the 'whole' patient, including their emotions and mental state, rather than focusing exclusively on physical symptoms.

There are thirty-eight different Bach Flower Remedies all relating to a specific negative emotion, personality type and mood. I find that it's nature's antidepressant with zero side effects. Today, I regularly use these Bach Flower Remedies when I feel stuck in a negative place filled with anxiety. After a few days of using it, my world brightens up.

20

Holding the healing space: embedding the wellness formula in a support system

We all hold the power to heal others, not with the tools of medicine, but with our natural ability to be present and pay attention – without trying to fix the person. When we share this gift with someone who is struggling, it's a way of holding the space for them to heal. Emotional pain with an autoimmune diagnosis is real and often unacknowledged. People start to heal the moment they feel heard. An integral part of my healing was the tremendous love that constantly poured out from my friends and family who held my healing space.

Having and maintaining a support system is a key element in our healing process. When someone at home is ill, it changes the dynamic for everyone. As a patient I needed to acknowledge this. Initially I felt so much guilt for the impact the diagnosis had on my family. The dynamics of our social life changed. No one complained. We all adapted. As a family, we became more conscious and appreciative of our blessings. Rajin used to say, 'Having a pessimistic attitude during difficult times is like having a flat tyre: if you don't change it, you can't go anywhere'.

The biggest shift as a family unit was our time distribution for the day. We spent more hours 'being' and fewer hours 'doing'. My family members turned off their words and listened with open hearts to the truth of my pain. They created the space that allowed me to draw on my inner strength. We became more present as a result of our gratitude. We started to enjoy every moment as a family. We encouraged each other to be fully present in the moment. We worked hard to keep the conversation from meandering into past drama. The more we practised this, the easier it became. Our children encouraged me to walk my talk.

I became honest about my feelings. I let my family know when I felt hurt or disrespected. We discussed my feelings and made changes. I stopped living by default and started living by design. I am the architect of my life. Some of the changes were dramatic, like saying no to important family events when the weather was too hot. Some of the changes went against society's rules, like the use of medicinal cannabis. I stopped associating with company that left me depleted of energy. What mattered most was getting me better and keeping me well. I drew strength and inspiration from the decisions my family helped me make. I soon realised that my family and I were on the same page when it came to managing my autoimmune conditions.

The understanding and encouragement I received from my friends was priceless. We all have busy lives and to witness how willingly my friends gave off their time to me was precious. As a patient, I valued their patience with my choice of vegan restaurants and venues where I would not be hot. Together we all learnt the value of good nutrition. We booked and cancelled events many times when I felt ill. Everyone understood. There was no need for explanations.

My friends and family stopped me from isolating myself and falling into a long-term depression. My sad days were short-lived. My friends encouraged my spiritual inner path. I geared my activities towards those that encouraged relaxation and meditation. When my actions started to reflect my desire to heal and feel joy again, the sad days were few and far between.

Rajin brings me a bouquet of roses every so often, which always makes me feel special. He lovingly commits to waking up early every day to make my green juice. We realise that, when it comes to managing a chronic condition like MS, the patient and spouse must function like two wings on the same bird. Rajin's sitting quietly with me, offering me his full attention and listening without intervention was the gift I enjoyed most. I make a conscious effort to express my gratitude to my husband often.

For a patient with an autoimmune disease who is already compromised physically, not having emotional support can leave them feeling emotionally paralysed. This is a very difficult place to try to rise from to start healing. Without support, the challenge of the illness is multiplied. Emotional support from friends and family is a lifeboat in stormy waters. Education is key for the support team to play a meaningful role in the healing process. The infinite compassion of God's cosmic plan for me was expressed through Tharsheyen's gap year. He was willing to walk alongside me, offering care and support that kept me joyful and catapulted my healing.

It was two years since I had been diagnosed when he completed his final year of schooling with outstanding results. He made the decision to study conventional medicine at a university overseas, hoping to one day shed new light on the autoimmune dilemma in medicine and help me get better. But he hadn't decided where he wanted to study yet. Since most of the universities outside South Africa start their academic year around August or September, he dedicated the early months of the year to helping me at home while he searched online for his university of choice.

Watching me battle to cope with MS and RA, he started spending more time googling ways to reverse autoimmune symptoms rather than applying to universities. He refused to accept my down days.

'Come on, Mum, it's time to get out of your bedroom and join me in the lounge', he would plead. 'Come watch me play FIFA Online'.

Not wanting to disappoint him, I would drag myself out of bed and cuddle up on the sofa to watch him play his video game. But he didn't just leave me to watch. He explained how the game was played and asked for my suggestions when selecting his team. He made me a part of the game. I soon found myself so engrossed in it, encouraging certain soccer moves, that I forgot how miserable my condition made me feel. We quickly fell into a FIFA routine and my days seemed to feel happier.

During the holidays when both the boys were home, my world was complete. They delighted in pampering me. Pavesan was quick to ensure that I was always spoken to with love and kindness. He constantly praised me for my efforts to understand the complexities of multiple autoimmune syndrome. It was impossible to cheat on my Wellness Formula in our children's presence. Together with their dad, they encouraged me all the time. Being part of a family steeped in science and wellness, they welcomed the idea that I was the experiment that could influence many lives. All four of us wanted the experiment to work.

Tharsheyen also managed my medicinal cannabis dose carefully, recording strains that I used, their efficacy and my tolerance levels. He ensured that the dose I used gave me relief while still keeping me functional. He respected my decision to stop using the cannabis once I felt better and more in control of my triggers. Watching my recovery using unconventional medical options made him rethink his career choice.

He came to a decision. 'You know, Mum, so many people in our country are suffering with their chronic diseases and are simply waiting for disability to set in as they get older. They have given up on healing. I think I can make a bigger difference to people's lives if I study naturopathic medicine'.

'That's fantastic!' I responded, intrigued at his new desire to shift his healing paradigm.

'There's such a huge need for education in our community about natural medicine and lifestyle change to manage chronic conditions. Just look at you! Your physical wellness is no reflection of your MRI scans'.

'That's certainly true', I said with a big smile.

'We have to start a culture of wellness. We need to create a culture of helping ourselves stay well. Long-term wellness will not happen with health care as we know it'.

'I agree. We have to make a determined effort to create a culture of health with our thoughts, choice of food, breathing and way of life. We have to learn how to live well'.

'Do you know what I've noticed, Mum? Some of the most affluent countries in the world, like the United States, have so much access to wellness information and healthy food choices, and yet those countries are spending trillions of dollars on health care'.

'It's tragic, isn't it?'

'Why is it that there are so many sick people in the world despite the advancement in healthcare technology? I read that people are so ill that analysts predict that we are living in an era where prescription drugs will see the fastest annual growth over the next decade.'

I was intrigued by my son's research and ideas and excited about his path forward. 'I think we have to apply ourselves to break and transcend the barriers we have set regarding wellness and healing', I said. 'The time is now for us to become conscious of the awesomeness of the human body and the intelligence that drives the complexity within every cell of our being.'

'Yes, Mum! I want to be part of the team that strives to break our limitations with who we think we are and how we view our body.'

'I like your thinking!'

'Just like you've done, I want to be able to promote health and treat disease using the body's inherent biological healing mechanisms to self-heal.'

Rajin and I were pleased with his decision to study natural medicine and delighted with his ability to see the bigger picture. He enrolled at the School of Natural Medicine at the University of the Western Cape to start the following year. He planned to study towards a Bachelor of Science in Complementary Medicine. After he'd announced his decision, I watched him move excitedly around the house beaming with joy for having found his passion.

My son's gap year was a blessing. He was there to reinforce my Wellness Formula 24-7. He dedicated his time to providing me with emotional and physical support – a tall order for an eighteen-year-old, but he did it with so much love and dedication, I couldn't help feeling better.

My son has taught me more about faith and discipline than all my reading has. My greatest healing therapy was the long discussions we enjoyed, seated on our veranda, unravelling the divine power of the human mind in conscious healing. It was so reassuring to have someone there to hold my hand and take me through those low times. We underestimate the value of having someone always available when we are ill. To this day he continues to send me reminders to stay true to my Wellness Formula.

21
Being malawell: finding opportunities and gifts in my challenges

Today, with absolute joy and appreciation, I find myself free of virtually all MS, RA, Hashimoto's and fibromyalgia symptoms. The severe, persistent nausea and headaches are gone. The painful Lhermitte's sign is no more. Even the excruciating MS hug released its grip on me. The long list of debilitating symptoms has rocketed away out of my body and mind. When a minor symptom does rear its head, I immediately know what triggered it. The disease has empowered me to become conscious of my thoughts, words and deeds.

I embrace my new dietary habits with gratitude. The odd times when I do eat out and my food is 'contaminated', I experience pain in my ankle the next morning. I increase my water consumption and, generally, by the end of the day the pain is gone.

On very hot days, even though I stay mainly in an air-conditioned space, I still experience tingling of my tongue, but this lasts a very short while.

I have an abundance of energy, most of which has been spent researching this book. I can make it through longer days, but I spend my time mindfully, doing peaceful activities. I do my best, which may be different from day to day, depending on triggers like heat. If I socialise for long hours, I experience slight tremors. Doing breathing exercises and going to bed early keeps the tremors away.

I'm enjoying company again and have learnt not to take thoughtless comments personally. I am able to hold challenging conversations with my husband without becoming emotional and going into a relapse as I did in the past. I have the courage to ask questions and express to him how I really feel.

The MS hug was the last symptom to disappear. This symptom only left when my meditation became regular and I kept my feelings positive and my thoughts in the present. As soon as I think negative thoughts, I feel a tightness in my ribcage. This means that my internal emotional overreaction to a situation, person or event needs to stop. It's a potent reminder to quickly shift out of my negative thought space and allow the free flow of life. I'm loving the lesson.

My memory has improved and I'm able to have intelligent discussions again. I remember the dance steps better and eagerly await my next dance lesson. Even though I am comfortable in crowds, I'm still adjusting to loud sounds.

On days when I skip my meditation, I find that my eye goes blurry during difficult conversations. When this happens, I return to the present. I isolate myself, turn on the Indian classical music and do my breathing, visualisations and meditation. It works every time.

I can drive long distances again, on my own, free of anxiety.

Choosing to eat better and to stay away from heat, flashing lights and loud noise is easy for me now. Letting go of wanting to have an emotional reaction when drama unfolds around me keeps me on my toes. The more often I achieve this, the easier it becomes. I applaud myself wholeheartedly every time I allow drama to simply pass by like a stranger on the street.

I feel in control of my conditions. The absence of symptoms is not merely an indication of remission, which implies that relief is temporary. Now that I have the Wellness Formula, the absence of the long list of symptoms I endured in the past implies a kind of cure for me. For the first time, I have the knowledge and understanding I need to control the disease conditions. This is empowering and liberating.

I exercise conscious awareness in everything I say and do. If I do slip into old habits, I am able to bring myself back into a space of wellness on my own within a short period of time. I have no desire to go back to my old way of being. As my Take-Charge Wellness Formula becomes my way of life, I can see myself enjoying a life free of autoimmune symptoms. I hold the key to my wellness.

I always looked well, and now I am so excited to finally *feel* well again. I see life with a different pair of eyes for having walked this path. I have a deeper appreciation for the wisdom of the cells in my body and the power of my thoughts. Although the way forward is clear to me, others sometimes still find it hard to grasp what my wellness hinges on. If Mala looks so well, does she really need to stay indoors on this beautiful warm day? She seems healthy, why can't she come to the party – everyone will be there! This is why I have decided to coin a word: malawell. My wellness might not meet everyone's expectations, but it is my own highest state of well-being. I am malawell.

malawell: Describes a person diagnosed with an incurable disease who is symptom-free as a result of being able to control the disease with disciplined lifestyle choices and by avoiding its triggers. It's different from remission, which implies a temporary solution. It's a state of wellness that allows total functionality for as long as the lifestyle triggers are respected and avoided at all costs.

Our financial challenges and the complexities of multiple autoimmune syndrome gave me the unique opportunity to practise all that I have come to learn in my life, to develop my Wellness Formula and to come back from the brink of disability to achieve malawellness. I thought it was so much easier to teach than to do. Now I know that it is so much more rewarding and exhilarating to do.

If we still the mind, we heal our world. To get different answers we need to keep asking different questions. The answer is in the question. We need to feel free to ask different questions. I believe that a rapid awakening is descending on humankind's search for wellness. It's not about looking for answers to chronic conditions; it's about asking the right questions to change and demystify our individual journey.

I found gratitude to be an integral part of my emotional wellness. An act of gratitude is an opportunity to step out of our drama and focus on something that is not about us. Gratitude dissolves entitlement. In a moment of gratitude and kindness, we give ourselves the chance to reflect on how much we have to be grateful for, no matter how difficult our circumstances may be. A simple act of gratitude and kindness is the catalyst to feeling joy.

When we live our truth, we ignore what other people think about us. I have learnt that, when medical science doesn't have all the answers, our body does. Looking back on my journey, I can see how often I had to think outside the box in order to move forward. The risks were there, but the faith and the effort were there too. The results were in our divine Creator's hands. Every challenge in my life, whether big or small, is a new opportunity to become creative and grow in ways unimaginable. And every challenge is an opportunity to exercise a choice: Do I want to focus on the old non-functional myelin sheath or the new functional myelin sheath in my neuroplastic brain? Both are there. The choice is mine.

For me the label incurable is directing us to go 'in' to make it 'curable'. It doesn't matter for how long we have been unwell, we need to have faith in our ability to go 'in' and stimulate the body to repair itself. When we go within the body and quieten the mind, we allow the intelligence that gave us life to orchestrate our healing.

As I stand in the ashes of who I used to be, I am discovering that who I am and all my talents and skills and the circumstances of my life are a gift from the divine Creator. How I use my gifts and talents, and how I respond to the circumstances in my life is my gift to Him. And, should I forget this, my husband is there to remind me that everything is perfect and as it needs to be.

While scientists work hard at unravelling the cellular and molecular mystery of autoimmune disease, we have a responsibility to ourselves to start listening to our bodies and take positive action. A chronic condition is nature calling for us to take personal action and bring the body and mind into balance, so that our body's own chemistry can solve the 'incurable riddle' and repair itself.

This is where my healing beliefs have led me. Where will your beliefs about managing and healing a chronic incurable disease take you?

Acknowledgements

To my spiritual guide, Baba Gurinder Singh Ji, thank you for awakening a strength in me I never knew possible and for continuing to bring into my space everything I need to heal and be joyful.

To all the medical professionals who encouraged me to continue on the path less travelled, a sincere thank you. Thank you for the time you took to look at the factors that were bringing me wellness. Thank you for the excitement you displayed when my MRI scans showed improvement.

A big thank you to all the awe-inspiring people in the world who have shaped my inner resilience through their books, talk shows, online videos and overall energy to help and grow the love consciousness within us all. Some of these people are John Kehoe, Deepak Chopra, Wayne Dyer, Eckhart Tolle, Hector Esponda Dubin, Chloe Faith Wordsworth, Oprah Winfrey, Sadhguru Jaggi Vasudev, Joe Dispenza, Mel Robbins and Robin Sharma. I read their works over and over again … and then some more. I just can't get enough of the wisdom dust that they sprinkle on my subconscious mind every time I read their books or watch their shows and videos.

Thank you to Heather Hannaway and Primi Chetty of Shuter & Shooter Publishers for their vision to see the book in me before I could. Writing this book encouraged me to consolidate my wellness regime and it sped up my healing. I believe that the mere act of writing it has inspired me to stay true to my healing formula. Heather Hannaway also contributed significantly towards seeing this book to print. I am truly grateful.

To my editor, Ingrid Lezar, thank you for believing in the book and wanting to be part of the process. Your effort and commitment to understanding this work is greatly appreciated. It was a pleasure working with you. You made this challenging process most enjoyable.

Special thanks to my typesetter Evan Clemitson, for your patience, creative skill and willingness to ensure that we always worked in a cool environment.

A special thank you to my friend Belinda Exter, whom I met while studying Resonance Repatterning, for spending many hours reading this manuscript and making significant comments.

My sincere thanks to anaesthesiologist Dr Jay Bhagwan and neuropharmacologist Prof. Santy Daya for your encouragement and invaluable contributions to this book.

To my friends in the medical profession, thank you for the insights you brought to the table with your pharmaceutical knowledge and wisdom on making decisions. I always feel heartened after talking to you.

A big thank you to the communities of Dalton, Wartburg and New Hanover for your ongoing support and prayers since I was diagnosed. The beautiful gifts, flower arrangements and delicious meals that reached my bedside will forever be remembered. You will never know the tremendous strength you gave Rajin with your hugs, tears and words of encouragement every time I relapsed and was hospitalised.

To my extended family and friends, thank you for coming on this journey with me. Thank you for your patience and tolerance on my 'bad days'. Your empathy and understanding at these times gave me the strength to persevere. Thank you for always going out of your way to accommodate and respect my dietary and temperature needs. Thank you for making me feel loved and appreciated.

A special thank you to my niece, Salehaa Gounden. Your love for dance has motivated me to follow my dream of dancing. Watching you come alive on the dance floor with both your classical Indian Bharatanatyam and your contemporary dance moves is awe-inspiring.

To fellow patients and the KwaZulu-Natal MS Society, thank you for the respect, trust, gratitude and encouragement you showed me when I shared my research and outlined the inconvenient truth about diet and lifestyle change in chronic conditions.

To my parents, Mike and Neela Gounden, thank you for the grounding and the values you instilled in me to never give up. Having my mum by my side has been an anchor in stormy waters. Thank you, Mum, for your patience, tolerance and unwavering faith in my healing formula. I will always be grateful to my late dad for introducing my spiritual path to me and instilling in me the love to read books that feed my soul.

I have been blessed with a family that is constantly evolving into a consciousness of love, meditation and a strong desire to help each other to heal and grow emotionally and spiritually. To my husband, my greatest teacher and best friend, who so gently (most of the time) nudges me back on course time and time again: thank you, Rajin, for standing by me and lifting me to heights I never knew possible. Thank you for the many months we spent discussing, debating and editing this work. The laughter we shared during this period was so precious.

My younger son, Tharsheyen, keeps me on track; there is no room to stay derailed. At the age of twenty he is already passionate and ruthless with finding and living his highest truth. There are no grey areas in his world. Thank you for spending your gap year facilitating my healing with so much love, patience and kindness.

My elder son, Pavesan, is my safety net, my pillow, my inspiration to be the person I am. At the young age of sixteen, he introduced us to conscious eating and high-intensity interval training. Thank you for your solid values and ability to see the bigger picture and bringing our family back on track with so much finesse.

These three men in my life have motivated, inspired and supported me to live from a place of love, gratitude and conviction. They have always shown me how proud they are of the person I am and the work I do. Little do they realise that it is they who bring out the magic in me.

References

1. Adams, L. n.d. Learning a new skill is easier said than done. *Gordon Training International.* http://www.gordontraining.com/free -workplace-articles/learning-a-new-skill-is-easier-said-than-done

2. Admin. 2015. New study unravels how myelin is repaired, may suggest new MS treatments. *Multiple Sclerosis News Today*, 7 September. https://multiplesclerosisnewstoday.com/2015/09/07/ new-study-unravels-myelin-repaired-may-suggest-new-ms -treatments/

3. Akiki, T. J., Averill, C. L., Wrocklage, K. M., Schweinsburg, B., Scott, J. C., Martini, B., Averill, L. A., Southwick, S. M., Krystal, J. H. and Abdallah, C. G. 2017. The association of PTSD symptom severity with localized hippocampus and amygdala abnormalities. *Chronic Stress.* https://doi.org/10.1177/2470547017724069

4. American Thyroid Association. *General Information/Press Room.* https://www.thyroid.org/media-main/press-room/

5. Angeloni, C., Hrelia, S. and Malaguti, M. 2017. Neuroprotective effects of glucosinolates. In J. M. Merillon and K. Ramawat (eds.), *Glucosinolates*. Reference Series in Phytochemistry. Cham: Springer International, 275–299.

6. Bach, E. 1931. *Heal Thyself: An Explanation of the Real Cause and Cure of Disease.* London: C. W. Daniel.

7. Backes, M. 2014. *Cannabis Pharmacy: The Practical Guide to Medicinal Marijuana.* New York: Black Dog & Leventhal.

8. Barks, C. 2003. *Rumi: The Book of Love: Poems of Ecstasy and Longing.* New York: HarperCollins.

9. Barrett, L. F. 2009. The future of psychology: connecting mind to brain. *Perspectives on Psychological Science* 4(4), 326–339. https://doi.org/10.1111/j.1745-6924.2009.01134.x

10. Baumgartner, T., Esslen, M. and Jäncke, L. 2006. From emotion perception to emotion experience: emotions

evoked by pictures and classical music. *International Journal of Psychophysiology* 60(1), 34–43. https://doi.org/10.1016/j.ijpsycho.2005.04.007

11. BBC News. 2018. South Africa's highest court legalises cannabis use, 18 September. https://www.bbc.com/news/world-africa-45559954

12. Beezhold, B. L. and Johnston, C. S. 2012. Restriction of meat, fish, and poultry in omnivores improves mood: a pilot randomized controlled trial. *Nutrition Journal* 11(9). https://doi.org/10.1186/1475-2891-11-9

13. Benito-Leon, J., Labiano-Fontcuberta, A., Mitchell, A. J., Moreno-García, S. and Martínez-Martín, P. 2014. Multiple sclerosis is associated with high trait anger: a case-control study. *Journal of the Neurological Sciences* 340(1–2), 69–74. https://doi.org/10.1016/j.jns.2014.02.029

14. Berger, G. M., Naidoo, J., Gounden, N. and Gouws, E. 1995. Marked hyperinsulinaemia in postmenopausal, healthy Indian (Asian) women. *Diabetic Medicine* 12(9), 788–795.

15. Bergland, C. 2016. Vagus nerve stimulation dramatically reduces inflammation. *Psychology Today*, 6 July. https://www.psychologytoday.com/intl/blog/the-athletes-way/201607/vagus-nerve-stimulation-dramatically-reduces-inflammation

16. Bernock, D. 2014. *Emerging With Wings: A True Story of Lies, Pain, and the Love that Heals.* 2nd ed. Shelby Charter Township, Michigan: 4F Media.

17. Blackwell, B., Bloomfield, S. S. and Buncher, C. R. 1972. Demonstration to medical students of placebo response and non-drug factors. *The Lancet* 1, 1279–1282. https://doi.org/10.1016/S0140-6736(72)90996-8

18. Bonaz, B., Bazin, T. and Pellissier, S. 2018. The vagus nerve at the interface of the microbiota-gut-brain axis. *Frontiers in Neuroscience* 12, 49. https://doi.org/10.3389/fnins.2018.00049

19. Bonaz, B., Sinniger, V. and Pellissier, S. 2016. Anti-inflammatory properties of the vagus nerve: potential therapeutic

implications of vagus nerve stimulation. *Journal of Physiology* 594(20), 5781–5790. https://doi.org/10.1113/JP271539

20. Boroch, A. 2017. *Healing Multiple Sclerosis: Diet, Detox & Nutritional Makeover for Total Recovery.* Los Angeles: Quintessential Healing.

21. Boyd-Brewer, C. and McCaffrey, A. 2004. Vibroacoustic sound therapy improves pain management and more. *Holistic Nursing Practice* 18(3), 111–118.

22. Bridgeman, M. B. and Abazia, D.T. 2017. Medicinal cannabis: history, pharmacology, and implications for the acute care setting. *P&T: Pharmacy and Therapeutics* 42(3), 180–188.

23. Browne, P., Chandraratna, D., Angood, C., Tremlett, H., Baker, C., Taylor, B. V. and Thompson, A. J. 2014. Atlas of multiple sclerosis 2013: a growing global problem with widespread inequity. *Neurology* 38(11), 1022–1024. https://doi.org/10.1212/WNL.0000000000000768

24. Caplan, J. 2006. Google's chief looks ahead. *Time*, 2 October. http://content.time.com/time/business/article/0,8599,1541446,00.html

25. Chaker, L., Bianco A. C., Jonklaas, J. and Peeters, R. P. 2017. Hypothyroidism. *The Lancet* 390(10101), 1550–1562. https://doi.org/10.1016/S0140-6736(17)30703-1

26. Chandrashekara, S. 2012. The treatment strategies of autoimmune disease may need a different approach from conventional protocol. *Indian Journal of Pharmacology* 44(6), 665–671. https://doi.org/10.4103/0253-7613.103235

27. Cho, Y., Lim, T. H., Kang, H., Lee, Y., Lee, H. and Kim, H. 2019. Socioeconomic status and depression as combined risk factors for acute myocardial infarction and stroke: a population-based study of 2.7 million Korean adults. *Journal of Psychosomatic Research*. https://doi.org/10.1016/j.jpsychores.2019.01.016

28. Chödrön, P. 2016. *When Things Fall Apart: Heart Advice for Difficult Times.* Boston: Shambala.

29. Chopra, D. 1989. *Quantum Healing: Exploring the Frontiers of Mind/Body Medicine.* New York: Bantam

30. Chopra, D. and Tanzi, R. E. 2013. *Super Brain: Unleashing the Explosive Power of Your Mind to Maximise Health, Happiness, and spiritual Well-being*. London: Rider.

31. Cignarella, F., Cantoni, C., Ghezzi, L., Salter, A., Dorsett, Y., Chen, L., Phillips, D., Weinstock, G. M., Fontana, L., Cross, A. H., Zhou, Y. and Piccio, L. 2018. Intermittent fasting confers protection in CNS autoimmunity by altering the gut microbiota. *Cell Metabolism* 27(6), 1222–1235. https://doi.org/10.1016/j.cmet.2018.05.006

32. Code, B. and Code, D. 2006. *Winning the Pain Game.* [s.l.]: Words of Wisdom Press.

33. Cousins, N. 1979. *Anatomy of an Illness: As Perceived by the Patient*. New York: Norton.

34. D'Acquisto, F. 2017. Affective immunology: where emotions and the immune response converge. *Dialogues of Clinical Neuroscience* 19(1), 9–19. https://www.dialogues-cns.org/contents-19-1/dialoguesclinneurosci-19-9

35. Daemen, M. J. 2013. The heart and the brain: an intimate and underestimated relation. *Netherlands Heart Journal* 21(2), 53–54. https://doi.org/10.1007/s12471-012-0371-x

36. Devidayal, N. 2015. 'Indian classical music is powerful in therapeutic processes'. *Times of India*, 29 March. https://timesofindia.indiatimes.com/india/Indian-classical-music-is-powerful-in-therapeutic-processes/articleshow/46731731.cms

37. Doidge, N. 2007. *The Brain That Changes Itself*. New York: Viking.

38. Doidge, N. 2015. *The Brain's Way of Healing*. New York: Viking.

39. Dolan, L. C., Matulka, R. A. and Burdock, G. A. 2010. Naturally occurring food toxins. *Toxins* 2(9), 2289–2332. https://doi.org/10.3390/toxins2092289

40. Dubin, H. E. 2004. *Living Meditation: A Journey Beyond Body and Mind*. Punjab: Radha Soami Satsang Beas.

41. Dyer, W. W. 2007. *Change Your Thoughts – Change Your Life: Living the Wisdom of the Tao*. Carlsbad, California: Hay House.

42. Edwards, L. 2003. Meditation as medicine. Benefits go beyond relaxation. *Advance for Nurse Practitioners* 11(5), 49–52.

43. Emoto, M. 2007. *The Healing Power of Water.* Carlsbad, California: Hay House.

44. Esch, T. and Stefano, G. B. 2011. The neurobiological link between compassion and love. *Medical Science Monitor* 17(3). https://doi.org/10.12659/MSM.881441

45. Fallon, S. 1999. *Nourishing Traditions.* Washington, D.C.: NewTrends.

46. Farhi, D. 1996. *The Breathing Book.* New York: Henry Holt and Company.

47. Fasano, A. 2011. Zonulin and its regulation of intestinal barrier function: the biological door to inflammation, autoimmunity, and cancer. *Physiological Reviews* 91(1), 151–75. https://doi.org/10.1152/physrev.00003.2008

48. Fasano, A. 2012a. Intestinal permeability and its regulation by zonulin: diagnostic and therapeutic implications. *Clinical Gastroenterology and Hepatology* 10(10), 1096–1100. https://doi.org/10.1016/j.cgh.2012.08.012

49. Fasano, A. 2012b. Zonulin, regulation of tight junctions, and autoimmune diseases. *Annals of the New York Academy of Sciences* 1258, 25–33. https://doi.org/10.1111/j.1749-6632.2012.06538.x

50. Fernández-Menéndez, S., Fernández-Morán, M., Fernández-Vega, I., Pérez-Álvarez, A. and Villafani-Echazú, J. 2016. Epstein-Barr virus and multiple sclerosis. From evidence to therapeutic strategies. *Journal of the Neurological Sciences* 361, 213–219. https://doi.org/10.1016/j.jns.2016.01.013

51. Firdous, J., Nanji, K., Qidwai, W. and Qasim, R. 2012. Fibromyalgia syndrome: an overview of pathophysiology, diagnosis and management. *Oman Medical Journal* 27(3), 192–195. https://doi.org/10.5001/omj.2012.44

52. Foster, J. A., Rinaman, L. and Cryan, J. F. 2017. Stress and the gut-brain axis: regulation by the microbiome. *Neurobiology of Stress* 7, 124–136. https://doi.org/10.1016/j.ynstr.2017.03.001

53. Fox, S. G. 2018. *Multiple Sclerosis Mission Remission: Healing MS Against All Odds.* Pennsauken, New Jersey: BookBaby.

54. Frankl, V. 1959. *Man's Search for Meaning.* Boston: Beacon Press.

55. Franks, I. 2016. Is MS hereditary? Yes, according to new study. *Multiple Sclerosis News Today,* 9 June. https://multiplesclerosisnewstoday.com/blog/2016/06/09/ms-hereditary-yes-according-new-study/

56. Friedman, M. and McDonald, G. M. 1997. Potato glycoalkaloids: chemistry, analysis, safety, and plant physiology. *Critical Reviews in Plant Sciences* 16(1), 55–132. https://doi.org/10.1080/713608144

57. Frisaldi, E., Piedimonte, A. and Benedetti, F. 2015. Placebo and nocebo effects: a complex interplay between psychological factors and neurochemical networks. *American Journal of Clinical Hypnosis* 57(3), 267–284. https://doi.org/10.1080/00029157.2014.976785

58. Genetic and Rare Diseases Information Center (GARD). 2015. Multiple sclerosis. https://rarediseases.info.nih.gov/diseases/10255/multiple-sclerosis

59. Gleason, T. 2015. Ballroom dance for multiple sclerosis? Why not? *Everyday Health.* https://www.everydayhealth.com/columns/trevis-gleason-life-with-multiple-sclerosis/ms-cha-cha-cha-ballroom-dance-helps-people-with-multiple-sclerosis/

60. Goldman, J. 2009. *The 7 vowel sounds* [online video], 30 November. https://youtu.be/iKDXFxUfyNw

61. Goldsby, T. L., Goldsby, M. E., McWalters, M. and Mills, P. J. 2017. Effects of singing bowl sound meditation on mood, tension and well-being: an observational study. *Journal of Evidence-Based Complementary and Alternative Medicine* 22(3), 401–406. https://doi.org/10.1177/2156587216668109

62. Gorbach, S. L. 1996. Microbiology of the gastrointestinal tract. In S. Baron (ed.), *Medical Microbiology,* 4th ed. Galveston, Texas: University of Texas Medical Branch at Galveston.

63. Goswami, A. 2004. *The Quantum Doctor: A Physicist's Guide to Health and Healing.* Charlottesville: Hampton Roads.

64. Gounden, N., Naidoo, J., Pegoraro, R. J. and Berger, G. M. 1995. Apolipoprotein E allele frequencies in a South African Indian female population. *Clinical Genetics* 48(5), 243–245.

65. Grewen, K. M. and Light, K. C. 2011. Plasma oxytocin is related to lower cardiovascular and sympathetic reactivity to stress. *Biological Psychology* 87(3). https://doi.org/10.1016/j.biopsycho.2011.04.003

66. Guggenmos, J., Schubart, A. S., Ogg, S., Andersson, M., Olsson, T., Mather, I. H. and Linington, C. 2004. Antibody cross-reactivity between myelin oligodendrocyte glycoprotein and the milk protein butyrophilin in multiple sclerosis. *Journal of Immunology* 172(1), 661–668. https://doi.org/10.4049 /jimmunol.172.1.661

67. Gustafson, C. 2014. Alan Goldhamer, DC: Water fasting – the clinical effectiveness of rebooting your body. *Integrative Medicine* 13(3), 52–57.

68. Helminski, K. (ed.). 1998. *The Rumi Collection: An Anthology of Translations of Mevlana Jalaluddin Rumi.* Boston: Shambala.

69. Tomatis. 2019. History. *Tomatis.* https://www.tomatis.com/en/history

70. Hochberg, M., Silman, A., Smolen, J., Weinblatt, M. and Weisman, M. 2008. *Rheumatoid Arthritis.* Philadelphia: Elsevier.

71. Howick, J., Friedemann, C., Tsakok, M., Watson, R., Tsakok, T., Thomas, J., Perera, R., Fleming, S. and Heneghan, C. 2016. Correction: are treatments more effective than placebos? A systematic review and meta-analysis. *Public Library of Science – One* 11(1). https://doi.org/10.1371/journal.pone.0147354

72. Isaac, S., Saini, B. and Chaar, B. B. 2016. The role of medicinal cannabis in clinical therapy: pharmacists' perspectives. *Public Library of Science – One* 11(15). https://doi.org/10.1371/journal.pone.0155113

73. Jelinek, G. 2016. *Overcoming Multiple Sclerosis: The Evidence-based 7 Step Recovery Program.* Crows Nest, New South Wales: Allen & Unwin.

74. Johnson, I. T. 2007. Phytochemicals and cancer. *Proceedings of the Nutrition Society* 66(2), 207–215. https://doi.org/0.1017/S0029665107005459

75. Johnson, R. L. and Wilson, C. G. 2018. A review of vagus nerve stimulation as a therapeutic intervention. *Journal of Inflammation Research* 11, 203–213. https://doi.org/10.2147/JIR.S163248

76. Kamath, A., Urval, R. P. and Shenoy, A. K. 2017. Effect of alternate nostril breathing exercise on experimentally induced anxiety in healthy volunteers using the simulated public speaking model: a randomized controlled pilot study. *BioMed Research International.* https://doi.org:/10.1155/2017/2450670

77. Katzung, B. G., Masters, S. B. and Trevor, A. J. 2012. *Basic & Clinical Pharmacology,* 12th ed. New York: McGraw-Hill.

78. Kehoe, J. (ed.). 2017. *Mind Power Into the 21st Century: Techniques to Harness the Astounding Powers of Thought.* Vancouver: Zoetic.

79. Khanna, S., Jaiswal, K. S. and Gupta, B. 2017. Managing rheumatoid arthritis with dietary interventions. *Frontiers in Nutrition* 4, 52. https://doi.org/10.3389/fnut.2017.00052

80. Landtblom, A.-M., Fazio, P., Fredrikson, S. and Granieri, E. 2010. The first case of history of multiple sclerosis: Augustus d'Este (1794–1848). *Neurological Sciences* 31(1), 29–33. https://doi.org/10.1007/s10072-009-0161-4

81. Lee, T., Jarome, T., Li, S. J., Kim, J. J. and Helmstetter, F. J. 2009. Chronic stress selectively reduces hippocampal volume in rats: a longitudinal MRI study. *NeuroReport* 20(17), 1554–1558. https://doi.org/10.1097/WNR.0b013e328332bb09

82. Leonard, G., Lapierre, Y., Chen, Y.-K., Wardini, R., Crane, J. and Ptito, A. 2017. Noninvasive tongue stimulation combined with intensive cognitive and physical rehabilitation induces neuroplastic changes in patients with multiple sclerosis: a multimodal neuroimaging study. *Multiple Sclerosis Journal – Experimental, Translational and Clinical* 3(1). https://doi.org/10.1177/2055217317690561

83. Levine, G. N., Lange, R. A., Bairey-Merz, C. N., Davidson, R. J., Jamerson, K., Metha, P. K., Michos, E. D., Norris, K., Ray, I. B., Saban, K. L., Shah, T., Stein, R., Smith Jr., S. C., American Heart Association Council on Clinical Cardiology, Council on Cardiovascular and Stroke Nursing and Council on Hypertension. 2017. Meditation and cardiovascular risk reduction. *Journal of the American Heart Association* 6(10). https://doi.org/10.1161/JAHA.117.002218

84. Light, D. W. 2014. New prescription drugs: a major health risk with few offsetting advantages. Harvard University, Edmond J. Safra Center for Ethics. https://ethics.harvard.edu/blog/new-prescription-drugs-major-health-risk-few-offsetting-advantages

85. Lipton, B. 2015. *The Biology of Belief: Unleashing the Power of Consciousness, Matter and Miracles.* London: Hay House UK.

86. Longo, V. D. and Mattson, M. P. 2014. Fasting: molecular mechanisms and clinical applications. *Cell Metabolism* 19(2), 181–192. https://doi.org/10.1016/j.cmet.2013.12.008

87. Ma, X., Yue, Z.-Q., Gong, Z.-Q., Zhang, H., Duan, N.-Y., Shi, Y.-T. Wei, G.X. and Li, Y.-F. 2017. The effect of diaphragmatic breathing on attention, negative affect and stress in healthy adults. *Frontiers in Psychology* 8, 874. https://doi.org/10.3389/fpsyg.2017.00874

88. MacAuley, D. 2005. Profile: Roger Bannister. *The Lancet* 366, Special Issue 1, 14–15. https://doi.org/10.1016/S0140-6736(05)67827-0

89. Malosse, D., Perron, H., Sasco, A. and Seigneurin, J. M. 1992. Correlation between milk and dairy product consumption and multiple sclerosis prevalence: a worldwide study. *Neuroepidemiology* 11, 304–312. https://doi.org/10.1159/000110946

90. Maman, F. 1997. *The Role of Music in the 21st Century.* Malibu, California: Tama-Do Academy.

91. Mason, K. L., Huffnagle, G. B., Noverr, M. C. and Kao, J. Y. 2008. Overview of gut immunology. *Advances in Experimental Medicine and Biology* 635, 1–14. https://doi.org/10.1007/978-0-387-09550-9_1

92. Maurer, M., Riesen, W., Muser, J., Hulter, H. N. and Krapf, R. 2003. Neutralization of Western diet inhibits bone resorption independently of K intake and reduces cortisol secretion in humans. *American Journal of Physiology – Renal Physiology* 284(1), F32–40. https://doi.org/10.1152/ajprenal.00212.2002

93. Mayo Clinic Staff. 2018. Hashimoto's disease. *Mayo Clinic.* https://www.mayoclinic.org/diseases-conditions/hashimotos-disease/symptoms-causes/syc-20351855

94. McCorry, L. K. 2007. Physiology of the autonomic nervous system. *American Journal of Pharmaceutical Education* 71(4), 78. https://www.ncbi.nlm.nih.gov/pmc/articles/PMC1959222

95. McLeod, S. 2018. Pavlov's dogs. *SimplyPsychology.* https://www.simplypsychology.org/pavlov.html

96. Mensinga, T. T., Sips, A. J., Rompelberg, C. J., van Twillert, K., Meulenbelt, J., van der Top, H. J. and van Egmond, H. P. 2005. Potato glycoalkaloids and adverse effects in humans: an ascending dose study. *Regulatory Toxicology and Pharmacology* 41(1), 66–72. https://doi.org/10.1016/j.yrtph.2004.09.004

97. Milas, K. 2018. Symptoms of Hashimoto's thyroiditis. *EndocrineWeb.* https://www.endocrineweb.com/conditions /hashimotos-thyroiditis/symptoms-hashimotos-thyroiditis

98. Minich, D. M. and Bland, J. S. 2007. Acid-alkaline balance: role in chronic disease and detoxification. *Alternative Therapies in Health and Medicine* 13(4), 62–65.

99. Morgan, J. J. B. and Webb Ewing, T. 2005. *Making the Most of Your Life.* Whitefish, Montana: Kessinger.

100. Morowitz, M. J., Carlisle, E. M. and Alverdy, J. C. 2011. Contributions of intestinal bacteria to nutrition and metabolism in the critically ill. *The Surgical Clinics of North America* 91(4), 771–785. https://doi.org/10.1016/j.suc.2011.05.001

101. Müller, P., Rehfeld, K., Schmicker, M., Hökelmann, A., Dordevic, M., Lessmann, V., Brigadski, T., Kaufmann, J. and Müller, N. G. 2017. Evolution of neuroplasticity in response to physical activity in old age: the case for dancing. *Frontiers in Aging Neuroscience* 9, 56. https://doi.org/10.3389/fnagi.2017.00056

102. Myers, A. 2015. *The Autoimmune Solution: Prevent and Reverse the Full Spectrum of Inflammatory Symptoms and Diseases.* New York: HarperCollins.

103. Myss, C. 2009. *Defy Gravity: Healing Beyond the Bounds of Reason.* Carlsbad, California: Hay House.

104. Naimy, M. 1948. *The Book of Mirdad: A Lighthouse and a Haven.* Beirut: Sader's Library.

105. National Multiple Sclerosis Society. n. d. Types of MS. *National Multiple Sclerosis Society.* https://www.nationalmssociety.org/What-is-MS/Types-of-MS

106. National Multiple Sclerosis Society. n. d. Who gets MS? (Epidemiology). *National Multiple Sclerosis Society.* https://www.nationalmssociety.org/What-is-MS/Who-Gets-MS

107. National Wellness Institute. About Wellness. *National Wellness Institute.* https://www.nationalwellness.org/page/AboutWellness

108. Nhât Hạnh, T. 1987. *Being Peace.* Berkeley: Parallax Press.

109. Okeniyi, J. A., Ogunlesi, T. A., Oyelami, O. A. and Adeyemi, L. A. 2007. Effectiveness of dried *Carica papaya* seeds against intestinal parasitosis: a pilot study. *Journal of Medicinal Food* 10(1), 194–196. https://doi.org/10.1089/jmf.2005.065

110. O'Mahony, S. M., Clarke, G., Borre, Y. E., Dinan, T. G. and Cryan, J. F. 2015. Serotonin, tryptophan metabolism and the brain-gut-microbiome axis. *Behavioural Brain Research* 277, 32–48. https://doi.org/10.1016/j.bbr.2014.07.027

111. Otaegui, D., Mostafavi, S., Bernard, C. C., Lopez de Munain, A., Mousavi, P., Oksenberg, J. R. and Baranzini, S. E. 2007. Increased transcriptional activity of milk related genes following the active phase of experimental autoimmune encephalomyelitis and multiple sclerosis. *Journal of Immunology* 179(6), 4074–4082. https://doi.org/10.4049/jimmunol.179.6.4074

112. Pacher, P., Bátkai, S. and Kunos, G. 2006. The endocannabinoid system as an emerging target of pharmacotherapy. *Pharmacological Reviews* 58(3), 389–462. https://doi.org/10.1124/pr.58.3.2

113. Padam, A., Sharma, N., Sastri, O. S. K. S., Mahajan, S., Sharma, R. and Sharma, D. 2017. Effect of listening to Vedic chants and Indian classical instrumental music on patients undergoing upper gastrointestinal endoscopy: a randomized control trial. *Indian Journal of Psychiatry* 59(2), 214–218. https://doi.org/10.4103/psychiatry.IndianJPsychiatry_314_16

114. Patel, B., Schutte, R., Sporns, P., Doyle, J., Jewel, L. and Fedorak, R. N. 2002. Potato glycoalkaloids adversely affect intestinal

permeability and aggravate inflammatory bowel disease. *Inflammatory Bowel Diseases* 8(5), 340–346.

115. Pender, M. P. and Burrows, S. R. 2014. Epstein-Barr virus and multiple sclerosis: potential opportunities for immunotherapy. *Clinical & Translational Immunology* 3(10). http://doi.org/10.1038/cti.2014.25

116. Pérez-Maceda, B., López-Bote, J. P., Langa, C. and Bernabeu, C. 1991. Antibodies to dietary antigens in rheumatoid arthritis: possible molecular mimicry mechanism. *Clinica Chimica Acta* 203(2–3), 153–165. https://doi.org/10.1016/0009-8981(91)90287-M

117. Perga, S., Martire, S., Montarolo, F., Giordani, I., Spadaro, M., Bono, G., Corvisieri, S., Messuti, I., Panzica, G., Orlandi, F. and Bertolotto, A. 2018. The footprints of poly-autoimmunity: evidence for common biological factors involved in multiple sclerosis and Hashimoto's thyroiditis. *Frontiers in Immunology* 20(9), 311. https://doi.org/10.3389/fimmu.2018.00311

118. Pertwee, R. (ed.). 2005. *Handbook of Experimental Pharmacology*, Vol. 168. Cannabinoids. Berlin: Springer.

119. Pietrocola, F., Pol, J. and Kroemer, G. 2016. Fasting improves anticancer immunosurveillance via autophagy induction in malignant cells. *Cell Cycle* 15(24), 3327–3328. https://doi.org/10.1080/15384101.2016.1224797

120. Porges, S. W. 2009. The polyvagal theory: new insights into adaptive reactions of the autonomic nervous system. *Cleveland Clinic Journal of Medicine* 76 (Suppl. 2), 86–90. https://doi.org/10.3949/ccjm.76.s2.17

121. Purce, J. 2012. *Sound creates form* [online video], 15 December. https://youtu.be/cUjV3SWXFiU

122. Purce, J. 2015. *Jill Purce discusses overtone chanting: space sound voice documentary* [online video], 6 March. https://youtu.be/guANw889h84

123. Purves, D., Augustine, G. J., Fitzpatrick, D., Katz, L. C., LaMantia, A.-C., McNamara, J. O. and Williams, S. M. (eds.). 2001. *Neuroscience*, 2nd ed. Sunderland, Massachusetts: Sinauer Associates.

124. Raefsky, S. M. and Mattson, M. P. 2017. Adaptive responses of neuronal mitochondria to bioenergetic challenges: roles in neuroplasticity and disease resistance. *Free Radical Biology and Medicine* 102, 203–216.
https://doi.org/10.1016/j.freeradbiomed.2016.11.045

125. Renoux, C., Vukusic, S., Mikaeloff, Y., Edan, G., Clanet, M., Dubois, B., Debouverie, M., Brochet, B., Lebrun-Frenay, C., Pelletier, J., Moreau, T., Lubetzki, C., Vermersch, P., Roullet, E., Magy, L., Tardieu, M., Suissa, S. and Confavreux, C., for the Adult Neurology Departments KIDMUS Study Group. 2007. Natural history of multiple sclerosis with childhood onset. *The New England Journal of Medicine* 356, 2603–2613.
https://doi.org/10.1056/NEJMoa067597

126. Robbins, M. 2017. *The 5 Second Rule: Transform Your Life, Work, and Confidence With Everyday Courage.* New York: Post Hill Press.

127. Rowland, I., Gibson, G., Heinken, A., Scott, K., Swann, J., Thiele, I. and Tuohy., K. 2018. Gut microbiota functions: metabolism of nutrients and other food components. *European Journal of Nutrition* 57(1), 1–24. https://doi.org/10.1007/s00394-017-1445-8

128. *Sar Bachan – The Yoga of Sound Current: An Abstract of the Teachings of Soamiji Maharaj, the Founder of the Radha Soami System of Philosophy and Spiritual Science.* 1955. Punjab: Radha Soami Satsang Beas.

129. Scialla, J. J. and Anderson, C. A. 2013. Dietary acid load: a novel nutritional target in chronic kidney disease? *Advances in Chronic Kidney Disease* 20(2), 141–149.
https://doi.org/10.1053/j.ackd.2012.11.001

130. Shaffer, J. 2016. Neuroplasticity and clinical practice: building brain power for health. *Frontiers in Psychology* 7, 1118.
https://doi.org/10.3389/fpsyg.2016.01118

131. Sikora, E. and Bodziarczyk, I. 2012. Composition and antioxidant activity of kale *(Brassica oleracea* L. var. *acephala)* raw and cooked. *Acta Scientarium Polonorum. Technologia Alimentaria* 11(3), 239–248.

132. Singh, C. 1995. *Die to Live.* Punjab: Radha Soami Satsang Beas.

133. Slingerland, A. E., Schwabkey, Z., Wiesnoski, D. H. and Jenq, R. R. 2017. Clinical evidence for the microbiome in inflammatory diseases. *Frontiers in Immunology* 8, 400. https://doi.org/10.3389/fimmu.2017.00400

134. Snow, S., Bernardi, N. F., Sabet-Kassouf, N., Moran, D. and Lehmann, A. 2018. Exploring the experience and effects of vocal toning. *Journal of Music Therapy* 55(2), 221–250. https://doi.org/10.1093/jmt/thy003

135. Somers, E. C., Thomas, S. L., Smeeth, L. and Hall. A. J. 2009. Are individuals with an autoimmune disease at higher risk of a second autoimmune disorder? *American Journal of Epidemiology* 169(6), 749–755. https://doi.org/ 10.1093/aje/kwn408

136. Sprouse-Blum, A. S., Smith, G., Sugai, D. and Parsa, F. D. 2010. Understanding endorphins and their importance in pain management. *Hawaii Medical Journal* 69(3), 70–71. https://www.ncbi.nlm.nih.gov/pmc/articles/PMC3104618

137. Stefferl, A., Schubart, A., Storch, M., Amini, A., Mather, I., Lassmann, H. and Linington, C. 2000. Butyrophilin, a milk protein, modulates the encephalitogenic T cell response to myelin oligodendrocytes glycoprotein in experimental autoimmune encephalomyelitis. *Journal of Immunology* 165(5), 2859–2865. https://doi.org/10.4049/jimmunol.165.5.2859

138. Stroobant, N., Van Nooten, G., Van Belleghem, Y. and Vingerhoets, G. 2010. The effect of CABG on neurocognitive functioning. *Acta Cardiologica* 65(5), 557–564. https://doi.org/10.2143/AC.65.5.2056243

139. Subramanian, R. K., Devaki, P. R. and Saikumar, P. 2016. Alternate nostril breathing at different rates and its influence on heart rates variability in non-practitioners of yoga. *Journal of Clinical and Diagnostic Research* 10(1), CM01–CM02. https://doi.org/10.7860/JCDR/2016/15287.7094

140. The Divine Life Society. 2011. Law of prosperity. *The Divine Life Society.* http://sivanandaonline.org/public_html /?cmd=displayrightsection&section _id=1480&parent=1339&format=html

141. Tolle, E. 1997. *The Power of Now: A Guide to Spiritual Enlightenment*. Novato: New World Library.

142. Tolle, E. 2003. *Stillness Speaks*. Novato: New World Library.

143. Tolle, E. 2005. *A New Earth*. New York: Dutton.

144. Tompkins, S. A., Roeder, J. A., Thomas, J. J. and Koch, K. K. 2013. Effectiveness of a relationship enrichment program for couples living with multiple sclerosis. *International Journal of MS Care* 15(1), 27–34. https://doi.org/10.7224/1537-2073.2012-002

145. Tooley, G. A., Armstrong, S. M., Norman, T. R. and Sali, A. 2000. Acute increases in night-time plasma melatonin levels following a period of meditation. *Biological Psychology* 53(1), 69–78. https://doi.org/10.1016/S0301-0511(00)00035-1

146. UC Davis Student Health and Counseling Services. n.d. What is Wellness? https://shcs.ucdavis.edu/wellness/what-is-wellness

147. University of Massachusetts Medical School. n. d. Publications. *Center for Mindfulness in Medicine, Health Care, and Society.* https://www.umassmed.edu/cfm/research/publications

148. van der Wall, E. E. and van Gilst, W. H. 2013. Neurocardiology: close interaction between heart and brain. *Netherlands Heart Journal* 21(2), 51–52. https://doi.org/10.1007/s12471-012-0369-4

149. Vickhoff, B., Malmgren, H., Aström, R., Nyberg, G., Ekström, S. R., Engwall, M., Snygg, J., Nilsson, M. and Jörnsten, R. 2013. Music structure determines heart rate variability of singers. *Frontiers in Psychology* 4, 334. https://doi.org/10.3389/fpsyg.2013.00334

150. Vighi, G. D., Marcucci, F., Sensi, L., Di Cara, G. and Frati, F. 2008. Allergy and the gastrointestinal system. *Clinical and Experimental Immunology* 153 (Suppl. 1), 3–6. https://doi.org/10.1111/j.1365-2249.2008.03713.x

151. Vina, J., Sanchis-Gomar, F., Martinez-Bello, V. and Gomez-Cabrera, M. C. 2012. Exercise acts as a drug: the pharmacological benefits of exercise. *British Journal of Pharmacology* 167(1), 1–12. https://doi.org/10.1111/j.1476-5381.2012.01970.x

152. Vojdani, A. 2015. Molecular mimicry as a mechanism for food immune reactivities and autoimmunity. *Alternative Therapies in Health and Medicine* 21 (Suppl. 1), 34–45.

153. Wahls, T. 2011. *Minding your mitochondria* [online video]. TEDx Talk, 30 November. https://youtu.be/KLjgBLwH3Wc

154. Wang, X. G. 1993. Teratogenic effect of potato glycoalkaloid. *Zhonghua Fu Chan Ke Za Zhi* 28(2), 73–75.

155. Wang, Z., Sadovnick, A. D., Traboulsee, A. L., Ross, J. P., Bernales, C. Q., Encarnacion, M., Yee, I. M., de Lemos, M., Greenwood, T., Lee, J. D., Wright, G., Ross, C. G., Zhang, S., Song, W. and Vilariño-Güell, C. 2016. Nuclear receptor NR1H3 in familial multiple sclerosis. *Neuron* 90(5), 948–954. https://doi.org/10.1016/j.neuron.2016.04.039

156. Ware, M. 2017. What are the health benefits of papaya? *Medical News Today,* 21 December. https://www.medicalnewstoday.com/articles/275517.php

157. Watanabe, F., Yabuta, Y., Bito, T. and Teng, F. 2014. Vitamin B12 containing plant food sources for vegetarians. Nutrients 6(5), 1861–1873. https://doi.org/10.3390/nu6051861

158. Weeks, N. 1973. *The Medical Discoveries of Edward Bach, Physician: What Flowers Do for the Human Body.* New Canaan, Connecticut: Keats.

159. Weil, A. 1999. *Breathing: The Master Key to Self Healing* [audio CD]. Louisville, Colorado: Sounds True.

160. Weiner, H. L. 2005. Multiple sclerosis: the history of a disease. *New England Journal of Medicine* 353, 1306–1307. https://doi.org/10.1056/NEJMbkrev38300

161. Weisse, A. B. 2017. Humor in medicine: can laughter help in healing? *Baylor University Medical Center Proceedings* 30(3), 378–381. https://www.ncbi.nlm.nih.gov/pmc/articles/PMC5468052

162. Welch, M. G., Margolis, K. G., Li, Z. and Gershon, M. D. 2014. Oxytocin regulates gastrointestinal mortality, inflammation, macromolecular permeability and mucosal maintenance in mice. *American Journal of Physiology – Gastrointestinal and Liver Physiology* 307(8), G848–G862. https://doi.org/10.1152/ajpgi.00176.2014

163. Wolk, A. 2017. Potential health hazards of eating red meat. *Journal of Internal Medicine* 281(2), 106–122. https://doi.org/10.1111/joim.12543

164. Wordsworth, C. F. 2002. Holographic repatterning: modalities for transforming resonance patterns[training material].

165. Wordsworth, C. F. 2007. *Quantum Change Made Easy: Breakthroughs in Personal Transformation, Self-Healing and Achieving the Best of Who You Are.* Scottsdale, Arizona: Resonance Repatterning Institute.

166. World Health Organization. 2008. *Atlas: multiple sclerosis resources in the world 2008.* Geneva: WHO Press. http://www.who.int/mental_health/neurology/Atlas_MS_WEB.pdf

167. World Health Organization. 2014. Mental health: a state of well-being. https://www.who.int/features/factfiles/mental_health/en/

168. Yano, J. M., Yu, K., Donaldson, G. P., Shastri, G. G., Ann, P., Ma, L., Nagler, C. R., Ismagilov, R. F., Mazmanian, S. K. and Hsiao, E. Y. 2015. Indigenous bacteria from the gut microbiota regulate host serotonin biosynthesis. *Cell* 161(2), 264–276. https://doi.org/10.1016/j.cell.2015.02.047

169. Zou, S. and Kumar, U. 2018. Cannabinoid receptors and the endocannabinoid system: signaling and function in the central nervous system. *International Journal of Molecular sciences* 19(3), 833. https://doi.org/10.3390/ijms19030833

Index

My Notes:

My Notes:

My Food Journal
Food is my Medicine

My Food Journal
Food is my Medicine

_____

_____

_____

_____

_____

_____

_____

_____

_____

_____

_____

_____

_____

_____

My Food Journal
Food is my Medicine

_____

_____

_____

_____

_____

_____

_____

_____

_____

_____

_____

_____

_____

_____

_____

_____

_____

_____

My Food Journal
Food is my Medicine

_____

_____

_____

_____

_____

_____

_____

_____

_____

_____

_____

_____

_____

My Food Journal
Food is my Medicine

_____

_____

_____

_____

_____

_____

_____

_____

_____

_____

_____

_____

_____

My Food Journal
Food is my Medicine

_____

_____

_____

_____

_____

_____

_____

_____

_____

_____

_____

_____

_____

_____

My Food Journal
Food is my Medicine

_____

_____

_____

_____

_____

_____

_____

_____

_____

_____

_____

_____

_____

My Food Journal
Food is my Medicine

_____

_____

_____

_____

_____

_____

_____

_____

_____

_____

_____

_____

_____

My Possible Triggers
I choose to remove that which worsens my condition

My Possible Triggers
I choose to remove that which worsens my condition

_____

_____

_____

_____

_____

_____

_____

_____

_____

_____

_____

_____

My Possible Triggers
I choose to remove that which worsens my condition

_____

_____

_____

_____

_____

_____

_____

_____

_____

_____

_____

_____

My Possible Triggers
I choose to remove that which worsens my condition

My Healing Affirmations
Powerful positive words to reset my biology

_____

_____

_____

_____

_____

_____

_____

_____

_____

_____

_____

_____

_____

_____

My Healing Affirmations
Powerful positive words to reset my biology

_____

_____

_____

_____

_____

_____

_____

_____

_____

_____

_____

_____

_____

My Healing Affirmations
Powerful positive words to reset my biology

_____

_____

_____

_____

_____

_____

_____

_____

_____

_____

_____

_____

_____

_____

My Healing Affirmations
Powerful positive words to reset my biology

_____

_____

_____

_____

_____

_____

_____

_____

_____

_____

_____

_____

_____

My Activity Journal
Physical movement making me stronger every day

_____

_____

_____

_____

_____

_____

_____

_____

_____

_____

_____

_____

_____

_____

My Activity Journal
Physical movement making me stronger every day

_____

_____

_____

_____

_____

_____

_____

_____

_____

_____

_____

_____

My Activity Journal
Physical movement making me stronger every day

_____

_____

_____

_____

_____

_____

_____

_____

_____

_____

_____

_____

_____

_____

_____

My Activity Journal
Physical movement making me stronger every day

_____

_____

_____

_____

_____

_____

_____

_____

_____

_____

_____

_____

_____

My Activity Journal
Physical movement making me stronger every day

_____

_____

_____

_____

_____

_____

_____

_____

_____

_____

_____

_____

_____

_____

_____

My Activity Journal
Physical movement making me stronger every day

_____

_____

_____

_____

_____

_____

_____

_____

_____

_____

_____

_____

My Activity Journal
Physical movement making me stronger every day

_____

_____

_____

_____

_____

_____

_____

_____

_____

_____

_____

_____

_____

_____

My Activity Journal
Physical movement making me stronger every day

_____

_____

_____

_____

_____

_____

_____

_____

_____

_____

_____

_____

_____

_____

My Empowering Gratitude Journal
Thank you, Thank you, Thank you

_____

_____

_____

_____

_____

_____

_____

_____

_____

_____

_____

_____

_____

_____

My Empowering Gratitude Journal
Thank you, Thank you, Thank you

My Empowering Gratitude Journal
Thank you, Thank you, Thank you

_____

_____

_____

_____

_____

_____

_____

_____

_____

_____

_____

_____

_____

_____

_____

My Empowering Gratitude Journal
Thank you, Thank you, Thank you

My Empowering Gratitude Journal
Thank you, Thank you, Thank you

_____

_____

_____

_____

_____

_____

_____

_____

_____

_____

_____

_____

_____

_____

My Empowering Gratitude Journal
Thank you, Thank you, Thank you

_____

_____

_____

_____

_____

_____

_____

_____

_____

_____

_____

_____